W9-CRL-579

ELASTIC LIQUIDS

ELASTIC LIQUIDS

An Introductory Vector Treatment of Finite-strain Polymer Rheology

A. S. LODGE

The Manchester College of Science and Technology
England

1964

ACADEMIC PRESS

LONDON and NEW YORK

ACADEMIC PRESS INC. (LONDON) LTD
Berkeley Square House
Berkeley Square
London, W.1

U.S. Edition published by
ACADEMIC PRESS INC.
111 Fifth Avenue
New York 3, New York

Library of Congress Catalog Card Number: 64–14224

Printed in Great Britain by
Spottiswoode, Ballantyne and Company Limited
London and Colchester

Preface

Polymer rheology may be described as the scientific study of the flow and deformation of materials that contain very long "high polymer" molecules and whose elastic and viscous properties are such that the classical theories of hydrodynamics and elasticity are inapplicable. The subject is of physical interest, partly because of the variety of the effects that can arise when materials with long stress relaxation periods are subjected to large changes of shape, and partly because of the considerable advances that have been made in our understanding of the molecular basis of elastic behaviour in the rubberlike state.

The subject is of wide technological relevance, because many processes in the rubber, plastics, textile, oil, paint, and foodstuffs industries involve the flow or deformation of polymeric materials, usually in concentrated solution or in the molten liquid state; the study of polymer rheology could, therefore, lead to a better understanding of existing processes and to the systematic development of new processes and new or modified products. The subject is also being studied in connection with certain physiological investigations of fluids and materials in the human body.

The aim of this book is to introduce scientists and engineers, as well as mathematicians, to phenomenological theories of visco-elastic liquids and solids subjected to large changes of shape. A novel approach to the presentation of the subject is made by devoting much more attention than is usually given to states of stress and strain or flow history that are *uniform* (or homogeneous). Most of the essential features of rheological interest are retained in this approach, and their treatment is considerably simplified by the absence of mathematical complications inherent in the treatment of non-uniform states.

Using reference vectors embedded in the deforming material as a basis for the descriptions of stress and strain, a treatment is developed from first principles that enables the reader to formulate admissible rheological equations of state and to calculate the main properties of the corresponding materials under conditions of uniform stress and flow history. Detailed consideration is given to large elastic recovery, stress relaxation, the Weissenberg effect, and other properties that are of special interest in relation to polymeric liquids.

The treatment is self-contained, and requires only a knowledge of the elements of vector analysis, determinants, and coordinate geometry, in addition to the standard equipment of algebra and calculus. The book should, therefore, be suitable for students in their final honours year or at post-graduate level. In contrast to all previous treatments, a knowledge of tensor analysis and matrix algebra is not required, except in the final chapter which is included in order to show that the "uniform state" treatment is a particular case of a general treatment valid for non-uniform states.

The book also includes outlines of molecular network theories of rubberlike solids and liquids (Chapters 4, 6); a unified treatment of the theory underlying experimental methods of determining the state of stress in shear flow (Chapter 9); an outline of observed properties of concentrated polymer solutions (Chapter 10); and problems for the reader to solve (Chapters 1–7), complete solutions being given in Chapter 11.

A. S. LODGE

Manchester
January 1964

Acknowledgments

In a subject that is essentially a development of classical physics and applied mathematics, it is not surprising to find that the foundations were laid by the great scientists of the last century, notably by Cauchy, Green, Kirchhoff, Joule, Maxwell, Boltzmann, and Poynting. For many references to the work of these and other scientists, I am indebted to the extensive bibliographies given by Truesdell (1952), Truesdell and Toupin (1960), Prager (1961), and Eringen (1962). For my own introduction to the subject, I should particularly like to thank Professor K. Weissenberg, whose ideas have stimulated most of my own work in this field; in particular, the basic idea that the stress in a flowing polymer solution may be isotropically related to finite strains which the solution has undergone is due to Weissenberg (1947), and the comparatively simple method of formulating obviously admissible rheological equations of state, which is given here in Chapters 4, 5, and 6, depends on the use of hypotheses due to Weissenberg (1949; cf. Grossman, 1961).

Much of the material in this book is the result of work initiated at the former British Rayon Research Association; I would like to record my gratitude to Mr J. Wilson who, as Director of Research, was largely responsible for creating excellent conditions in which work of this kind could be carried out, and also to my former colleagues Drs L. R. G. Treloar and D. W. Saunders, Messrs N. Adams and A. Kaye, for their help over many years. I am also indebted to Professor J. G. Oldroyd for showing me, in advance of publication, drafts of his papers (1950a,b) on convected coordinate systems which greatly influenced my own work and the present treatment; the present notation has been chosen to agree with that of Oldroyd. The present treatment carries the use of convected coordinate systems further than other treatments have done, and should help to make clear the great advantages of these systems; in particular, the results in Appendix 1 should dispel doubts that have been voiced concerning the physical picture presented by the body stress components π^{ij}, which vary with time under conditions of steady flow in which the space stress components p^{ij} do not; it is shown that in general the state of stress in a deforming material cannot be constant, and so it is the space components that give a misleading picture.

I should also like to express my indebtedness to Messrs R. A. Barker, D. G. Backhouse, G. L. Wakefield and students in the Department of

Printing and Photographic Technology in this College for the photographs reproduced in Chapter 10; to Dr L. R. G. Treloar for Fig. 10.1; to Drs E. R. Howells and J. J. Benbow for the data used in Figs. 10.7 and 10.10; to Dr R. K. Bullough for Appendix 2; to Mr W. F. O. Pollett for the data in Table 10.2; to Mr J. E. Roberts and the Armaments Research and Development Establishment for the recipe of the elastic liquid used in Fig. 10.6; to Dr D. B. Scully and Mr G. F. Roach for their great kindness in reading the manuscript; to the staff of Academic Press for producing this book with speed and care; and finally to Professor G. J. Kynch for his support of this work in general and for his suggestion in particular that I should give a course of lectures on rheology to a post-graduate audience drawn from industry and university. These lectures form the basis of the present book.

A. S. LODGE

Contents

CHAPTER 1

Vector Analysis

Fundamental Operations

The physical quantities with which we have to deal in the present treatment may be divided into two categories: *vectors* and *scalars*. The vector quantities include force, traction, displacement and the relative position of a pair of particles; they will be represented by bold-face symbols. The scalar quantities include length, area, volume, time, angle, and the magnitude of force; they will be represented by italic symbols.

A vector $\mathbf{e}$ has direction and magnitude, and may be represented by a directed line $\overrightarrow{\mathrm{PQ}}$ (Fig. 1.1) whose length represents the *magnitude* $e = |\mathbf{e}|$ of the vector. In some cases the position of the point P is unimportant, and the same vector can be represented by any other parallel

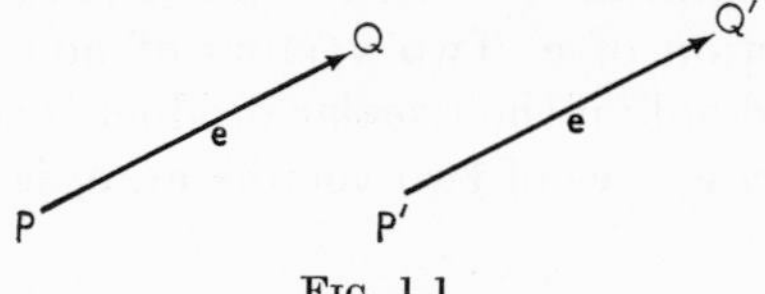

FIG. 1.1.

line P′Q′ of the same sense and equal length; two vectors are said to be equal if they may be represented by parallel lines of equal length and like sense. A scalar has magnitude only, and may be represented by a number.

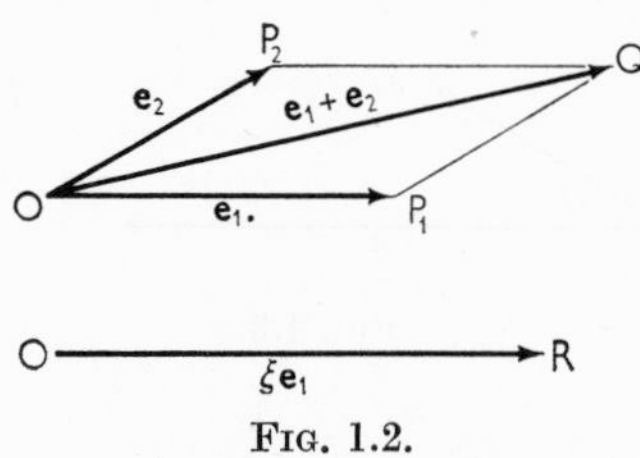

FIG. 1.2.

Two fundamental operations performed with vectors are *addition* and *multiplication by a scalar*. If two vectors $\mathbf{e}_1$, $\mathbf{e}_2$ are represented by the lines $\overrightarrow{\mathrm{OP}_1}$, $\overrightarrow{\mathrm{OP}_2}$, the sum $\mathbf{e}_1+\mathbf{e}_2$ is a vector represented by the diagonal $\overrightarrow{\mathrm{OQ}}$ (Fig. 1.2) of the parallelogram $\mathrm{OP}_1\mathrm{P}_2\mathrm{Q}$. If ξ is a positive scalar, the product $\xi\mathbf{e}_1$ is a vector represented by a line $\overrightarrow{\mathrm{OR}}$ in the same direction as $\overrightarrow{\mathrm{OP}_1}$ such that $\mathrm{OR} = \xi\mathrm{OP}$; if ξ is negative, $\xi\mathbf{e}_1$ is represented by $\overrightarrow{\mathrm{RO}}$. It is a straightforward matter to show that the usual commutative, distributive and associative laws hold for these operations (see, for example, Weatherburn, 1942):

$$\mathbf{e}_1+\mathbf{e}_2 = \mathbf{e}_2+\mathbf{e}_1.$$

$$\xi(\eta\mathbf{e}) = (\xi\eta)\,\mathbf{e}.$$

$$(\mathbf{e}_1+\mathbf{e}_2)+\mathbf{e}_3 = \mathbf{e}_1+(\mathbf{e}_2+\mathbf{e}_3).$$

$$\xi(\mathbf{e}_1+\mathbf{e}_2) = \xi\mathbf{e}_1+\xi\mathbf{e}_2.$$

The *scalar product* $\mathbf{e}_1.\mathbf{e}_2$ of two vectors $\mathbf{e}_1$, $\mathbf{e}_2$ is a scalar defined by the equation

$$\mathbf{e}_1.\mathbf{e}_2 = e_1 e_2 \cos\theta, \tag{1.1}$$

where θ denotes the "angle between the vectors", i.e. the angle between lines representing the vectors. If $\mathbf{e}_1 = \mathbf{e}_2$, then $\theta = 0$ and $\mathbf{e}_1.\mathbf{e}_2 = (e_1)^2$. A vector of unit magnitude is called a *unit vector*; clearly $\mathbf{e}/e$ is a unit vector in the direction of $\mathbf{e}$. Two vectors of non-zero magnitude are perpendicular if and only if their scalar product is zero.

The *vector product* $\mathbf{e}_1 \wedge \mathbf{e}_2$ of two vectors $\mathbf{e}_1$, $\mathbf{e}_2$ is a vector defined by the equation

$$\mathbf{e}_1 \wedge \mathbf{e}_2 = e_1 e_2 \sin\theta\,\mathbf{n}, \tag{1.2}$$

where $\mathbf{n}$ is a unit vector perpendicular to $\mathbf{e}_1$ and $\mathbf{e}_2$ such that $\mathbf{e}_1$, $\mathbf{e}_2$, $\mathbf{n}$ form a right-handed system (Fig. 1.3).

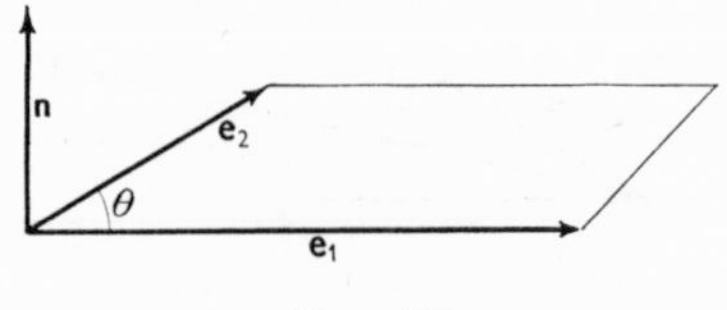

FIG. 1.3.

Vectors $\mathbf{e}_1$, $\mathbf{e}_2$, $\mathbf{n}$, where $\mathbf{n}$ is perpendicular to the plane of $\mathbf{e}_1$ and $\mathbf{e}_2$, form a *right-handed system* if, to a person looking along the direction in which $\mathbf{n}$ points, $\mathbf{e}_2$ could be obtained from $\mathbf{e}_1$ by a clockwise rotation through an angle of less than 180°. Vectors $\mathbf{e}_1$, $\mathbf{e}_2$, $\mathbf{e}_3$, where $\mathbf{e}_3$ is not necessarily perpendicular to the plane of $\mathbf{e}_1$ and $\mathbf{e}_2$, are said to form a right-handed system if the angle between $\mathbf{e}_3$ and $\mathbf{n}$ is less than 90° and

$\mathbf{e}_1$, $\mathbf{e}_2$, $\mathbf{n}$ form a right-handed system. The above systems are *left-handed* if the word "clockwise" is replaced by "anticlockwise". If $\mathbf{e}_1$ and $\mathbf{e}_2$ are parallel, $\mathbf{n}$ is undefined but $\sin\theta = 0$ and hence $\mathbf{e}_1 \wedge \mathbf{e}_2 = 0$. Changing the order of factors in a vector product changes the sign, for $\mathbf{e}_2$, $\mathbf{e}_1$, $-\mathbf{n}$ form a right-handed system. The value of a scalar product is independent of the order of its factors. Scalar and vector products obey the following distributive and associative laws.

$$(\xi\mathbf{e}_1).\mathbf{e}_2 = \xi(\mathbf{e}_1.\mathbf{e}_2);$$

$$\mathbf{r}.(\mathbf{e}_1+\mathbf{e}_2) = \mathbf{r}.\mathbf{e}_1+\mathbf{r}.\mathbf{e}_2;$$

$$(\xi\mathbf{e}_1)\wedge\mathbf{e}_2 = \xi(\mathbf{e}_1\wedge\mathbf{e}_2);$$

$$\mathbf{r}\wedge(\mathbf{e}_1+\mathbf{e}_2) = \mathbf{r}\wedge\mathbf{e}_1+\mathbf{r}\wedge\mathbf{e}_2.$$

The proofs of these results may be found in any standard textbook on vector analysis (e.g. Weatherburn, 1942); the last result is non-trivial.

Theorem. *The area A of a parallelogram is given, in terms of vectors $\mathbf{e}_1$, $\mathbf{e}_2$ representing two adjacent sides, by the equations*

$$A = |\mathbf{e}_1\wedge\mathbf{e}_2|; \tag{1.3}$$

$$A^2 = \begin{vmatrix} \mathbf{e}_1.\mathbf{e}_1 & \mathbf{e}_1.\mathbf{e}_2 \\ \mathbf{e}_2.\mathbf{e}_1 & \mathbf{e}_2.\mathbf{e}_2 \end{vmatrix}. \tag{1.4}$$

The vertical lines denote the magnitude of the vector in the first of these equations and the determinant in the second.

Proof. The area of the parallelogram $\mathrm{OP_1QP_2}$ in Fig. 1.2 is twice the area of the triangle $\mathrm{OP_1P_2}$; this area is $\frac{1}{2}e_1e_2\sin\theta$. Hence $A = e_1e_2\sin\theta = |\mathbf{e}_1\wedge\mathbf{e}_2|$, by (1.2); this proves (1.3). Further, we have

$$\begin{aligned} A^2 &= (e_1e_2\sin\theta)^2 \\ &= (e_1)^2(e_2)^2-(e_1e_2\cos\theta)^2 \\ &= (\mathbf{e}_1.\mathbf{e}_1)(\mathbf{e}_2.\mathbf{e}_2)-(\mathbf{e}_1.\mathbf{e}_2)(\mathbf{e}_2.\mathbf{e}_1) \\ &= \begin{vmatrix} \mathbf{e}_1.\mathbf{e}_1 & \mathbf{e}_1.\mathbf{e}_2 \\ \mathbf{e}_2.\mathbf{e}_1 & \mathbf{e}_2.\mathbf{e}_2 \end{vmatrix}, \end{aligned}$$

which proves (1.4).

The orientation of a given plane can be described by a unit vector $\mathbf{n}$ normal to the plane; the sense of this vector is arbitrary and is usually specified explicitly in any given example. If we mark out a particular region of the plane, of area A, we may associate with this the vector $A\mathbf{n}$

which is usually called the *vector area*, although the term *areal vector* is preferable since it is a vector and not an area. For a parallelogram of adjacent edges $\mathbf{e}_1$, $\mathbf{e}_2$ (Fig. 1.3), the areal vector is

$$(1.5) \qquad A\mathbf{n} = \mathbf{e}_1 \wedge \mathbf{e}_2 \qquad \text{by (1.2) and (1.3),}$$

if we choose the sign so as to make $\mathbf{e}_1$, $\mathbf{e}_2$ and the areal vector form a right-handed system.

(1.6) **Theorem.** *The sum of the inward-drawn areal vectors of the faces of a tetrahedron is zero.*

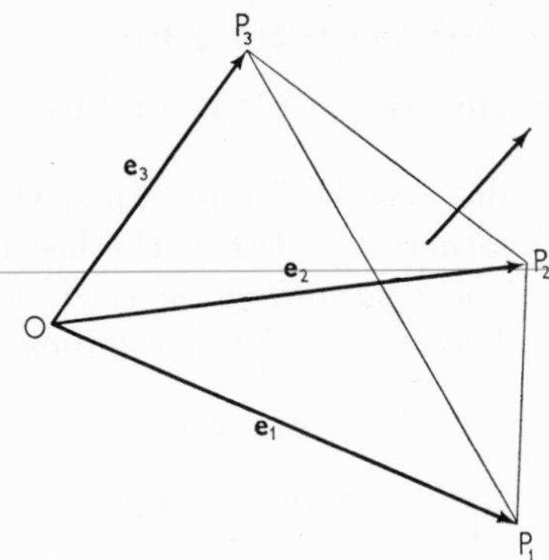

FIG. 1.4.

Proof. Let $OP_1P_2P_3$ be the tetrahedron (Fig. 1.4), and let $\overrightarrow{OP_i} = \mathbf{e}_i$ $(i = 1, 2, 3)$. Then $\overrightarrow{P_1P_2} = \mathbf{e}_2 - \mathbf{e}_1$, $\overrightarrow{P_1P_3} = \mathbf{e}_3 - \mathbf{e}_1$, and hence the inward-drawn areal vector for the face $P_1P_2P_3$ is

$$\begin{aligned} \tfrac{1}{2}\overrightarrow{P_1P_3} \wedge \overrightarrow{P_1P_2} &= \tfrac{1}{2}(\mathbf{e}_3 - \mathbf{e}_1) \wedge (\mathbf{e}_2 - \mathbf{e}_1) \\ &= \tfrac{1}{2}\mathbf{e}_3 \wedge \mathbf{e}_2 - \tfrac{1}{2}\mathbf{e}_3 \wedge \mathbf{e}_1 - \tfrac{1}{2}\mathbf{e}_1 \wedge \mathbf{e}_2; \end{aligned}$$

when this is added to the sum of the other three inward-drawn areal vectors, viz.

$$\tfrac{1}{2}\mathbf{e}_1 \wedge \mathbf{e}_2 + \tfrac{1}{2}\mathbf{e}_2 \wedge \mathbf{e}_3 + \tfrac{1}{2}\mathbf{e}_3 \wedge \mathbf{e}_1,$$

the result is clearly zero, which proves the theorem.

It is clear that the theorem is still true if all the areal vectors are outward-drawn; and it is not difficult to see that a similar theorem is true for a polyhedron of any number of faces; for this can be divided into tetrahedra by adding suitable planes, and the contributions to the sum of areal vectors arising from each of the additional planes will be zero.

Theorem. *The volume v of a parallelepiped is given, in terms of vectors* $\mathbf{e}_1, \mathbf{e}_2, \mathbf{e}_3$ *representing three edges drawn from one corner, by the expression*

$$v = \pm(\mathbf{e}_1 \wedge \mathbf{e}_2).\mathbf{e}_3. \tag{1.7}$$

The positive or negative sign is taken according as $\mathbf{e}_1, \mathbf{e}_2, \mathbf{e}_3$ form a right- or left-handed system.

Proof. Let $\mathbf{e}_1, \mathbf{e}_2, \mathbf{e}_3$ form a right-handed system (Fig. 1.5). Then $\mathbf{e}_1 \wedge \mathbf{e}_2 = A\mathbf{n}$ (1.5), where A is the area of the base OP_1QP_2 of the parallelepiped and $\mathbf{n}$ is the unit normal to this base making an angle not

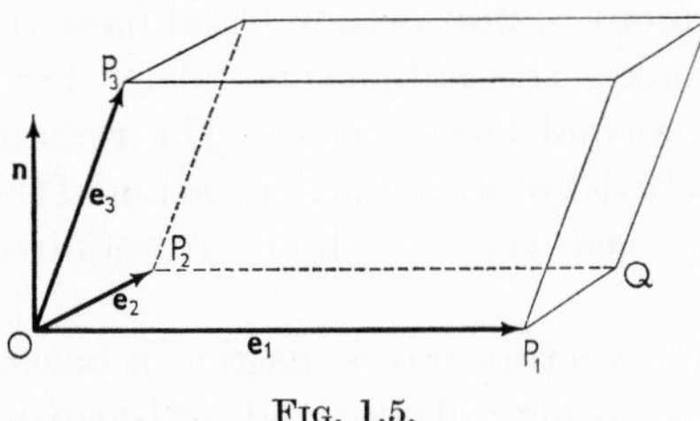

FIG. 1.5.

exceeding 90° with the third vector $\mathbf{e}_3$. Hence $\mathbf{n}.\mathbf{e}_3$ is equal to the height of the parallelepiped, and therefore

$$(\mathbf{e}_1 \wedge \mathbf{e}_2).\mathbf{e}_3 = A\mathbf{n}.\mathbf{e}_3 = (\text{area of base}) \times (\text{height}) = v.$$

If $\mathbf{e}_1, \mathbf{e}_2, \mathbf{e}_3$ form a left-handed system, then $\mathbf{e}_2, \mathbf{e}_1, \mathbf{e}_3$ form a right-handed system, and hence $(\mathbf{e}_1 \wedge \mathbf{e}_2).\mathbf{e}_3 = -(\mathbf{e}_2 \wedge \mathbf{e}_1).\mathbf{e}_3 = -v$, by the result just proved.

In the *scalar triple product* $(\mathbf{e}_1 \wedge \mathbf{e}_2).\mathbf{e}_3$, the brackets may, if desired, be omitted without ambiguity, for the vector product must be formed first and the scalar product second if the expression is to have a meaning. From the theorem just proved, it is easy to see that the value of a scalar triple product is unaltered by any cyclic interchange of the vectors, is multiplied by -1 if two vectors are interchanged, is unaltered by interchange of the symbols "$\wedge$" and "$.$", and is zero if two of the vectors are equal or parallel or if one vector is a linear combination of the other two, for in each of the last three cases the three vectors are coplanar and the volume of the parallelepiped is zero. These properties may be summarized in the form

$$(\mathbf{e}_i \wedge \mathbf{e}_j).\mathbf{e}_k = \mathbf{e}_i.(\mathbf{e}_j \wedge \mathbf{e}_k) = v, -v, \text{or } 0, \tag{1.8}$$

according as i, j, k is an even or an odd permutation of 1, 2, 3, or two or three of i, j, k are equal. This applies when $\mathbf{e}_1, \mathbf{e}_2, \mathbf{e}_3$ form a right-handed system.

The Base Vectors $\mathbf{e}_1$, $\mathbf{e}_2$, $\mathbf{e}_3$

The use of a set of reference or base vectors $\mathbf{e}_1$, $\mathbf{e}_2$, $\mathbf{e}_3$, which are not restricted to be at right angles to one another or to be of unit length, is essential to the present treatment of rheology. These vectors are taken (Chapter 2) to be embedded in and to deform with the material continuum considered, and thus if they are unit and orthogonal in one state of the material they will not in general be so in another. A set of three mutually orthogonal unit vectors is called an *orthonormal* set or basis ("normal" because the vectors are "normalized" to unit length). Although the treatment of non-orthonormal base vectors is to be found in standard textbooks, the subject is rather less familiar than the treatment of orthonormal base vectors. The remainder of the present chapter will be largely devoted to the derivation of the equations relating to non-orthonormal base vectors which are required in the rest of the book.

In order that three vectors can be used as a basis, they must be non-zero (i.e. have non-zero magnitude) and be *linearly independent*, i.e. in any relation of the form

$$a^1\mathbf{e}_1 + a^2\mathbf{e}_2 + a^3\mathbf{e}_3 = 0, \tag{1.9}$$

the (scalar) coefficients a^i must each be zero. This implies that if three linearly independent vectors $\mathbf{e}_i$ ($i = 1, 2, 3$) are drawn from a common origin O (Fig. 1.5), the parallelepiped having edges $\mathbf{e}_i$ must be non-degenerate (i.e. have non-zero volume) for if, on the contrary, the volume is zero, one vector, $\mathbf{e}_3$ say, must be zero or must lie in the plane of the other two, in which case it is expressible in the form $\mathbf{e}_3 = a\mathbf{e}_1 + b\mathbf{e}_2$, for some values of a, b; this contradicts equation (1.9). We shall refer to the parallelepiped having base vectors $\mathbf{e}_i$ as edges as a *basic parallelepiped*.

Theorem. *An arbitrary vector* $\mathbf{r}$ *can be expressed in terms of a set of base vectors* $\mathbf{e}_i$ *by an equation of the form*

$$\mathbf{r} = \xi^1\mathbf{e}_1 + \xi^2\mathbf{e}_2 + \xi^3\mathbf{e}_3 = \sum_{i=1}^{3} \xi^i\mathbf{e}_i \tag{1.10}$$

for suitable values of the scalar coefficients ξ^1, ξ^2, ξ^3.

Proof. Let $\mathbf{r}$ be represented by a position vector $\overrightarrow{\mathrm{OR}}$ (Fig. 1.6), where O is a corner of the basic parallelepiped having edges $\overrightarrow{\mathrm{OP}_i} = \mathbf{e}_i$. Let the line through R parallel to OP_3 meet the plane $\mathrm{OP}_1\mathrm{P}_2$ in a point M, and let the line through M parallel to OP_2 meet the line OP_1 in L. Then

$\overrightarrow{OL} = \xi^1 \mathbf{e}_1$, where $|\xi^1| = OL/OP_1$; $\overrightarrow{LM} = \xi^2 \mathbf{e}_2$, where $|\xi^2| = LM/OP_2$; and $\overrightarrow{MR} = \xi^3 \mathbf{e}_3$, where $|\xi^3| = MR/OP_3$. But

$$\overrightarrow{OR} = \overrightarrow{OM} + \overrightarrow{MR} = \overrightarrow{OL} + \overrightarrow{LM} + \overrightarrow{MR} \quad \text{(cf. Fig. 1.2);}$$

hence $\mathbf{r} = \overrightarrow{OR} = \xi^1 \mathbf{e}_1 + \xi^2 \mathbf{e}_2 + \xi^3 \mathbf{e}_3$, which proves the theorem. (The usual notation $|\xi|$ means the positive value of ξ; $|\mathbf{e}|$, the magnitude of $\mathbf{e}$, is necessarily positive or zero.)

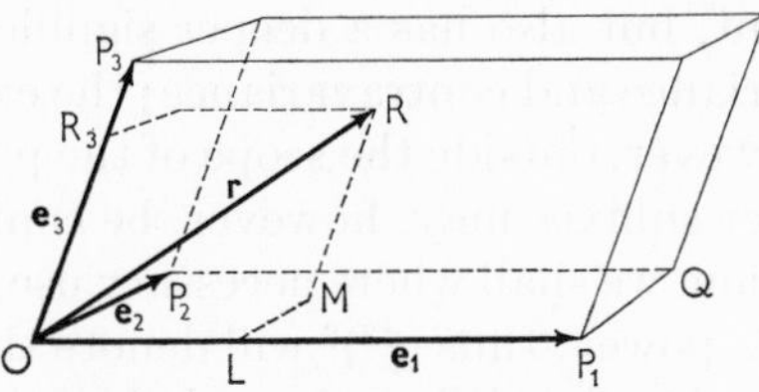

FIG. 1.6. The basic parallelepiped.

When the basis $\mathbf{e}_i$ is orthonormal, an explicit expression for the coefficients ξ^i in terms of the base vectors $\mathbf{e}_i$ and the given vector $\mathbf{r}$ can be obtained simply by taking the scalar product of each side of equation (1.10) with each base vector in turn: thus

$$\text{(1.11)} \qquad \mathbf{r}.\mathbf{e}_j = \sum_{i=1}^{3} \xi^i \mathbf{e}_i.\mathbf{e}_j = \xi^j,$$

since

$$\text{(1.12)} \qquad \mathbf{e}_i.\mathbf{e}_j = \begin{cases} 0 & \text{if } i \neq j, \\ 1 & \text{if } i = j. \end{cases} \qquad \text{(orthonormal basis)}$$

Quantities, such as those occurring in the last equation, having two suffixes i, j and having the value one or zero according as the suffixes are equal or unequal are of such frequent occurrence that it is worth while introducing a special notation for them: we define the symbols δ_{ij} by the equation

$$\text{(1.13)} \qquad \delta_{ij} = \begin{cases} 1 & \text{if } i = j, \\ 0 & \text{if } i \neq j. \end{cases} \qquad (i, j = 1, 2, 3)$$

These symbols are known as the "Kronecker deltas"; their use is typified by the equation

$$\text{(1.14)} \qquad \sum_{i=1}^{3} \xi^i \delta_{ij} = \sum_{k=1}^{3} \xi^k \delta_{kj} = \xi^j.$$

The second expression has been included to emphasize the point that the letter (i or k, in this case) used for a suffix which occurs in a summation (a so-called "dummy" suffix) can be changed without altering the value of the sum.

A further comment on notation should be made at this stage. We use suffixes in upper as well as in lower positions to denote different quantities; thus ξ^1, ξ_1 stand for different variables, and the vector $\mathbf{e}^1$, which is introduced in the next paragraph, is different from $\mathbf{e}_1$. The use of suffixes in upper and lower positions adds considerably to the clarity of the present treatment, but also has a deeper significance in relation to the concepts of covariance and contravariance; the explicit treatment of these concepts is, however, outside the scope of the present book (except in Chapter 12). Upper suffixes may, however, be confused with powers; to avoid such confusion, we shall where necessary use brackets to enclose a quantity raised to a power; thus $(\xi^3)^2$ will denote the square of ξ^3, and $(e_2)^3$ will denote the cube of e_2. Where a symbol, such as r, is used in the text without upper suffixes ever being attached to it, brackets are unnecessary and we may, for example, use r^2 to denote the square of r, as usual.

The Reciprocal Vectors $\mathbf{e}^1$, $\mathbf{e}^2$, $\mathbf{e}^3$

When the basis $\mathbf{e}_i$ is not orthonormal, it is convenient to introduce three vectors $\mathbf{e}^i$ defined (when $\mathbf{e}_1$, $\mathbf{e}_2$, $\mathbf{e}_3$ form a right-handed set) by the equations

$$\left.\begin{aligned}\mathbf{e}^1 &= \frac{1}{v}\mathbf{e}_2 \wedge \mathbf{e}_3,\\ \mathbf{e}^2 &= \frac{1}{v}\mathbf{e}_3 \wedge \mathbf{e}_1,\\ \mathbf{e}^3 &= \frac{1}{v}\mathbf{e}_1 \wedge \mathbf{e}_2,\end{aligned}\right\}$$

which we may write in the form

$$\mathbf{e}^i = \frac{1}{v}\mathbf{e}_j \wedge \mathbf{e}_k \qquad (i, j, k = 1, 2, 3 \text{ in cyclic order}). \tag{1.15}$$

In these equations, v denotes the volume of the basic parallelepiped and is given by (1.7) or (1.8). The set of vectors $\mathbf{e}^i$ so defined is said to be *reciprocal* to the set $\mathbf{e}_i$. The vectors $\mathbf{e}^i$ are clearly normal to the faces of the basic parallelepiped, and are therefore non-coplanar and linearly independent.

The most important property of the vectors $\mathbf{e}^i$ is expressed by

$$\mathbf{e}^i . \mathbf{e}_j = \delta_{ij}, \tag{1.16}$$

which can in fact be used (instead of (1.15)) as a definition of the reciprocal vectors $\mathbf{e}^i$ when $\mathbf{e}_i$ are given, or of $\mathbf{e}_i$ when $\mathbf{e}^i$ are given (Examples 1, Nos. 3, 6). Equations (1.16) are a generalization of equation (1.12).

The proof of equation (1.16) is immediate, for

$$\mathbf{e}_l . \mathbf{e}^i = \frac{1}{v} \mathbf{e}_l . \mathbf{e}_j \wedge \mathbf{e}_k \qquad \text{by (1.15)},$$

$$= \begin{cases} 1 & \text{if } l = i, \\ 0 & \text{if } l \neq i, \end{cases} \qquad \text{by (1.8)}.$$

If $\mathbf{e}_1$, $\mathbf{e}_2$, $\mathbf{e}_3$ form a left-handed set, the sign could be changed in the definition (1.15) to preserve the validity of (1.16). From now on, however, we shall for definiteness take $\mathbf{e}_1$, $\mathbf{e}_2$, $\mathbf{e}_3$ as a right-handed set, unless the contrary is explicitly stated.

We may note, from (1.5) and (1.15), that $v\mathbf{e}^1$, $v\mathbf{e}^2$, $v\mathbf{e}^3$ *are the inward-drawn areal vectors of the faces* OP_2P_3, OP_3P_1, OP_1P_2 *of the basic parallelepiped* (Fig. 1.6).

The simplest example of the use of the reciprocal vectors $\mathbf{e}^i$ is in obtaining expressions for the coefficients ξ^i in the resolution (1.10) of an arbitrary vector $\mathbf{r}$ relative to the basis $\mathbf{e}_i$. For, on taking the scalar product of each side of (1.10) with $\mathbf{e}^j$, we see that

$$\mathbf{r} . \mathbf{e}^j = \sum_i \xi^i \mathbf{e}_i . \mathbf{e}^j = \sum_i \xi^i \delta_{ij} = \xi^j, \tag{1.17}$$

on using (1.16). Clearly (1.17) is a generalization of (1.11).

The Quantities γ_{ij}, γ^{ij}

The scalar products of base vectors $\mathbf{e}_i$ and reciprocal base vectors $\mathbf{e}^i$ have values given by (1.16). The scalar products of base vectors with themselves and the scalar products of reciprocal base vectors with themselves are of such frequent occurrence in the present treatment that it is worth introducing special symbols for them. We shall write

$$\mathbf{e}_i . \mathbf{e}_j = \gamma_{ij}, \quad \mathbf{e}^i . \mathbf{e}^j = \gamma^{ij}. \tag{1.18}$$

The quantities γ_{ij}, γ^{ij} so defined have properties expressed by the following equations:

$$\gamma_{ij} = \gamma_{ji}, \quad \gamma^{ij} = \gamma^{ji}; \tag{1.19}$$

$$\mathbf{e}^i = \sum_j \gamma^{ij}\,\mathbf{e}_j, \quad \mathbf{e}_i = \sum_j \gamma_{ij}\,\mathbf{e}^j; \tag{1.20}$$

$$\sum_j \gamma_{ij}\gamma^{jk} = \delta_{ik}; \tag{1.21}$$

$$\gamma \equiv \det \gamma_{ij} = v^2, \quad \det \gamma^{ij} = v^{-2} = \gamma^{-1}; \tag{1.22}$$

$$\gamma^{ij} = \frac{1}{\gamma}\Gamma^{ij}, \quad \gamma_{ij} = \gamma\Gamma_{ij}, \tag{1.23}$$

where

$$\begin{cases} \Gamma^{ij} = \text{cofactor of } \gamma_{ji} \text{ in } \det\gamma_{ij}, \\ \Gamma_{ij} = \text{cofactor of } \gamma^{ji} \text{ in } \det\gamma^{ji}. \end{cases} \tag{1.24}$$

Moreover, equations (1.23) are valid for any quantities γ_{ij}, γ^{ij} which are related by (1.21), provided only that $\gamma \neq 0$; in particular, it is not necessary that (1.19) be satisfied for (1.23) to be valid.

Proof of (1.19). This follows at once from the definition (1.18) and the fact that a scalar product has a value which is independent of the order of its factors. Double-suffix quantities, such as γ_{ij}, which satisfy an equation of the form (1.19), are said to be *symmetric*. This symmetry implies that, of the nine quantities $\gamma_{ij}(i,j = 1,2,3)$, only six are independent.

Proof of (1.20). To prove the first of equations (1.20), we observe that any vector, and $\mathbf{e}^i$ in particular, may be expressed as a linear combination of the base vectors $\mathbf{e}_k$: thus we may write

$$\mathbf{e}^i = \sum_k x^{ik}\,\mathbf{e}_k, \tag{1.25}$$

where the coefficients x^{ij} are to be determined. Taking the scalar product of each side of this equation with $\mathbf{e}^j$, we have

$$\begin{aligned} \gamma^{ij} &= \mathbf{e}^i . \mathbf{e}^j & &\text{by (1.18)} \\ &= \sum_k x^{ik}\,\mathbf{e}_k . \mathbf{e}^j & &\text{by (1.25)} \\ &= \sum_k x^{ik}\,\delta_{kj} & &\text{by (1.16)} \\ &= x^{ij}. \end{aligned}$$

When these values for the coefficients x^{ij} are inserted in (1.25), we obtain the required equation (1.20). The second of equations (1.20) may be proved in a similar manner by expressing $\mathbf{e}_i$ as a linear combination of the reciprocal base vectors $\mathbf{e}^k$; this is always possible since these vectors are linearly independent.

Proof of (1.21). To prove (1.21), we rewrite the first of equations (1.20) in the form

$$\mathbf{e}^j = \sum_k \gamma^{jk} \mathbf{e}_k,$$

by changing the suffixes from i, j to j, k. We then substitute the expression so obtained for $\mathbf{e}^j$ in the second of equations (1.20), obtaining the result

$$\begin{aligned}\mathbf{e}_i &= \sum_j \gamma_{ij} \Big(\sum_k \gamma^{jk} \mathbf{e}_k \Big) \\ &= \sum_k \Big(\sum_j \gamma_{ij} \gamma^{jk} \Big) \mathbf{e}_k.\end{aligned}$$

It should be noted that in a double summation the order in which the summations are performed is immaterial but it is necessary to use different suffix letters for the different summations if (as in the equations just considered) the summation signs are to be interchanged or written together.

It will be seen that the equation just obtained represents a set of linear relations between the vectors $\mathbf{e}_i$; since these are linearly independent, it follows that the coefficient of $\mathbf{e}_k$ on the right-hand side must be zero if $k \neq i$ and must be unity if $k = i$. This is just what is expressed by the required equation (1.21).

Proof of (1.22). The proof of the first of equations (1.22) is more lengthy and is recommended as an exercise for the reader; it is included as Example No. 8 at the end of the present chapter, the solution being given in Chapter 11. The second of equations (1.22) can be readily deduced from the first for, if we apply the rule for multiplying determinants (the notation $\det \gamma_{ij}$ is used for the determinant whose elements are γ_{ij}) to the previous equation (1.21), we see that

$$\begin{aligned}(\det \gamma_{ij})(\det \gamma^{ij}) &= \det \Big(\sum_j \gamma_{ij} \gamma^{jk} \Big) \\ &= \det \delta_{ik} \\ &= 1.\end{aligned}$$

Proof of (1.23). To derive (1.23) from (1.21) without using (1.18) or (1.19), we may first suppose that γ_{ij} are given quantities (with $\gamma \neq 0$) and that γ^{ij} are defined in terms of them by (1.21).

In $\gamma \equiv \det \gamma_{ij}$, the elements of column j are γ_{1j}, γ_{2j}, γ_{3j}, and their cofactors are Γ^{j1}, Γ^{j2}, Γ^{j3} according to the notation (1.24); hence

$$\Gamma^{j1}\gamma_{1j} + \Gamma^{j2}\gamma_{2j} + \Gamma^{j3}\gamma_{3j} = \gamma.$$

The cofactors of the elements in any other column k are Γ^{k1}, Γ^{k2}, Γ^{k3}; hence

$$\Gamma^{k1}\gamma_{1j} + \Gamma^{k2}\gamma_{2j} + \Gamma^{k3}\gamma_{3j} = 0, \quad \text{when } k \neq j.$$

These two equations may be written in the form

$$\sum_i \Gamma^{ki}\gamma_{ij} = \gamma\delta_{kj}. \tag{1.26}$$

Multiplying both sides of this equation by γ^{jl} and summing over j, we have

$$\sum_i \sum_j \Gamma^{ki}\gamma_{ij}\gamma^{jl} = \gamma \sum_j \delta_{kj}\gamma^{jl};$$

using (1.21) (with k replaced by l) on the left-hand side, we have

$$\sum_i \Gamma^{ki}\delta_{il} = \gamma\gamma^{kl},$$

or

$$\Gamma^{kl} = \gamma\gamma^{kl},$$

which proves the first of equations (1.23).

The second of equations (1.23) can be proved by a similar argument in which γ_{ij} and γ^{ij} are interchanged.

The following theorem is frequently used in later chapters.

(1.27) **Theorem.** *If a symmetric set of constants $A^{ij} = A^{ji}$ satisfy an equation*

$$\sum_{i=1}^{3} \sum_{j=1}^{3} A^{ij} l_i l_j = 0 \tag{1.28}$$

for all real values of three variables l_i subject to the condition

$$\sum_i \sum_j \gamma^{ij} l_i l_j = 1, \tag{1.29}$$

where γ^{ij} are defined by (1.18), *then the constants must all be zero*, i.e.

$$A^{ij} = 0 \qquad (i,j = 1,2,3). \tag{1.30}$$

Corollary 1. If (1.28) is satisfied for all values of l_i, then (1.30) must hold. For, taking $l_1 = 1$, $l_2 = l_3 = 0$, it follows from (1.28) that $A^{11} = 0$; similarly, $A^{22} = A^{33} = 0$. Taking $l_2 = l_3 = 1$, $l_1 = 0$, it follows that $A^{23} + A^{32} = 0$, and hence that $A^{23} = 0$ since $A^{23} = A^{32}$; similarly $A^{31} = A^{12} = 0$, which proves the corollary.

Corollary 2. The values of a symmetric set of constants $B^{ij} = B^{ji}$ *are uniquely determined if the values of the expression*

$$\sum_i \sum_j B^{ij} l_i l_j$$

are given for all values of l_i *subject to* (1.29). For if B^{ij} and C^{ij} denote two possible sets of values for the coefficients, then

$$\sum_i \sum_j B^{ij} l_i l_j = \sum_i \sum_j C^{ij} l_i l_j$$

for all values of l_i subject to equation (1.29), and hence $B^{ij} - C^{ij} \equiv A^{ij}$ satisfies the conditions of the theorem and must be zero. Thus $B^{ij} = C^{ij}$, and so B^{ij} are uniquely determined.

Corollary 3. For the validity of the theorem and Corollary 2, it is sufficient to consider six suitably chosen sets of values for l_i. *In particular, if*

$$\gamma^{ij} = \delta_{ij}, \tag{1.31}$$

then one suitable choice for the six sets of values for (l_1, l_2, l_3) *is the following:*

$$\begin{cases} (1,\ 0,\ 0), & (0,\ 1,\ 0), & (0,\ 0,\ 1), \\ (0,\ 2^{-1/2},\ 2^{-1/2}), & (2^{-1/2},\ 0,\ 2^{-1/2}), & (2^{-1/2},\ 2^{-1/2},\ 0). \end{cases} \tag{1.32}$$

To prove the last statement, we note that when (1.31) is satisfied, the condition (1.29) becomes

$$(l_1)^2 + (l_2)^2 + (l_3)^2 = 1, \tag{1.33}$$

which is satisfied by each of the sets of values for l_i given in (1.32); the number $2^{-1/2}$ occurs because l_i are components of unit vectors. As in the proof of Corollary 1, substitution of the first three sets (1.32) in turn in (1.28) leads to the conclusion that $A^{11} = A^{22} = A^{33} = 0$; and a similar use of the second three sets (1.32) leads to the conclusion that $A^{23} = A^{31} = A^{12} = 0$, on using the fact that $A^{ij} = A^{ji}$. This proves the second part of Corollary 3.

All that remains is to prove the first part of Corollary 3, for the truth of the theorem itself will then be apparent. For this purpose, we need to show that the replacing of (1.31) by (1.29) makes no essential difference to the argument just used. If then we take $l_2 = l_3 = 0$, (1.29) becomes

$$\gamma^{11}(l_1)^2 = 1,$$

and hence $l_1 = \pm\sqrt{\gamma^{11}}$, since $\gamma^{11} = (e^1)^2 \neq 0$, by (1.18); thus $(l_1, 0, 0)$ is a possible set of values for l_i, with $l_1 \neq 0$, and hence it follows from (1.28) that $A^{11} = 0$. Similarly, $A^{22} = A^{33} = 0$.

Finally, if we take $l_1 = 0$ and $l_2 = l_3$, then (1.29) becomes

$$(\gamma^{22}+\gamma^{33}+2\gamma^{23})(l_2)^2 = 1,$$

which determines a non-zero value for l_2; hence $(0, l_2, l_2)$ is a possible set of values for l_i, with $l_2 \neq 0$, and hence it follows from (1.28) that $A^{23} = 0$. Similarly, $A^{31} = A^{12} = 0$, which completes the proof. We may note, incidentally, that the value just determined for l_2 is necessarily finite for, from (1.18), using θ to denote the angle between $\mathbf{e}^2$ and $\mathbf{e}^3$, we have

$$\begin{aligned}\gamma^{22}+\gamma^{33}+2\gamma^{23} &= (e^2)^2+(e^3)^2+2e^2e^3\cos\theta \\ &= (e^2-e^3)^2+4e^2e^3\cos^2\frac{\theta}{2} \geqslant 0.\end{aligned}$$

The equality sign here could occur only if $e^2 = e^3$ and $\theta = n\pi$ (n odd); this would mean that $\mathbf{e}^2 = -\mathbf{e}^3$, which contradicts the assumption that they are linearly independent. The coefficient of $(l_2)^2$ is therefore necessarily positive, and the value of l_2 finite.

The Display of Double-suffix Quantities

As is evident from the equations already developed, much use is made of sets of three quantities, such as $\mathbf{e}_i$, represented by a symbol with a single-letter suffix, and with sets of nine quantities, such as γ_{ij}, represented by a symbol with two-letter suffixes. Unless the contrary is stated, *letter suffixes will throughout be understood to assume the values 1, 2, 3,* and the summation over these values of a suffix j, say, will be denoted by the sign $\sum_j$. "The set of quantities $\mathbf{e}_i$" will be taken to mean all members of the set, viz. $\mathbf{e}_1, \mathbf{e}_2, \mathbf{e}_3$; similarly, "the quantities γ_{ij}" will be taken to mean all members of the set, viz.

$$\gamma_{11}, \gamma_{22}, \gamma_{33}; \quad \gamma_{23}, \gamma_{31}, \gamma_{12}; \quad \gamma_{32}, \gamma_{21}, \gamma_{13}.$$

It will sometimes be necessary to display all the members of a two-suffix quantity. This could be done by printing the members along a single line, as above, but it is usually better to write them out in three lines according to the system illustrated by the following example.

$$\gamma_{ij} = \begin{pmatrix}\gamma_{11} & \gamma_{12} & \gamma_{13} \\ \gamma_{21} & \gamma_{22} & \gamma_{23} \\ \gamma_{31} & \gamma_{32} & \gamma_{33}\end{pmatrix}. \tag{1.34}$$

Here the values of the suffix i determine the row in which a quantity is placed, while the values of the suffix j determine the column. The large containing brackets are included for clarity. The array (1.34) represents nine numbers (or variables) and should not be confused with the determinant

$$\gamma = \det \gamma_{ij} = \begin{vmatrix} \gamma_{11} & \gamma_{12} & \gamma_{13} \\ \gamma_{21} & \gamma_{22} & \gamma_{23} \\ \gamma_{31} & \gamma_{32} & \gamma_{33} \end{vmatrix}, \tag{1.35}$$

which represents a single number (or a single combination of the variables γ_{ij}).

In what is known as the matrix calculus, rules are laid down and methods are developed for the manipulation of such arrays of quantities. We shall, however, not assume any knowledge of the matrix calculus, nor shall we use matrix notation as such, for the rather modest requirements of the present treatment can be met simply by noting the following obvious implications of the display notation as introduced above.

Multiplication by a single number

If b denotes any number, the symbol $b\gamma_{ij}$ stands for the set of quantities $b\gamma_{11}, b\gamma_{22}, b\gamma_{33}; b\gamma_{23}, b\gamma_{31}, b\gamma_{12}; b\gamma_{32}, b\gamma_{21}, b\gamma_{13}$, and hence the display notation will read as follows.

$$b\gamma_{ij} = b\begin{pmatrix} \gamma_{11} & \gamma_{12} & \gamma_{13} \\ \gamma_{21} & \gamma_{22} & \gamma_{23} \\ \gamma_{31} & \gamma_{32} & \gamma_{33} \end{pmatrix} = \begin{pmatrix} b\gamma_{11} & b\gamma_{12} & b\gamma_{13} \\ b\gamma_{21} & b\gamma_{22} & b\gamma_{23} \\ b\gamma_{31} & b\gamma_{32} & b\gamma_{33} \end{pmatrix} \tag{1.36}$$

It follows from this that

$$\det(b\gamma_{ij}) = b^3 \det \gamma_{ij}. \tag{1.37}$$

Addition

If γ_{ij}, Γ_{ij} are any two double-suffix quantities, the sum $\gamma_{ij}+\Gamma_{ij}$ represents the set of quantities $\gamma_{11}+\Gamma_{11}$, $\gamma_{22}+\Gamma_{22}$, $\gamma_{33}+\Gamma_{33}$, $\gamma_{23}+\Gamma_{23}$, etc., and thus we have

$$\gamma_{ij}+\Gamma_{ij} = \begin{pmatrix} \gamma_{11}+\Gamma_{11} & \gamma_{12}+\Gamma_{12} & \gamma_{13}+\Gamma_{13} \\ \gamma_{21}+\Gamma_{21} & \gamma_{22}+\Gamma_{22} & \gamma_{23}+\Gamma_{23} \\ \gamma_{31}+\Gamma_{31} & \gamma_{32}+\Gamma_{32} & \gamma_{33}+\Gamma_{33} \end{pmatrix}. \tag{1.38}$$

By using this result and (1.36) with $b = -1$, we obtain a similar result for the difference $\Gamma_{ij}-\gamma_{ij}$. More generally, by successive application of these results, we can obtain a similar result for the sum of any number of double-suffix quantities with arbitrary coefficients; in particular, if we allow b and γ_{ij} to depend on a parameter t, we see that

$$\int b\gamma_{ij}\,dt = \begin{pmatrix} \int b\gamma_{11}\,dt & \int b\gamma_{12}\,dt & \int b\gamma_{13}\,dt \\ \int b\gamma_{21}\,dt & \int b\gamma_{22}\,dt & \int b\gamma_{23}\,dt \\ \int b\gamma_{31}\,dt & \int b\gamma_{32}\,dt & \int b\gamma_{33}\,dt \end{pmatrix}. \tag{1.39}$$

Elements, such as γ_{11}, γ_{22}, γ_{33}, which are said to lie on the "main diagonal" of an array (1.34), sometimes have a different physical significance to the other "off-diagonal" elements γ_{23}, γ_{31}, γ_{12}, γ_{32}, γ_{21}, γ_{13}. For example, in the case of γ_{ij} itself, it follows from (1.1) and (1.18) that

$$\gamma_{ij} = \begin{pmatrix} (e_1)^2 & e_1 e_2 \cos\theta_{12} & e_1 e_3 \cos\theta_{13} \\ e_1 e_2 \cos\theta_{12} & (e_2)^2 & e_2 e_3 \cos\theta_{23} \\ e_1 e_3 \cos\theta_{13} & e_2 e_3 \cos\theta_{23} & (e_3)^2 \end{pmatrix}, \tag{1.40}$$

where e_1, e_2, e_3 are the lengths of the edges of the basic parallelepiped, and θ_{23}, θ_{13}, θ_{12} are the angles between them.

Examples 1

1. If $\mathbf{e}_1$, $\mathbf{e}_2$, $\mathbf{e}_3$ are vectors such that $\mathbf{e}_1 \wedge \mathbf{e}_2 . \mathbf{e}_3 \equiv v \neq 0$, give an analytical proof that the vectors $\mathbf{e}^i \equiv v^{-1}\mathbf{e}_j \wedge \mathbf{e}_k$ $(i,j,k = 1,2,3$ in cyclic order) are linearly independent.

2. If $\mathbf{r}.\mathbf{e}_i = 0$ $(i = 1,2,3)$ and $\mathbf{e}_i$ are linearly independent, prove that $\mathbf{r} = 0$.

3. If $\mathbf{e}_i$ are linearly independent vectors, prove that there is only one set of vectors $\mathbf{e}^i$ which satisfy the equations

$$\mathbf{e}^i . \mathbf{e}_j = \delta_{ij} \qquad (i,j = 1,2,3).$$

4. If $\mathbf{e}_i$ are linearly independent vectors and $\mathbf{e}^i$ are their reciprocal vectors, prove that, for any vector $\mathbf{r}$,

$$\sum_j \mathbf{r}.\mathbf{e}^j \mathbf{e}_j = \mathbf{r} = \sum_j \mathbf{r}.\mathbf{e}_j \mathbf{e}^j.$$

5. Prove the formula

$$\mathbf{u} \wedge (\mathbf{v} \wedge \mathbf{w}) = \mathbf{u}.\mathbf{w}\mathbf{v} - \mathbf{u}.\mathbf{v}\mathbf{w}$$

for the *triple vector product* of any three vectors $\mathbf{u}$, $\mathbf{v}$, $\mathbf{w}$.

6. If $\mathbf{e}_i$ are linearly independent, and $\mathbf{e}^i$ are their reciprocal vectors (defined by (1.7) and (1.15)), prove that

$$\mathbf{e}^i \wedge \mathbf{e}^j = \bar{v}\mathbf{e}_k \qquad (i,j,k = 1,2,3 \text{ in cyclic order}),$$

where $\bar{v} = \mathbf{e}^1 \wedge \mathbf{e}^2 . \mathbf{e}^3$. Prove also that $\bar{v} = v^{-1}$.

(This example shows that the relations between $\mathbf{e}_i$ and $\mathbf{e}^i$ are "reciprocal" in the sense that equations of the same form are obtained whether one starts with $\mathbf{e}_i$ or with $\mathbf{e}^i$.)

7. If (in the usual notation) $\gamma^{ij} = (e^i)^2\delta_{ij}$, show that $\mathbf{e}_i = (e^i)^{-2}\mathbf{e}^i = (e_i)^2\mathbf{e}^i$.

8. If $\mathbf{f}_i$, $\mathbf{e}_i$ are any six given vectors, prove that

$$(\mathbf{f}_1 \wedge \mathbf{f}_2 . \mathbf{f}_3)(\mathbf{e}_1 \wedge \mathbf{e}_2 . \mathbf{e}_3) = \begin{vmatrix} \mathbf{f}_1 . \mathbf{e}_1 & \mathbf{f}_1 . \mathbf{e}_2 & \mathbf{f}_1 . \mathbf{e}_3 \\ \mathbf{f}_2 . \mathbf{e}_1 & \mathbf{f}_2 . \mathbf{e}_2 & \mathbf{f}_2 . \mathbf{e}_3 \\ \mathbf{f}_3 . \mathbf{e}_1 & \mathbf{f}_3 . \mathbf{e}_2 & \mathbf{f}_3 . \mathbf{e}_3 \end{vmatrix}.$$

Deduce that $\det \gamma_{ij} = v^2$ (1.22).

9. If $\gamma (\equiv \det \gamma_{ij})$ and γ^{ij}, defined by the equations

$$\sum_j \gamma^{ij}\gamma_{jk} = \delta_{ik} \qquad (i,k = 1,2,3),$$

are regarded as functions of nine independent variables $\gamma_{ij} (\neq \gamma_{ji})$, prove that

$$\frac{\partial \gamma}{\partial \gamma_{ij}} = \gamma\gamma^{ji} \quad \text{and} \quad \frac{\partial \gamma^{ij}}{\partial \gamma_{rs}} = -\gamma^{ir}\gamma^{sj}.$$

CHAPTER 2

The Description of Uniform Strain

The rheological properties of materials are essentially macroscopic properties, and in describing them we may ignore the fact that matter must be regarded as being discontinuous on a molecular scale. In attemping to explain the properties, it may be necessary to take account of the molecular structure of matter, but explanations of this type are not the main concern of this book.

It will therefore be assumed that the materials we consider are *continuous* in the sense that they may be regarded as continuous distributions of point-particles filling a three-dimensional region of space in each state. By the term *state*, or *configuration*, we simply mean that the particles of the material occupy given places in space; we shall use symbols such as t_0, t, t' to distinguish between different states. The values assumed by these symbols may be discrete (as in the labelling of a finite number of states of an elastic solid, for example) or part of a continuous range (as in the flow of a liquid, when the variable t will usually denote time). A change of state $t_0 \rightarrow t$ will be called a *deformation* when only two states are involved and a *flow* when a continuous range of states is involved and the material is a liquid.

The deformations considered will be assumed to be *continuous* in the following sense. Let $0x_1x_2x_3$ be a rectangular cartesian coordinate system, fixed in space. Let x_i denote the coordinates of the *place* which a typical particle P occupies in state t, and let x'_i denote the coordinates of the place which the same particle occupies in another state t'. The particles of the material, or body, set up a correspondence between the places in the two regions of space which the body occupies in the two states. If this correspondence is one–one and is represented by functional relations

(2.1) $$x'_i = x'_i(x_1, x_2, x_3) \qquad (i = 1, 2, 3)$$

which have a unique inverse

(2.2) $$x_i = x_i(x'_1, x'_2, x'_3) \qquad (i = 1, 2, 3)$$

and are differentiable a "sufficient" number of times (i.e. as many times as needed in the subsequent analysis), then the deformation $t \rightarrow t'$ is said to be continuous. Continuity of a deformation thus involves not only the obvious requirement that no two particles occupy the same place but also the requirement that neighbouring particles (i.e. particles at x_i, x_i+dx_i, where dx_i are differentials) in one state are neighbouring particles in the other; this implies that no breaks occur in the material.

The term *deformation* as used here includes a degenerate change of state represented by a translation and rotation of the body as a rigid whole in which no part of the body undergoes any change of shape. The *shape* of a body is determined by the separations between all pairs of particles in the body. The term *strain* will be used to mean *change of shape*. Thus in general a given deformation will involve a rigid displacement and a strain. It is of fundamental importance to separate these aspects of deformation, for the equations which govern the motion of a continuous material fall naturally into two groups: the stress equations of motion, and the rheological equations of state.

The *stress equations of motion* (or equilibrium) relate spatial gradients of stress (defined in Chapter 3) and forces of gravity and inertia; these equations are derived from purely mechanical considerations, namely the conditions for the motion or equilibrium of a typical infinitesimal volume element of the body under the action of gravity and forces exerted on its surface by the material in its immediate neighbourhood, and accordingly apply to all continuous materials. Under conditions of uniform stress and zero body force (our main concern in this book), the equations are satisfied identically and do not need to be considered.

The *rheological equations of state*, or constitutive equations, relate the stress in a given volume element to the *changes of shape* which that element has undergone up to the instant considered. That such relations exist is a basic assumption of the subject. The form of these equations depends on the material, and is the main concern of this book.

In considering the possible forms which rheological equations of state might take, it is therefore convenient to use quantities which describe changes of shape but which are independent of any translatory or rotatory motion which the material element may undergo; this is the object of the present chapter. A corresponding description of stress is developed in Chapter 3.

Properties of Uniform Strain

When the relations (2.1) between the cartesian coordinates x_i, x'_i are linear, the strain (and the deformation) $t \to t'$ are said to be *uniform* or *homogeneous*. For a uniform strain, we therefore have equations of the form

$$x'_i = \sum_j a_{ij} x_j + b_i \qquad (i = 1, 2, 3), \tag{2.3}$$

where the quantities a_{ij}, b_i are independent of x_i and x'_i.

Since the transformation $x_i \to x_i''$, resulting from two linear transformations $x_i \to x_i'$, $x_i' \to x_i''$, is itself linear, it follows that the resultant $t \to t''$ of any two uniform strains $t \to t'$, $t' \to t''$ is a uniform strain. Hence the resultant of any number of uniform strains is a uniform strain. The continuity of the deformation $t \to t'$ (i.e. the continuity and differentiability of (2.1)) ensures that particles lying on any given surface in state t will lie on a surface in state t'. We may therefore speak of a *material surface* or a *material plane* as a surface or plane always composed of the same particles. The intersection of two material surfaces or planes is a *material curve* or *material line*, always composed of the same particles. In uniform strain, material planes and lines have the following special properties.

(2.4) Parallel planes deform into parallel planes.

(2.5) Parallel lines deform into parallel lines.

(2.6) The ratio of separations of any three collinear particles is constant.

(2.7) The ratio of separations of any three parallel planes is constant.

Proof. The equation of a plane may be written in the form

$$\sum_{i=1}^{3} B_i x_i = 1 \tag{2.8}$$

where the coefficients B_i are constants whose *ratios* determine the direction of the normal to the plane. Thus the equations of any two planes parallel to the plane (2.8) can be written in the form

$$\sum \lambda B_i x_i = 1, \quad \sum \mu B_i x_i = 1, \tag{2.9}$$

for suitable values of the constants λ, μ.

The constants b_i in (2.3) evidently represent a translation of the body as a rigid whole. Such a translation clearly has no effect on the properties of planes and lines under consideration, and we may therefore for simplicity put $b_i = 0$ without loss of generality. Furthermore, equations (2.3), being a particular case of (2.1), must have an inverse; with $b_i = 0$, the inverse equations must be of the form

$$x_i = \sum_j A_{ij} x_j', \tag{2.10}$$

where the constants A_{ij} are determined by the constants a_{ij}.

If we now substitute this expression for x_i in the equations (2.8), (2.9) of the planes, we obtain the equations

$$\sum B_j' x_j' = 1, \quad \sum \lambda B_j' x_j' = 1, \quad \sum \mu B_j' x_j' = 1,$$

where $B_j' = \sum_i B_i A_{ij}$, for the material surfaces in state t'. But these equations evidently represent parallel planes, which proves (2.4).

The proof of (2.5) follows at once from (2.4), because any two parallel lines can be regarded as the intersections of two parallel planes with a transverse plane.

To prove (2.6), we use the fact that if P, Q, R are collinear particles occupying places of coordinates X_i, Y_i, Z_i in state t, the coordinates of Q may be written in the form

$$Y_j = \frac{\lambda X_j + \mu Z_j}{\lambda + \mu}, \tag{2.11}$$

where $\mu : \lambda = \mathrm{PQ} : \mathrm{QR}$. For the coordinates Y'_i of Q in state t', we have

$$\begin{aligned} Y'_i &= \sum_j a_{ij} Y_j && \text{by (2.3) with } b_i = 0, \\ &= \frac{\lambda \sum_j a_{ij} X_j + \mu \sum_j a_{ij} Z_j}{\lambda + \mu} && \text{by (2.11)}, \\ &= \frac{\lambda X'_i + \mu Z'_i}{\lambda + \mu}, \end{aligned}$$

where X'_i, Z'_i are the coordinates of P, R in state t'. Since this equation has the same form as (2.11), it follows that the particles P, Q, R are collinear in state t' and that the ratio PQ : QR of their separations is still $\mu : \lambda$.

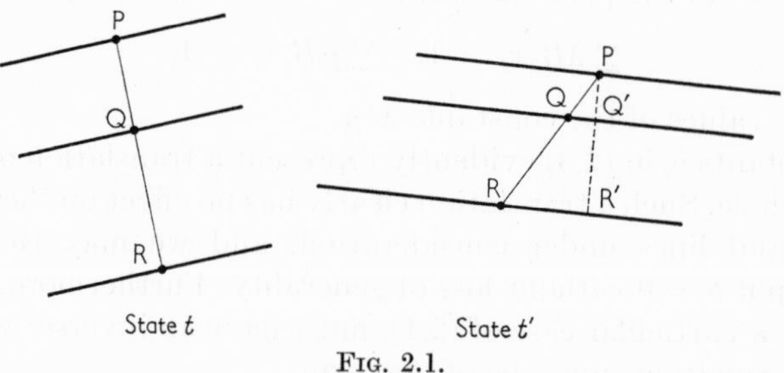

FIG. 2.1.

It is instructive to prove the remaining property (2.7) from (2.6). We consider any three parallel planes in state t. Let any line normal to these planes meet them in particles P, Q, R (Fig. 2.1). In state t', the material line PQR will not in general be normal to the planes because these, while remaining parallel, will have undergone a relative lateral displacement as well as a change of separation. However, if we construct a new normal PQ′R′ in state t', we see by similar triangles that the ratio PQ′ : Q′R′ of the separations of planes equals PQ : QR, the ratio of separations of particles, which, by (2.6), has the same value in both states. This proves (2.7).

It is perhaps necessary to emphasize the point made in the last paragraph that a material line normal to a material plane in one state will not after general uniform strain be normal to that plane in another state. Thus *the normal to a material plane is not in general a material line.*

We may note that the property (2.6) justifies the use of the term *uniform* to describe the type of strain here considered. In the familiar use of this term in connection with the elongation of an elastic filament of negligible width, an elongation is said to be uniform if the ratio of initial and final lengths of an element is the same for all elements of the filament. It follows from (2.6) that in uniform strain every material line in a three-dimensional body undergoes elongation (or contraction) that is uniform in this sense.

It is the property (2.6) which, more than any other, makes it worth while to introduce the concept of embedded vectors on which the present treatment depends.

Embedded Vectors

Definition. A vector $\mathbf{e}$ associated with a deforming continuum is said to be an *embedded vector* if it is always represented by the directed line joining the same pair of particles P, R. An embedded vector, which may also be called a *convected vector* or a *body vector,* is thus represented by a material line and varies as the state of the material varies. To emphasize this, we may write $\overrightarrow{\mathrm{PR}} = \mathbf{e}(t)$.

The material line representing an embedded vector always contains the same particles and may be regarded as a one-dimensional space; the embedded vector may be used as a basis for this space. Thus any particle Q on the line PR may be represented (with respect to the moving origin P and moving base vector $\mathbf{e}$) by the embedded vector

$$\overrightarrow{\mathrm{PQ}} = \xi\overrightarrow{\mathrm{PR}} = \xi\mathbf{e}(t) \tag{2.12}$$

where $\xi = \mathrm{PQ}/\mathrm{QR}$ if Q and R lie on the same side of P, and $\xi = -\mathrm{PQ}/\mathrm{QR}$ if Q and R lie on opposite sides of P.

It follows from (2.6) that *the coefficient* ξ, which may be called the *convected coordinate* of the particle Q, *is constant throughout any sequence of uniform strains.*

The extension of this idea to three dimensions is straightforward. Let O, P_1, P_2, P_3, (Fig. 1.6) be any four non-coplanar particles. (Particles which are non-coplanar in one state are non-coplanar in every state reached by uniform strain, by (2.4).) In any state t, we may take the embedded vectors

$$\mathbf{e}_i(t) = \overrightarrow{\mathrm{OP}_i} \qquad (i = 1, 2, 3) \tag{2.13}$$

as a basis for the whole material, in terms of which the embedded vector $\mathbf{r} = \overrightarrow{\mathrm{OR}}$ for any given particle R can be expressed by an equation of the form

$$\mathbf{r}(t) = \sum_{i=1}^{3} \xi^i \mathbf{e}_i(t). \tag{2.14}$$

In this equation, *the coefficients* ξ^i *are independent of* t. For the plane through the particle R parallel to the material plane $\mathrm{OP_1P_2}$ is a material plane, by (2.4), and therefore meets the material line $\mathrm{OP_3}$ in a particle, $\mathrm{R_3}$ say (Fig. 1.6). $\mathrm{OR_3}$ and MR are parallel, by construction; hence $\mathrm{OR_3} = \mathrm{MR} = \pm \xi^3 \mathrm{OP_3}$ (the sign depending on whether $\mathrm{R_3}$ and P lie on the same side of O or not). Since $\mathrm{OR_3}/\mathrm{OP_3}$ is constant in any uniform deformation, by (2.6), it follows that ξ^3 is constant. Similarly, ξ^1 and ξ^2 are constant.

In relation to a given basis of embedded vectors $\mathbf{e}_i$, we may therefore speak of "the particle ξ^i" without ambiguity and without having to specify the state.

It should be noted that, in general, *the reciprocal vectors* $\mathbf{e}^i$ *are not embedded vectors* because they are normal to the material planes defining the faces of the basic parallelepiped, and the normal to a material plane is not in general a material line.

Separations of Particles

The *shape* of a body is determined if we are given the separations of every pair of particles in the body. Let us first consider the case of a pair of particles O, R, where O is the particle at the origin of our basic parallelepiped and R is an arbitrary particle, of convected coordinates ξ^i, say. For the square of the separation of O and R, we have

$$\begin{aligned} r^2 = \mathrm{OR}^2 &= \overrightarrow{\mathrm{OR}} . \overrightarrow{\mathrm{OR}} \\ &= \left(\sum_i \xi^i \mathbf{e}_i(t)\right) \cdot \left(\sum_j \xi^j \mathbf{e}_j(t)\right) \qquad \text{by (2.14)} \\ &= \sum_i \sum_j \xi^i \xi^j \mathbf{e}_i(t) . \mathbf{e}_j(t). \end{aligned}$$

According to our definition (1.18) of γ_{ij}, this equation may be written in the form

$$(2.15) \qquad [r(t)]^2 = \sum_i \sum_j \xi^i \xi^j \gamma_{ij}(t).$$

The quantities γ_{ij}, being scalar products of the embedded base vectors, depend on the state t.

A similar equation may be readily obtained for the separation of any pair of particles R, S (neither of which is at the origin) of coordinates ξ^i, $\bar{\xi}^i$, say: we have $\overrightarrow{\mathrm{OS}} = \overrightarrow{\mathrm{OR}} + \overrightarrow{\mathrm{RS}}$, and hence

$$\begin{aligned}\overrightarrow{\mathrm{RS}} &= \overrightarrow{\mathrm{OS}} - \overrightarrow{\mathrm{OR}} \\ &= \sum_i \bar{\xi}^i \mathbf{e}_i - \sum_i \xi^i \mathbf{e}_i \\ &= \sum_i (\bar{\xi}^i - \xi^i)\, \mathbf{e}_i.\end{aligned}$$

Therefore

$$(2.16) \qquad \mathrm{RS}^2 = \sum_i \sum_j (\bar{\xi}^i - \xi^i)(\bar{\xi}^j - \xi^j)\, \gamma_{ij}.$$

This equation is of the same form as (2.15), with the "relative coordinates" $\bar{\xi}^i - \xi^i$ of particles R, S in place of ξ^i, the coordinates of R relative to the particle O at the origin.

We see, therefore, that, relative to a specified system of embedded base vectors (i.e. when the particles $\mathrm{OP_1P_2P_3}$ at the ends of these base vectors are specified), *the separations of all particles of the material are completely described by the quantities* γ_{ij}. Moreover, these quantities are unaffected by any rigid-body motion, as the following theorem shows.

(2.17) **Theorem.** *A necessary and sufficient condition that a uniform motion be a rigid-body motion is that* γ_{ij} *be constant.* The truth of this theorem is obvious when it is recalled that the quantities γ_{ij} are determined by the lengths and mutual inclinations of the edges of the basic parallelepiped (1.40), but it is worth while giving a formal proof.

Proof. The condition is sufficient, for if γ_{ij} be constant, equation (2.16) shows that the separation of every pair of particles is constant, and therefore the motion is a rigid-body motion.

The condition is necessary, for, if the motion be a rigid-body motion, the separation of particles O, P must be the same in any two states t, t', and therefore

$$\begin{aligned}0 &= [r(t)]^2 - [r(t')]^2 \\ &= \sum_i \sum_j \xi^i \xi^j [\gamma_{ij}(t) - \gamma_{ij}(t')], \qquad \text{by (2.15).}\end{aligned}$$

This equation must hold for arbitrary values of the coordinates ξ^i, since P can be any particle, and therefore, by Theorem (1.27), Corollary 1, the coefficients of $\xi^i \xi^j$ must be zero, i.e.

$$\gamma_{ij}(t) = \gamma_{ij}(t').$$

Thus the quantities γ_{ij} are constant.

It follows that *the quantities γ_{ij} describe the shape of the material and are unaffected by rigid-body motions*; the differences $\gamma_{ij}(t) - \gamma_{ij}(t')$ describe completely the strain for any deformation $t \to t'$. They could, therefore, be used as the strain variables in a rheological equation of state. For any given state or motion, the actual values of the quantities γ_{ij} will depend on the particular choice of base vectors, but the properties of the material, and therefore the *form* of the rheological equations of state, must be independent of any such choice. In deriving certain possible forms of rheological equations of state, we shall adopt methods which ensure that these requirements are met (Chapters 4, 5, 6).

We note that, owing to the symmetry conditions $\gamma_{ij} = \gamma_{ji}$ (1.19), only six of the quantities γ_{ij} are independent. The three base vectors $\mathbf{e}_i$, on the other hand, are equivalent to nine independent quantities (three components for each vector); the extra three quantities correspond to the fact that the base vectors contain information as to the orientation of the material in space as well as the shape. The base vectors in fact vary during a rigid motion; their scalar products γ_{ij} do not.

In the flow of a liquid, or in any continuously varying deformation, expressions for the rates of change of particle separations may be obtained by differentiating equation (2.15) the required number of times, remembering that the coordinates ξ^i are constant. Thus

$$\text{(2.18)} \qquad \frac{d^n(r^2)}{dt^n} = \sum_i \sum_j \xi^i \xi^j \frac{d^n \gamma_{ij}}{dt^n} \qquad (n = 1, 2, 3, \ldots).$$

Separations of Parallel Material Planes

Although the quantities γ_{ij}, which are simply related to the separations of pairs of particles, satisfactorily describe strain, it is convenient to derive a second set of quantities which also describe strain. In geometrical language, the second description may be called the *dual* of the first, being more simply related to the separation of material planes than to the separation of particles.

In a general uniform deformation $t \to t'$, a given pair of parallel material planes will in general undergo a relative tangential displacement as well as a change of separation; it is therefore not at first sight obvious that a knowledge of changes of separation of pairs of parallel planes of all orientations gives a complete description of strain, but this is in fact the case, as we shall now show.

In relation to a given basic parallelepiped $OP_1P_2P_3$, a material plane may be specified in either of two ways: (a) we may specify the unit normal $\mathbf{n}$ and the perpendicular distance h from the origin O, or (b) we may specify the particles A_1, A_2, A_3 of intersection of the plane with the three main edges OP_1, OP_2, OP_3 of the parallelepiped (Fig. 2.2). We now derive the relations between these two specifications.

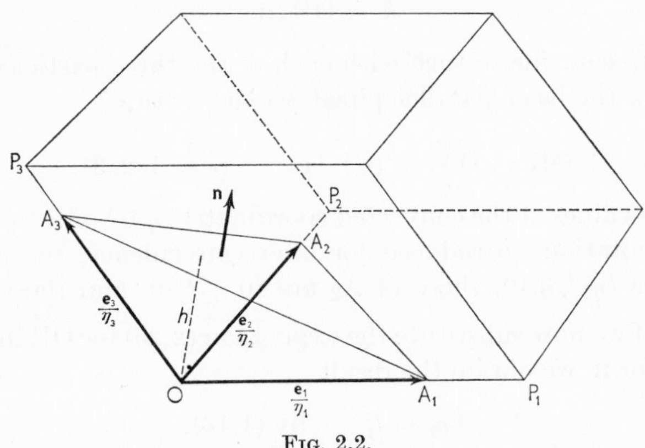

FIG. 2.2.

We may express the unit normal $\mathbf{n}$, drawn from O to the plane, as a linear combination of the reciprocal base vectors $\mathbf{e}^i$, since these are linearly independent:

(2.19) $$\mathbf{n} = \sum_i l_i \mathbf{e}^i.$$

The coefficients l_i are the analogues for a non-orthonormal basis of the actual direction cosines of the normal $\mathbf{n}$; taking the scalar product of each side of the equation with $\mathbf{e}_j$, we have

(2.20) $$l_j = \mathbf{n}.\mathbf{e}_j \qquad \text{by (1.16).}$$

Since $\mathbf{n}$ is of unit length, the values of l_i must be subject to a restriction; in fact, they satisfy the relation

$$1 = \mathbf{n}.\mathbf{n} = \sum_i \sum_j l_i l_j \mathbf{e}^i.\mathbf{e}^j,$$

which may be written in the form

(2.21) $$\sum_i \sum_j \gamma^{ij} l_i l_j = 1 \qquad \text{by (1.18).}$$

When the basis is orthonormal, $\gamma^{ij} = \gamma_{ij} = \delta_{ij}$, and the relation (2.21) reduces to the familiar form

$$(l_1)^2 + (l_2)^2 + (l_3)^2 = 1.$$

Equation (2.21) shows that the quantities l_i vary with the state t since the quantities γ^{ij} do.

To obtain an expression for the distance h of the plane from the origin O, we note that if R is any particle on the plane, the distance h is equal to the projection of OR on the unit normal, i.e.

$$h = \overrightarrow{\mathrm{OR}} \cdot \mathbf{n}. \tag{2.22}$$

Taking R to coincide in turn with each of the three particles A_i on the edges OP_i of the basic parallelepiped, we may write

$$\overrightarrow{\mathrm{OR}} = \overrightarrow{\mathrm{OA}_i} = (\eta_i)^{-1}\mathbf{e}_i \qquad (i = 1, 2, 3), \tag{2.23}$$

for suitable values of the convected coordinates $(\eta_i)^{-1}$ of the particles A_i; with this notation, introduced for later convenience, the coordinates ξ^i of A_1 are $(\eta_1^{-1}, 0, 0)$, those of A_2 are $(0, \eta_2^{-1}, 0)$, and those of A_3 are $(0, 0, \eta_3^{-1})$. If we now substitute the expression (2.23) for $\overrightarrow{\mathrm{OR}}$ in (2.22) and use (2.19) for $\mathbf{n}$, we obtain the result

$$h\eta_i = l_i \qquad \text{by (1.16)}. \tag{2.24}$$

On substituting this expression for l_i in (2.21), we finally obtain the required equation

$$\frac{1}{h^2} = \sum_i \sum_j \gamma^{ij} \eta_i \eta_j. \tag{2.25}$$

This equation gives the separation h between an arbitrary material plane of "coordinates" η_i and a parallel plane through the origin. The plane coordinates η_i, being equal to convected coordinates of particles, are constant; the separation h and the quantities γ^{ij} are not. The equation (2.25) is similar in form to the corresponding equation (2.15) for the separation of particles.

In the flow of a liquid, or in any continuously varying deformation in which γ^{ij} is a sufficiently differentiable function of t, we may differentiate (2.25) to obtain the following equation for the nth order rate of change of the inverse square of the separation of planes:

$$\frac{d^n}{dt^n}\left(\frac{1}{h^2}\right) = \sum_i \sum_j \frac{d^n \gamma^{ij}}{dt^n} \eta_i \eta_j. \tag{2.26}$$

On multiplying this equation by h^2 and using (2.24), we see that

$$h^2 \frac{d^n}{dt^n}\left(\frac{1}{h^2}\right) = \sum_i \sum_j \frac{d^n \gamma^{ij}}{dt^n} l_i l_j, \tag{2.27}$$

where the quantities l_i refer to the state t.

For two distinct states t, t_0, the difference of separations h, h_0 is given by the equation

$$\frac{1}{h^2} - \frac{1}{h_0^2} = \sum_i \sum_j \eta_i \eta_j [\gamma^{ij}(t) - \gamma^{ij}(t_0)]. \tag{2.28}$$

On multiplying this equation by h^2 and using (2.24), we obtain the following equation for the relative difference of squares of separations:

$$\frac{h^2 - h_0^2}{h_0^2} = -\sum \sum l_i l_j [\gamma^{ij}(t) - \gamma^{ij}(t_0)]; \tag{2.29}$$

here, the quantities l_i refer to the state t.

Equation (2.25) shows that the quantities γ^{ij} give complete information about the separations of pairs of material planes of arbitrary orientation when one of the planes passes through the origin. From the nature of uniform strain, we should expect that the stipulation that one plane pass through the origin would involve no loss of generality, and it is easy to see that this is in fact the case. Let σ, σ' be any two parallel planes and let s be a third plane, parallel to σ, σ', passing through the origin; let h be the separation of s, σ and let h' be the separation of σ, σ'. From the fundamental property (2.7) of uniform deformation, the ratio h'/h has the same value in any two states t, t_0, i.e.

$$\left(\frac{h'}{h}\right)_t = \left(\frac{h'}{h}\right)_{t_0},$$

and therefore

$$\frac{h'}{h'_0} = \frac{h}{h_0},$$

where h, h_0 denote the values in states t, t_0. It follows at once from (2.29) that

$$\frac{h'^2 - h_0'^2}{h_0'^2} = -\sum_i \sum_j l_i l_j [\gamma^{ij}(t) - \gamma^{ij}(t_0)], \tag{2.30}$$

since the quantities l_i depend only on the normal to the family of parallel planes (cf. (2.20)). This equation is of the same form as the corresponding equation (2.29), showing that, as far as this equation is concerned, it is immaterial whether one of the parallel planes passes through the origin or not.

The coordinates η_i determine a plane completely and therefore have different values for different members of a family of parallel planes. If η_i, η_i' be the coordinates for planes σ, σ', then $h = l_i/\eta_i$, by (2.24), and $h+h' = l_i/\eta_i'$, since $h+h'$ is the separation between σ' and the origin. On subtracting one of these equations from the other, we thus see that

$$h'\zeta_i = l_i, \tag{2.31}$$

where

$$\frac{1}{\zeta_i} = \frac{1}{\eta_i'} - \frac{1}{\eta_i} \tag{2.32}$$

may be regarded as the "relative coordinates" of planes σ, σ', in the sense that, if A_i, A_i', be the particles in which the planes σ, σ' intersect the edge OP_i of the basic parallelepiped, then $\overrightarrow{A_iA_i'} = \zeta_i^{-1}\mathbf{e}_i$. On substituting for l_i from (2.31) in (2.21), we obtain the equation

$$\frac{1}{h'^2} = \sum_i \sum_j \gamma^{ij}\zeta_i\zeta_j, \tag{2.33}$$

which has the same form as the corresponding equation (2.25). Thus a knowledge of the quantities γ^{ij} is sufficient to determine the separation of any pair of parallel planes, whether one passes through the origin or not.

(2.34) **Theorem.** *A necessary and sufficient condition that a motion be a rigid-body motion is that the quantities γ^{ij} be constant.*

This theorem is similar to the corresponding theorem (2.17) for the quantities γ_{ij}. It could be proved in a similar manner, but it is instructive to prove it instead from the previous theorem (2.17) by taking account of the fact that there are relations (1.21) which can be solved to give γ^{ij} in terms of γ_{ij}, or vice versa. We shall consider the case in which γ_{ij} and γ^{ij} are differentiable functions of t.

Proof. On differentiating (1.21), we have

$$\sum_j \left(\frac{d\gamma_{ij}}{dt}\gamma^{jk} + \gamma_{ij}\frac{d\gamma^{jk}}{dt}\right) = 0.$$

On multiplying this equation by γ^{li} and summing over i, we have

$$\begin{aligned} \sum_i \sum_j \gamma^{li}\frac{d\gamma_{ij}}{dt}\gamma^{jk} &= -\sum_i \sum_j \gamma^{li}\gamma_{ij}\frac{d\gamma^{jk}}{dt} \\ &= -\sum_j \delta_{lj}\frac{d\gamma^{jk}}{dt} \qquad \text{by (1.21)} \\ &= -\frac{d\gamma^{lk}}{dt}. \end{aligned} \tag{2.35}$$

The stated condition is therefore necessary, for if the motion be rigid-body, then $d\gamma_{ij}/dt = 0$ and therefore $d\gamma^{jk}/dt = 0$, by the equation just derived. In a similar manner, we could obtain an equation giving $d\gamma_{jk}/dt$ in terms of $d\gamma^{ij}/dt$ and thereby prove that the condition is also sufficient.

We complete the general discussion of the quantities γ_{ij}, γ^{ij} with the following theorem, which plays a fundamental role in the method of deriving properly invariant rheological equations of state used later in this book.

(2.36) **Theorem.** *Let h_0, h be the values of the separation of a pair of parallel material planes in any two states t_0, t related by a uniform deformation. The strain $t_0 \to t$ is completely determined by the values of the separation ratio h/h_0 for planes of all possible orientations or of six suitably chosen orientations.*

The geometrical implications of this theorem are as follows. In a general uniform deformation, an arbitrary pair of parallel material planes will undergo a relative tangential displacement and a stretching or deformation in themselves (which may involve a change of area of any marked region in the planes) as well as a change of separation. The theorem shows that both the tangential displacement and the deformation in the planes are determined if the change of separation is specified for a sufficient number of planes. Six planes are sufficient to determine the quantities $\gamma^{ij}(t_0)$, because only six of these are independent.

Proof. We may suppose that the base vectors $\mathbf{e}_i$ are specified in one state, say t. The values of γ_{ij} and γ^{ij} in this state are therefore known. Planes of given orientation then have known values of the quantities l_i which satisfy (2.21). For this proof, the symbols h, l_i, γ^{ij} (without suffix t, t_0 or argument t, t_0) will be understood to stand for the appropriate values in state t. It follows from (2.21) and (2.29) that

$$\left(\frac{h}{h_0}\right)^2 = \sum_i \sum_j l_i l_j \gamma^{ij}(t_0). \tag{2.37}$$

If, therefore, the value of the separation ratio h/h_0 is given for all planes, i.e. for all values of l_i subject to (2.21), then the quantities $\gamma^{ij}(t_0)$ are determined, by Theorem (1.27). The values of $\gamma_{ij}(t_0)$ are therefore determined, by (1.23). For any specified pair of particles, the coordinates, ξ^i and $\bar{\xi}^i$ say, and the square of their separation $\sum\sum(\xi^i - \bar{\xi}^i)(\xi^j - \bar{\xi}^j)\gamma_{ij}$ in state t are known; since (as we have seen) $\gamma_{ij}(t_0)$ is determined, it follows that the square of the separation, $\sum\sum(\xi^i - \bar{\xi}^i)(\xi^j - \bar{\xi}^j)\gamma_{ij}(t_0)$, in state t_0 is also determined. Since this is true for every pair of particles, the shape of the material in state t_0 is determined; but the shape in state

t is given, and therefore the strain $t_0 \rightarrow t$ is determined, as stated in the theorem.

From Theorem (1.27), Corollary 3, it can be seen that the above argument still applies if the values of h/h_0 are given for six suitably chosen sets of values of l_i; the six sets (1.32) are a possible choice when the basis is taken to be orthonormal in state t. Thus the strain $t_0 \rightarrow t$ is determined by the values of h/h_0 for planes of six suitably chosen orientations, which completes the proof of the theorem.

Principal Axes of Strain

(2.38) **Theorem.** *In any uniform deformation* $t_0 \rightarrow t$, *there are three material lines passing through any particle which are mutually orthogonal in both states* t_0, t. These lines are called the *principal axes of strain.*

A sphere of unit radius and centre at the given particle, if embedded in the material, will become an ellipsoid after any uniform deformation of the material, because such a deformation is represented by a linear transformation (2.3); the surface in the second state will therefore be represented by an equation of the second degree, and must be an ellipsoid, rather than a paraboloid or hyperboloid, from the continuity of the deformation. The material lines coinciding with the main axes of this ellipsoid are in fact the principal axes of strain as defined in the theorem stated above; they are of course orthogonal in the final state. The proof that they are orthogonal in the initial state is left as an exercise for the reader (Examples 2, No. 2); the solution, which is both important and lengthy, is given in Chapter 11.

The lengths λ_a, λ_b, λ_c of the main semi-axes of the ellipsoid are called *principal values* of strain, or *principal elongation ratios.* The use of sets of quantities other than γ_{ij} for describing strain leads naturally to the definition of other functions (e.g. $\lambda_a^2 - 1$, etc.) as principal values of strain in the literature, but the use of the terms principal elongation ratios or principal extension ratios for the lengths of the semi-axes seems now to be well established. When no ambiguity is likely to arise, the word principal may be omitted and the term elongation ratio used.

There are two degenerate cases to consider. If $\lambda_a = \lambda_b = \lambda_c$, the ellipsoid is itself a sphere; in this case, any three mutually orthogonal material lines can be taken as principal axes. If $\lambda_a = \lambda_b \neq \lambda_c$, one principal section of the ellipsoid is a circle; any two orthogonal material lines in the plane of this circle together with the main axis perpendicular to the plane of the circle may be taken as principal axes. These two cases require a separate proof, which is also given in Chapter 11.

We note that any two of the principal axes at a given particle define a plane which is a material plane since the principal axes are material lines. *The three principal axes define three material planes which are evidently mutually orthogonal in both states t_0, t.* These planes, which we call *principal planes*, form an exception to the general rule in that their normals (in states t_0 and t) are material lines.

The General Uniform Strain

Let us consider any two states t_0, t of a material which are related by a uniform deformation. At any particle O, we may choose a set of embedded base vectors $\mathbf{e}_i$, orthonormal in state t_0, lying along the principal axes

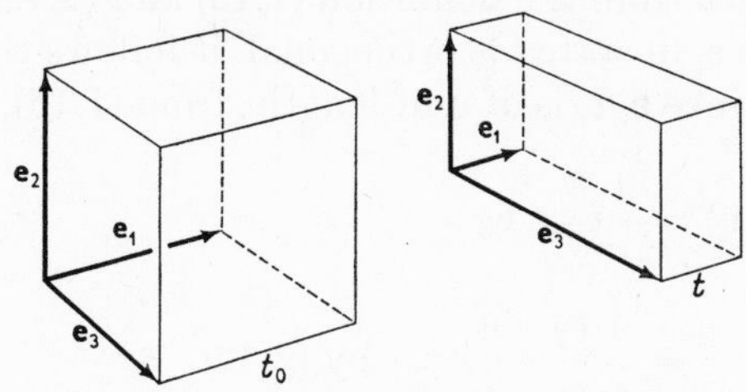

FIG. 2.3.

at 0 for the strain $t_0 \to t$. By Theorem (2.38), this basis will be orthogonal in state t, and the lengths of its axes will be equal to the principal elongation ratios:

(2.39) $$e_i(t) = (\lambda_a, \lambda_b, \lambda_c).$$

From (1.12) and (1.18), it follows that

(2.40) $$\gamma_{ij}(t_0) = \delta_{ij} = \begin{pmatrix} 1 & 0 & 0 \\ 0 & 1 & 0 \\ 0 & 0 & 1 \end{pmatrix} \quad \text{(orthonormal basis)},$$

(2.41) $$\gamma_{ij}(t) = (e_i)^2 \delta_{ij} = \begin{pmatrix} (e_1)^2 & 0 & 0 \\ 0 & (e_2)^2 & 0 \\ 0 & 0 & (e_3)^2 \end{pmatrix} \quad \text{(orthogonal basis)}.$$

With this choice of base vectors, the basic parallelepiped is a unit cube in state t_0 and a rectangular block in state t (Fig. 2.3). All material lines parallel to a given principal axis $\mathbf{e}_i$ undergo the same elongation, by a factor e_i, and remain at right angles to all material lines parallel to the corresponding principal plane (of normal $\mathbf{e}^i$). Planes parallel to this principal plane increase their separation by a factor e_i, and undergo no relative tangential displacement. Planes which are not parallel to a principal plane in general undergo a relative tangential displacement, as we shall see below when we consider simple shear.

To obtain the reciprocal vectors $\mathbf{e}^i$, we first note that

$$v(t_0) = 1, \quad v(t) = e_1 e_2 e_3. \tag{2.42}$$

The basis $\mathbf{e}_i(t_0)$, being orthonormal, is "self-reciprocal" i.e.

$$\mathbf{e}^i(t_0) = \mathbf{e}_i(t_0); \tag{2.43}$$

this follows at once from the definition (1.15) and (2.42).

Since the basis $\mathbf{e}_i$ in state t is orthogonal, it follows that the basis $\mathbf{e}_i/e_i$ is orthonormal, since $\mathbf{e}_i/e_i$ is of unit length; from (1.15), we have

$$\begin{aligned} \mathbf{e}^1 &= \frac{1}{v}\mathbf{e}_2 \wedge \mathbf{e}_3 \\ &= \frac{1}{e_1}\frac{\mathbf{e}_2}{e_2} \wedge \frac{\mathbf{e}_3}{e_3} \qquad \text{by (2.42)} \\ &= \frac{1}{e_1}\frac{\mathbf{e}_1}{e_1}, \quad \text{since } \frac{\mathbf{e}_i}{e_i} \text{ are orthonormal.} \end{aligned}$$

With similar results for $\mathbf{e}^2$ and $\mathbf{e}^3$, we therefore have

$$\mathbf{e}^i(t) = [e_i(t)]^{-2}\,\mathbf{e}_i(t) \tag{2.44}$$

From (2.43), (2.44), and (1.18) it follows that

$$\gamma^{ij}(t_0) = \delta_{ij} = \begin{pmatrix} 1 & 0 & 0 \\ 0 & 1 & 0 \\ 0 & 0 & 1 \end{pmatrix} \quad \text{(orthonormal basis)} \tag{2.45}$$

$$\gamma^{ij}(t) = \frac{\delta_{ij}}{(e_i)^2} = \begin{pmatrix} (e_1)^{-2} & 0 & 0 \\ 0 & (e_2)^{-2} & 0 \\ 0 & 0 & (e_3)^{-2} \end{pmatrix} \quad \text{(orthogonal basis).} \tag{2.46}$$

These equations could alternatively be derived from (2.40) and (2.41) by means of (1.23) and (1.24).

In Fig. 2.3, we have for simplicity drawn the base vectors so that $\mathbf{e}_i(t_0)$ is parallel to $\mathbf{e}_i(t)$, but the above analysis makes no use of this fact; the values of γ_{ij} and γ^{ij} are, as remarked earlier, unaffected by any rigid displacement of the body.

It is an obvious consequence of Theorem (2.38) that any uniform deformation $t_0 \to t$ can be resolved into (i) a rigid *translation*, in which any chosen particle O is brought from its initial to its final place; (ii) a rigid *rotation*, in which the principal axes at O are brought from their initial to their final orientations in space; and (iii) a *strain*, in which the three mutually orthogonal families of lines in the directions of the principal axes are uniformly elongated by the appropriate factors λ_a, λ_b, λ_c. A *deformation* in which there is no rotation of type (ii) is called a *pure strain*; the most general type of pure strain is therefore that represented in Fig. 2.3.

Simple Elongation at Constant Volume

If two of the principal values of strain are equal, the strain is called *simple elongation*. Let us take

$$e_2 = e_3. \tag{2.47}$$

Then

$$1 = v = e_1 e_2 e_3, \tag{2.48}$$

since the volume is constant. This type of strain is of particular interest; it is appropriate to the extension of a filament of rubber, for example. From (2.47), (2.48), we have

$$e_2 = e_3 = (e_1)^{-1/2}, \tag{2.49}$$

and therefore (2.41) and (2.46) become

$$\gamma_{ij}(t) = \begin{pmatrix} (e_1)^2 & 0 & 0 \\ 0 & (e_1)^{-1} & 0 \\ 0 & 0 & (e_1)^{-1} \end{pmatrix}, \quad \gamma^{ij}(t) = \begin{pmatrix} (e_1)^{-2} & 0 & 0 \\ 0 & e_1 & 0 \\ 0 & 0 & e_1 \end{pmatrix} \tag{2.50}$$

Steady Elongational Flow

We have seen that for any two states, related by a uniform deformation, the most general possible strain is that represented in Fig. 2.3 and is completely described when the material lines which are principal axes are specified, together with their corresponding elongation ratios. When deformations involving more than two states have to be considered, as in the flow of a liquid, a new factor arises because a given material line which is a principal axis for one pair of states may or may not be a principal axis for another pair of states; a useful distinction may be drawn between flows for which all principal axes are "constant in the material" and flows for which some (or all) principal axes are not constant in the material. (A principal axis is *constant in the material* if the same material line is a principal axis for every pair of states in the flow considered.) This is perhaps the main distinction to be drawn between the two important types of flow known as elongational flow and shear flow.

In *elongational flow*, all three principal axes of strain are constant in the material; one principal axis defines the direction of elongation, and the principal elongation ratios for the other two principal axes are equal for any given pair of states. We can represent elongational flow by means of the equations just derived for simple elongation $t_0 \to t$ if we regard the state t_0 as an arbitrarily chosen reference state (in which the basis $\mathbf{e}_i$ is orthonormal) and the state t as a variable state, at the current time t, say. We again take the volume to be constant, since this is the case of chief interest in polymer rheology; the general case, with non-constant volume, can easily be dealt with in the present formalism, if required. An elongational flow will be said to be *steady* if the rate of change of length *per unit instantaneous length* in the direction of elongation is constant, i.e. if

$$\frac{1}{e_1}\frac{de_1}{dt} = \bar{G}, \tag{2.51}$$

where $\bar{G}$ is constant. The constant $\bar{G}$ will be called the *elongation rate*; the bar is used to distinguish the symbol from the shear rate G, an analogous quantity defined below. By integrating (2.51), using the inital condition $e_1 = 1$ at $t = t_0$ we obtain the result

$$\begin{cases} e_1(t) = \exp \bar{G}(t-t_0), \\ e_2(t) = e_3(t) = \exp \frac{1}{2}\bar{G}(t_0-t) \qquad \text{by (2.49).} \end{cases} \tag{2.52}$$

Thus in elongational flow the lengths of material lines in the principal directions vary exponentially with time.

From (2.50) and (2.52), we see that

$$\gamma^{ij}(t) = \begin{pmatrix} \exp 2\bar{G}(t_0-t) & 0 & 0 \\ 0 & \exp \bar{G}(t-t_0) & 0 \\ 0 & 0 & \exp \bar{G}(t-t_0) \end{pmatrix}. \tag{2.53}$$

Differentiating this equation and using (2.52), we obtain the result

$$\frac{d\gamma^{ij}}{dt} = \begin{pmatrix} -2\bar{G}(e_1)^{-2} & 0 & 0 \\ 0 & \bar{G}e_1 & 0 \\ 0 & 0 & \bar{G}e_1 \end{pmatrix}.$$

By differentiating this equation and using (2.51) repeatedly, we obtain the result

$$\frac{d^n \gamma^{ij}}{dt^n} = \begin{pmatrix} (-2\bar{G})^n(e_1)^{-2} & 0 & 0 \\ 0 & \bar{G}^n e_1 & 0 \\ 0 & 0 & \bar{G}^n e_1 \end{pmatrix}. \tag{2.54}$$

Thus the higher time derivatives of strain all contain non-zero components; we shall see that this is in contrast to the case of steady shear flow, for which time derivatives of order higher than two are zero.

Dilatation

A uniform strain $t_0 \to t$ in which all three principal values of strain are equal is called a *dilatation* or *isotropic expansion* (or compression). In such a case, we have

$$e_1 = e_2 = e_3 = v^{1/3}, \qquad \text{by (2.48)}, \tag{2.55}$$

and hence, from (2.41) and (2.46), we have

$$\begin{cases} \gamma_{ij}(t) = v^{2/3}\,\delta_{ij} = \begin{pmatrix} v^{2/3} & 0 & 0 \\ 0 & v^{2/3} & 0 \\ 0 & 0 & v^{2/3} \end{pmatrix}, \\ \gamma^{ij}(t) = v^{-2/3}\,\delta_{ij} = \begin{pmatrix} v^{-2/3} & 0 & 0 \\ 0 & v^{-2/3} & 0 \\ 0 & 0 & v^{-2/3} \end{pmatrix}, \end{cases} \tag{2.56}$$

where v is the ratio of volumes of a given material element in states t and t_0. In this type of strain, there is a change of volume but no change of inclination of any pair of material lines (cf. Examples 2, No. 5).

Pure Shear

(2.57) A uniform deformation $t_0 \to t$ is called a *pure shear* if

(i) there is no change of length along one principal axis;
(ii) the volume is constant;
(iii) there is no rotation of the principal axes.

Using the above basis $\mathbf{e}_i$ (orthonormal in state t_0) with $\mathbf{e}_3$ along the principal axis which does not change in length, we have

$$e_3 = 1, \quad e_2 = (e_1)^{-1} \qquad \text{by (2.48)}, \tag{2.58}$$

and hence (2.41) and (2.46) become

$$(2.59)\quad \gamma_{ij}(t) = \begin{pmatrix} (e_1)^2 & 0 & 0 \\ 0 & (e_1)^{-2} & 0 \\ 0 & 0 & 1 \end{pmatrix}, \quad \gamma^{ij}(t) = \begin{pmatrix} (e_1)^{-2} & 0 & 0 \\ 0 & (e_1)^2 & 0 \\ 0 & 0 & 1 \end{pmatrix},$$

while

$$(2.60)\qquad \gamma_{ij}(t_0) = \gamma^{ij}(t_0) = \begin{pmatrix} 1 & 0 & 0 \\ 0 & 1 & 0 \\ 0 & 0 & 1 \end{pmatrix},$$

as in (2.40) and (2.45).

Simple Shear

(2.61) A uniform deformation $t_0 \to t$ is called a *simple shear* if there is a family of parallel material planes, called *shearing planes*, with the following properties:

(i) each shearing plane moves rigidly along a straight line, called a *line of shear*, in its own plane;
(ii) the lines of shear for all shearing planes are parallel;
(iii) the separation of each pair of shearing planes is constant;
(iv) the relative displacement of a pair of shearing planes, divided by their separation, has the same value for all pairs of shearing planes and is called the *magnitude of shear*;
(v) the volume is constant.

The above properties are not all independent; it is clear, for example, that (ii) implies (iii), and that (i) and (iii) imply (v). In fact, by taking account of the properties of uniform deformation, all the above properties can easily be derived from the independent conditions that one plane does not move and that the volume is constant (Examples 2, No. 3).

It should be noted that the sign of the magnitude of shear can be significant; for example, if a shear of magnitude s takes a material from a state t_0 to a state t, then an "equal and opposite shear" of magnitude $-s$ will take the material back to its original state t_0. From this point of view, the use of the word "magnitude" is misleading, in view of its use to denote the positive value of a number. A shear of magnitude s is sometimes called a shear of $|s|$ *shear units*; thus $|s| = 1$ defines one shear unit.

It should also be noted that the term "*line of shear*" is preferable to the term "direction of shear", because, taking any one shear plane as a reference plane, shear planes on one side will have a direction of displacement opposite to that of shear planes on the other side.

We now evaluate the shape variables γ_{ij}, γ^{ij} for a simple shear $t_0 \to t$ using a basic parallelepiped for which one pair of faces, normal to $\mathbf{e}^2$, are shearing planes. For later use, it is convenient to choose the basis $\mathbf{e}_i$ so as to be orthonormal in state t. Let us take any particle O, in any chosen shearing plane, as origin, and let us take $\mathbf{e}_1$ along the line of shear. It should be noted that the choice whether $\mathbf{e}_1$ points in one direction, or the opposite, along the line of shear is arbitrary, even when the shear is specified; let us then choose one direction for $\mathbf{e}_1$. There is now a similar arbitrariness of choice for the direction of $\mathbf{e}_2$, which we take to be normal to the shearing planes in state t; again, let us choose definitely one such direction for $\mathbf{e}_2$. Finally, $\mathbf{e}_3$ is now determined by the stipulation that $\mathbf{e}_1$, $\mathbf{e}_2$, $\mathbf{e}_3$ form a right-handed set.

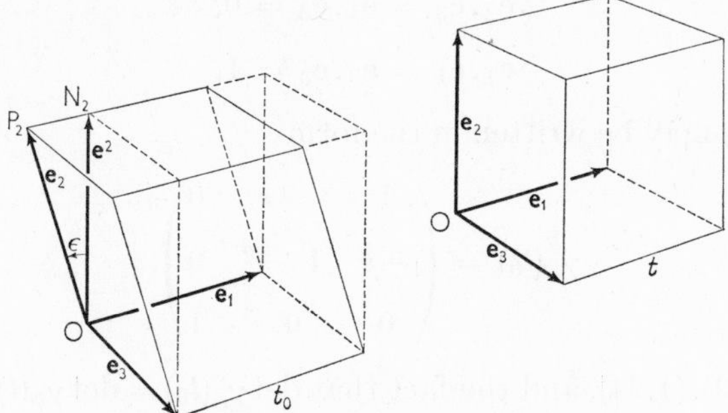

FIG. 2.4. Base vectors for simple shear.

Relative to a definite basis $\mathbf{e}_i$ chosen in this way, we can adopt a sign convention for shear; we shall say that a shear $t_0 \to t$ is positive, i.e. is of magnitude s, where s is positive, if shearing planes on the positive side of O (with respect to the vector $\mathbf{e}_2$) move relative to O in the direction of $\mathbf{e}_1$. Thus the shear $t_0 \to t$ shown in Fig. 2.4 is positive. For a negative shear, planes on the positive side of O move in the direction of $-\mathbf{e}_1$.

In state t, the basis $\mathbf{e}_i$, being orthonormal, is self-reciprocal, and hence we have

$$(2.62) \qquad \gamma_{ij}(t) = \gamma^{ij}(t) = \begin{pmatrix} 1 & 0 & 0 \\ 0 & 1 & 0 \\ 0 & 0 & 1 \end{pmatrix},$$

by (1.12) and (1.18).

The vectors $\mathbf{e}_1$, $\mathbf{e}_3$, being embedded in a rigid plane and orthonormal in state t, must be orthonormal in state t_0; the embedded vector $\mathbf{e}_2$, however, changes in length and orientation (relative to $\mathbf{e}_1$) in the shear, as shown in Fig. 2.4. The *angle of shear* ϵ, may be defined as the inclination of the vector $\mathbf{e}_2$ in state t_0 to the shearing plane normal $\mathbf{e}^2$; with the sign convention that ϵ is positive if $\mathbf{e}^2$, $\mathbf{e}_2$ and $\mathbf{e}_3$ form a right-handed set, the angle of shear and the magnitude of shear s are related by the equation

(2.63) $$s = \tan\epsilon.$$

From Fig. 2.4, it can be seen that, in state t_0, $e_2 = \sec\epsilon$, and

$$\mathbf{e}_1 . \mathbf{e}_2 = e_2 \cos\left(\frac{\pi}{2}+\epsilon\right) = -\tan\epsilon,$$

$$\mathbf{e}_2 . \mathbf{e}_2 = (e_2)^2 = 1+\tan^2\epsilon,$$

remembering that the shearing planes shown have unit separation; also

$$\mathbf{e}_2 . \mathbf{e}_3 = \mathbf{e}_1 . \mathbf{e}_3 = 0,$$

$$\mathbf{e}_1 . \mathbf{e}_1 = \mathbf{e}_3 . \mathbf{e}_3 = 1.$$

These results may be written in the form

(2.64) $$\gamma_{ij}(t_0) = \begin{pmatrix} 1 & -s & 0 \\ -s & 1+s^2 & 0 \\ 0 & 0 & 1 \end{pmatrix}.$$

Using (1.23), (1.24), and the fact that $\det\gamma_{ij}(t_0) = \det\gamma_{ij}(t) = 1$ because the volume is constant, it is a straightforward matter to derive from (2.64) the result

(2.65) $$\gamma^{ij}(t_0) = \begin{pmatrix} 1+s^2 & s & 0 \\ s & 1 & 0 \\ 0 & 0 & 1 \end{pmatrix}.$$

From (2.62), (2.64), and (2.65), we see that

(2.66) $$\gamma_{ij}(t_0)-\gamma_{ij}(t) = \begin{pmatrix} 0 & -s & 0 \\ -s & s^2 & 0 \\ 0 & 0 & 0 \end{pmatrix}, \quad \gamma^{ij}(t_0)-\gamma^{ij}(t) = \begin{pmatrix} s^2 & s & 0 \\ s & 0 & 0 \\ 0 & 0 & 0 \end{pmatrix}.$$

In the classical theory of elasticity, the strains are taken to be infinitesimally small in the sense that, in the case of simple shear, the magnitude s is a first order infinitesimal and second and higher order infinitesimals are neglected. It is seen from (2.66) that, to this order, the diagonal terms in the strain variables $\gamma^{ij}(t_0)-\gamma^{ij}(t)$ are zero, while the non-zero off-diagonal terms are of first order. For finite strains, on the other hand, the diagonal terms are not all zero and for large enough strains can dominate the non-zero off-diagonal terms.

We may therefore expect that the transition from infinitesimally small strains to finite strains will involve not only the replacement of linear by non-linear relations in known "classical" effects but also the occurrence of new effects which have no classical analogue. According to certain theories, some of which are dealt with later in this book, the "Poynting effects" and "Weissenberg effects" are cases in point.

It is seen that material lines parallel to $\mathbf{e}_3$ are orthogonal to the material plane defined by $\mathbf{e}_1$ and $\mathbf{e}_2$ in both states t_0, t; it is to be expected therefore that $\mathbf{e}_3$ defines a principal axis for the simple shear $t_0 \to t$. The calculation

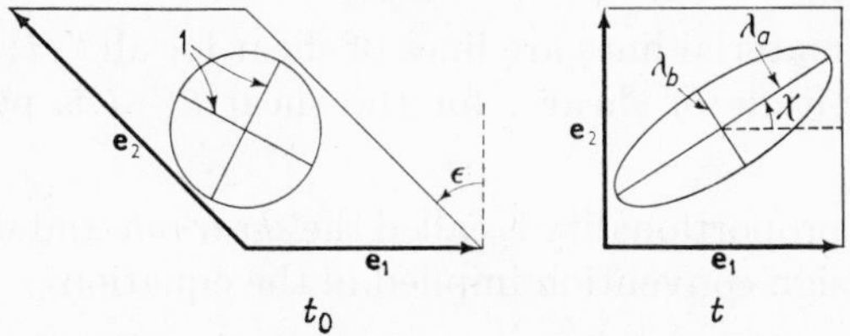

FIG. 2.5. Principal axes for simple shear.

of the principal axes and principal values of strain is set as an exercise for the reader (Examples 2, No. 4); the solution (given in Chapter 11) confirms this expectation, and shows that the other two principal axes lie in the plane of $\mathbf{e}_1$ and $\mathbf{e}_2$ and make angles of $\chi, \chi+(\pi/2)$ with $\mathbf{e}_1$ (Fig. 2.5) where

$$s = 2\cot 2\chi = \cot\chi - \tan\chi, \tag{2.67}$$

and the corresponding principal elongation ratios are

$$\lambda_a = \cot\chi, \quad \lambda_b = \tan\chi, \quad \lambda_c = 1. \tag{2.68}$$

It follows, in particular, that a simple shear is a deformation at constant volume in which there is no change of length along one principal axis, and therefore differs from a pure shear (2.57) only by a rotation of the principal axes. The *strain* (i.e. change of shape) in simple shear is the same as the strain in pure shear, and the distinction between the two is therefore rheologically unimportant where only two states (e.g. the stress-free and stressed states in a perfectly elastic solid, defined in Chapter 4) are rheologically significant; where more than two states are significant (as in an elastic liquid, defined in Chapter 4) and a succession of shears is involved (as in "pure shear flow" and steady shear flow), there is an important difference between the two types of shear: in pure shear flow, the principal axes of strain for every pair of states are represented by the same orthogonal families of material lines, whereas in steady shear flow the principal axes other than $\mathbf{e}_3$ are represented by different material lines for different pairs of states. This can be seen from (2.67) and Fig. 2.5, where the principal axis defined by the value of χ in state t depends on the initial state t_0 through the variable s.

Steady Shear Flow

A continuously varying deformation in which, for every pair of states t' and t, the deformation $t' \to t$ is a simple shear *having the same family of material surfaces as shearing planes* is called a *shear flow*. A shear flow is said to be *steady* if

(i) the same material lines are lines of shear for all t', t; and
(ii) the magnitude of shear s for the shear $t' \to t$ is proportional to $t - t'$;

the constant of proportionality is called the *shear rate* and will be denoted by G, with the sign convention implied in the equation

$$s = G(t-t') \qquad (t' \leqslant t) \tag{2.69}$$

where t', t are understood to denote instants of time.

The shear rate can be seen to be equal to the velocity gradient and is often called the velocity gradient; this is not, however, a very good term for the purpose, as we shall see when we consider generalized types of shear flow involving curved shearing surfaces (Chapter 9); it can be seen, for example, that the superposition of a rigid rotation at constant angular velocity about a fixed axis parallel to $\mathbf{e}_3$ would alter the value of the velocity gradient but would of course have no effect on the changes of shape.

For later use, it is convenient to evaluate time derivatives of the shape variables γ^{ij} relative to a basis $\mathbf{e}_i$ which is *instantaneously* orthonormal at the current instant t in a steady shear flow; we may use the same basis and equations as in the treatment of simple shear $t_0 \to t$, if we use t' instead of t_0 to denote a state at an arbitrary instant t' previous to t. From (2.65) and (2.69) we therefore have

$$\gamma^{ij}(t') = \begin{pmatrix} 1+G^2(t-t')^2 & G(t-t') & 0 \\ G(t-t') & 1 & 0 \\ 0 & 0 & 1 \end{pmatrix}. \tag{2.70}$$

Differentiating this equation with respect to t', we see that

$$\text{(2.71)} \quad \frac{d\gamma^{ij}(t')}{dt'} = \begin{pmatrix} 2G^2(t'-t) & -G & 0 \\ -G & 0 & 0 \\ 0 & 0 & 0 \end{pmatrix}, \quad \frac{d^2\gamma^{ij}(t')}{dt'^2} = \begin{pmatrix} 2G^2 & 0 & 0 \\ 0 & 0 & 0 \\ 0 & 0 & 0 \end{pmatrix},$$

$$\text{(2.72)} \qquad \frac{d^n\gamma^{ij}(t')}{dt'^n} = 0 \quad (n \geqslant 3).$$

In the first of these expressions, the diagonal element arises from the non-orthogonality of the basis at time t'. Having carried out the necessary differentiations, we may let t' tend to t in these equations thus obtaining the following expressions for the required time derivatives relative to a basis ($\mathbf{e}_i$ at t) which is instantaneously orthonormal:

$$\text{(2.73)} \quad \frac{d\gamma^{ij}}{dt} = \lim_{t'\to t} \frac{d\gamma^{ij}(t')}{dt'} = \begin{pmatrix} 0 & -G & 0 \\ -G & 0 & 0 \\ 0 & 0 & 0 \end{pmatrix}, \quad \gamma^{ij} = \begin{pmatrix} 1 & 0 & 0 \\ 0 & 1 & 0 \\ 0 & 0 & 1 \end{pmatrix};$$

$$\text{(2.74)} \qquad \frac{d^2\gamma^{ij}}{dt^2} = \lim_{t'\to t} \frac{d^2\gamma^{ij}(t')}{dt'^2} = \begin{pmatrix} 2G^2 & 0 & 0 \\ 0 & 0 & 0 \\ 0 & 0 & 0 \end{pmatrix}.$$

Here and elsewhere we omit the argument t referring to the current state when there is no danger of ambiguity.

It will be noted that the time derivatives cannot be obtained by differentiating (2.62); the reason is that the required time derivative is equal to $\lim\{\gamma^{ij}(t)-\gamma^{ij}(t')\}/\{t-t'\}$, where $\gamma^{ij}(t)$ and $\gamma^{ij}(t')$ are evaluated with respect to the same system of embedded vectors. Equation (2.62) gives the value of $\gamma^{ij}(t)$ relative to a basis which is instantaneously orthonormal at t and is not orthonormal at t'; the differentiation of (2.62) would correspond to the evaluation of the above limit in which $\gamma^{ij}(t)$ and $\gamma^{ij}(t')$ were both referred to orthonormal bases which could not therefore be a common system of embedded vectors.

It is seen from (2.72) that, in steady shear flow, third and higher order time derivatives of the shape variables γ^{ij} are all zero; from (2.64) and (2.69), it is easy to see that the same is true of γ_{ij}. This is in contrast to the situation with steady elongational flow (as remarked above) for which the corresponding time derivatives of all orders have non-zero components.

It is also seen, from (2.74), that in steady shear flow the second time derivative $d^2\gamma^{ij}/dt^2$ (sometimes called the strain acceleration, or second rate-of-strain) has a non-zero component. As a simple example to show what this implies in geometrical terms, we may substitute the expressions (2.73) and (2.74) for the first and second time-derivatives in equation (2.27), obtaining the equations

$$(2.75) \qquad h^2\frac{d}{dt}\left(\frac{1}{h^2}\right) = -2Gl_1 l_2, \quad h^2\frac{d^2}{dt^2}\left(\frac{1}{h^2}\right) = G^2 l_1^2,$$

which give the time derivatives of h, the separation of an arbitrary pair of parallel material planes, in terms of the actual direction cosines l_i of their normal $\mathbf{n}$ at time t. In particular, for planes normal to the lines of shear, the unit normal $\mathbf{n} = \mathbf{e}_1$; $l_i = \mathbf{e}_1 . \mathbf{e}_i = (1,0,0)$; and hence

$$h^2\frac{d}{dt}\left(\frac{1}{h^2}\right) = 0, \quad h^2\frac{d^2}{dt^2}\left(\frac{1}{h^2}\right) = G^2.$$

This implies that, in the motion of any pair of parallel material planes which are (always) parallel to the embedded vector $\mathbf{e}_3$, the quantity $1/h^2$ has a minimum value, and therefore the separation h has a maximum value, at the instant that the planes are perpendicular to the lines of shear.

This result, which is otherwise obvious, implies that at the current instant t every pair of material planes instantaneously perpendicular to the lines of shear has undergone a steady increase in separation throughout the previous flow history. Weissenberg has used this fact as the basis of an heuristic argument (1949) which suggests that, for materials for which the stress depends on a finite flow history, there should be across planes instantaneously perpendicular to the lines of shear a tensile normal component of stress, if the normal component of stress across the shearing planes, say, is taken as the zero of pressure.

Oscillatory Shear Superposed on Steady Shear Flow

From the definition of *steady* shear flow given above, it is evident that a shear flow will be non-steady if

(i) the shear rate is not constant, or if
(ii) the lines of shear are not "constant in the material", i.e. are not represented by the same family of (parallel) material lines.

A shear flow in which the lines of shear are constant in the material will be called *uni-directional*. As an example of a uni-directional shear flow of experimental interest (Jobling and Roberts, 1959), we consider a combination of a sinusoidally-varying shear and a steady shear flow. We first extend the definition of shear rate to apply to a shear rate which is not constant.

Let $s = s(t,t')$ denote the magnitude of a simple shear $t' \to t$; then

$$s(t,t) = 0. \tag{2.76}$$

Defining the shear rate $\dot{s}$ by the equation

$$\dot{s} = \dot{s}(t) = \lim_{t'\to t} \frac{s(t,t')}{t-t'} = \lim_{t'\to t} \frac{s(t,t')-s(t,t)}{t-t'}, \qquad \text{by (2.76)}, \tag{2.77}$$

we see that

$$\dot{s}(t) = -\left[\frac{\partial s(t,t')}{\partial t'}\right]_{t'=t}. \tag{2.78}$$

For a steady shear flow, it follows from (2.69) and (2.78) that $\dot{s} = G$, in agreement with the previous definition.

To obtain a shear flow in which the shear rate is a sum of a constant and a sinusoidally varying term, let us consider the case

$$\frac{-\partial s(t,t')}{\partial t'} = G + \alpha\omega \cos \omega t', \tag{2.79}$$

where G, ω, and α are constants.

Integrating this equation with respect to t' (t being treated as a constant) and using (2.76) to determine the constant of integration, we obtain the result

$$s = s(t,t') = G(t-t') + \alpha[\sin \omega t - \sin \omega t'], \tag{2.80}$$

which evidently represents a sinusoidally varying shear, of amplitude α and angular frequency ω, superposed on a steady shear flow of shear rate G. From (2.78) and (2.79), the shear rate is given by the equation

$$\dot{s}(t) = G + \alpha\omega \cos \omega t. \tag{2.81}$$

These equations will be used in Chapter 6. We may note here that the presence of the square of s in the diagonal term in γ^{ij} (2.66) will give rise to terms involving the product of G and α and hence may be expected to give rise to effects which can be regarded as arising from an interaction between the steady and oscillatory parts of the flow. There will also be terms involving $\sin 2\omega t$ and $\cos 2\omega t$.

Examples 2

1. If S_{ij} and A_{ij} are any quantities satisfying the relations

$$S_{ij} = S_{ji}; \quad A_{ij} = -A_{ji}; \quad (i,j = 1, 2, 3),$$

prove that $\sum_i \sum_j S_{ij} A_{ij} = 0$. (Quantities such as A_{ij} are said to be *anti-symmetric.*)

2. Prove that in any uniform deformation $t_0 \to t$ there are three material lines through any particle O which are mutually orthogonal in both states t_0, t (Theorem 2.38). The following procedure is suggested.

(i) Consider particles ξ^i lying on the surface of a sphere of centre O and radius unity in state t_0. Determine the values of ξ^i for the particles at the extremities of the main axes of the corresponding ellipsoid in state t by determining the stationary values of $r^2 = \sum_i \sum_j \xi^i \xi^j \gamma_{ij}(t)$ for variations in ξ^i subject to the condition

$$1 = \sum_i \sum_j \xi^i \xi^j \gamma_{ij}(t_0).$$

(ii) Show that the lengths of the main semi-axes of this ellipsoid are the roots in λ of the equation

$$\det[\gamma_{ij}(t) - \lambda^2 \gamma_{ij}(t_0)] = 0.$$

(iii) Show that, when the roots of this equation are all different, the material lines coinciding with the main axes of the ellipsoid are orthogonal in state t_0 and in state t.

3. In a given uniform, non-rigid deformation $t_0 \to t$, the volume is constant, and there is one material plane α every particle of which remains in its original position. Prove that the deformation is a simple shear by deriving the following properties:

(i) Every material plane parallel to α moves rigidly, along a straight line in itself, at constant distance from α.

(ii) For all such planes on one side of α, the displacements are parallel and of magnitude proportional to the distance from α; for planes on the opposite side of α, the displacement is in the opposite direction.

4. Show that, for a simple shear $t_0 \to t$ of magnitude s, the principal elongation ratios have the values

$$\lambda_a = \cot\chi, \quad \lambda_b = \tan\chi, \quad \lambda_c = 1 \qquad (2.68),$$

where $$2\cot 2\chi = s \qquad (2.67),$$

and that the principal axis corresponding to λ_a lies in the plane of $\mathbf{e}_1$ and $\mathbf{e}_2$ (Fig. 2.5) and is inclined to $\mathbf{e}_1(t)$ at an angle χ.

If $s > 0$ and $0 \leqslant \chi \leqslant \pi/2$, show that

$$\lambda_a > 1 \quad \text{and} \quad 0 < \chi < \pi/4.$$

5. Prove that in a uniform dilatation (2.55) there is no change of inclination of any pair of material lines.

6. In any flow at constant volume, prove that

$$\sum_i \sum_j \gamma^{ij} \frac{d\gamma_{ij}}{dt} = 0$$

and

$$\sum_i \sum_j \gamma_{ij} \frac{d\gamma^{ij}}{dt} = 0.$$

7. Let h_0 and h denote the initial and final values of the separation of a pair of parallel material planes in a body which is given an arbitrary uniform deformation $t_0 \to t$; it has been shown that the *separation ratio* h/h_0 has the same value for all pairs of material planes parallel to the given planes and may therefore be regarded as a function of the common unit normal $\mathbf{n}$.

A quantity J_1, called a *strain invariant*, is defined by the equation

$$J_1 = J_1(t_0, t) = \sum_{\mathbf{n}} \left(\frac{h}{h_0}\right)^2,$$

where the summation extends over three mutually orthogonal unit normals $\mathbf{n}$. Prove that, for a given deformation $t_0 \to t$:

(i) J_1 has the same value for every set of three mutually orthogonal normals.

(ii) $J_1 = \lambda_a^2 + \lambda_b^2 + \lambda_c^2$, where λ_a, λ_b, and λ_c are the principal elongation ratios for the deformation $t_0 \to t$.

(iii) The value of

$$\sum_i \sum_j \gamma_{ij}(t)\, \gamma^{ij}(t_0) \qquad (= J_1)$$

is independent of the choice of (embedded) base vectors $\mathbf{e}_i$ used to define γ_{ij}, γ^{ij}.

8. For any uniform deformation $t_0 \to t$, the *relative displacement vector* $\mathbf{r}$ for any given pair of parallel material planes may be defined as follows: let the normal in state t_0 from any particle O on one of the planes meet the other plane in a particle P; then $\mathbf{r} = (\overrightarrow{\mathrm{OP}})_t$.

Prove that

$$\mathbf{r} = \frac{h_0^2}{h} \sum_i \sum_j \gamma^{ij}(t_0)\, l_i\, \mathbf{e}_j,$$

where h_0 and h denote the separations of the planes in states t_0 and t; l_i are the components of the unit normal $\mathbf{n}$ in state t referred to any given embedded basis whose vectors are $\mathbf{e}_i$ in state t. A (second) strain invariant J_2 is defined by the equation

$$J_2 = J_2(t_0, t) = \sum_{\mathbf{n}} \frac{r^2 h^2}{h_0^4},$$

where the summation extends over the terms associated with three mutually orthogonal unit normals $\mathbf{n}$, and r denotes the magnitude of the relative displacement vector $\mathbf{r}$. Prove that:

(i) J_2 has the same value for every set of three mutually orthogonal unit normals $\mathbf{n}$.

(ii) $J_2 = \lambda_a^4 + \lambda_b^4 + \lambda_c^4$, where λ_a, λ_b, and λ_c are the principal elongation ratios for the deformation $t_0 \to t$.

(iii) The value of the expression

$$\sum_i \sum_j \sum_k \sum_m \gamma^{ij}(t_0)\, \gamma_{jk}(t)\, \gamma^{km}(t_0)\, \gamma_{mi}(t)$$

is independent of the choice of (embedded) base vectors used in the evaluation of γ_{ij}, γ^{ij}.

9. In a uniform deformation $t_0 \to t$, the principal elongation ratios are $\lambda_a, \lambda_b, \lambda_c$; $\gamma_0 \equiv \det \gamma_{ij}(t_0)$, and $\gamma \equiv \det \gamma_{ij}(t)$. Prove that:

(i) $$J_3(t_0, t) \equiv \gamma/\gamma_0 = \lambda_a^2 \lambda_b^2 \lambda_c^2;$$

(ii) $$\det\{\Delta^{ij} - (\lambda^2 - 1)\gamma^{ij}\} = 0$$

where $\Delta^{ij} = \gamma^{ij}(t_0) - \gamma^{ij}(t)$, and $\lambda = \lambda_a, \lambda_b$, or λ_c;

(iii) $$K_3 = (\lambda_a^2 - 1)(\lambda_b^2 - 1)(\lambda_c^2 - 1),$$

where $K_3 = K_3(t_0, t) \equiv \gamma \det \Delta^{ij}$.

10. In any uniform flow, the principal values of the nth order time derivative of the shape variables γ_{ij} may be defined as the roots in ω_n of the cubic equation

$$\det\left\{\frac{d^n \gamma_{ij}}{dt^n} - \omega_n \gamma_{ij}\right\} = 0,$$

and the principal axis corresponding to a principal value ω_n as any line parallel to the vector $\mathbf{u} = \sum_i u^i \mathbf{e}_i$, where u^i satisfy the simultaneous equations

$$\sum_j \left\{ \frac{d^n \gamma_{ij}}{dt^n} - \omega_n \gamma_{ij} \right\} u^j = 0 \qquad (i = 1, 2, 3).$$

Prove that:

(i) In steady shear flow of shear rate G, the principal values of $d\gamma_{ij}/dt$ are 0, G, and $-G$.

(ii) In any flow for which one principal axis of $d\gamma_{ij}/dt$ is always parallel to a given material line, one principal axis of $d^n \gamma_{ij}/dt^n$ (for $n = 2, 3, \ldots$) is also always parallel to this line, and

$$\omega_{n+1} = \frac{d\omega_n}{dt} + \omega_1 \omega_n \qquad (n = 1, 2, 3, \ldots),$$

where ω_1, ω_n are the corresponding principal values of

$$\frac{d\gamma_{ij}}{dt}, \quad \frac{d^n \gamma_{ij}}{dt^n}.$$

11. Let $\overrightarrow{\mathrm{OP}} = \sum_i \xi^i \mathbf{e}_i$ be the position vector of a particle P.

(i) Show that the coordinates η_i (cf. (2.23), (2.24)) of the material plane through P perpendicular to $\overrightarrow{\mathrm{OP}}$ are given by the equations

$$\eta_i = \frac{1}{h^2} \sum_j \xi^j \gamma_{ji},$$

where $h = \mathrm{OP}$ is the distance from O to the plane.

(ii) In any given uniform deformation $t_0 \to t$, let OP be a principal axis and λ the corresponding principal elongation ratio. Show that the coordinates η_i of the corresponding principal plane, defined as a material plane through P perpendicular to $\overrightarrow{\mathrm{OP}}$ in state t, satisfy the equations

$$\sum_i \{\gamma^{ji}(t_0) - \lambda^2 \gamma^{ji}(t)\} \eta_i = 0 \qquad (j = 1, 2, 3),$$

and give an analytical proof that this plane is also perpendicular to $\overrightarrow{\mathrm{OP}}$ in state t_0.

CHAPTER 3

The Description of Uniform Stress

The forces which can act on a volume element of a continuous material are of two kinds: *body forces* (due to gravity and inertia), which are proportional to the mass (and therefore to the volume) and whose lines of action are distributed over the whole volume of the element; and *surface forces* (exerted by the material immediately outside the volume element), which act only over the surface of the volume element. Other types of force are conceivable (e.g. a point force, acting on a given particle, is a mathematical possibility; a body couple, proportional to the volume, is a physical possibility in a material, having a volume distribution of electric dipole moment, in an external electric field), but we shall not need to consider them in this book.

It will be assumed that the surface forces acting across any region of a material plane have the following properties: the material on one side of the plane exerts on the material on the other side a force which is proportional to the area of the region, in the limit when this area tends to zero; the material on the other side (since action and reaction must be equal and opposite) exerts an equal and opposite force (which therefore has the same limiting property) on the material on the first side of the plane. Thus *the ratio of surface force to area tends to a finite limit as the area tends to zero*; this limit is a vector called the *traction* and will be denoted by $\mathbf{f}$.

If we express the fact that the traction across a plane depends on its orientation by regarding $\mathbf{f} = \mathbf{f}(\mathbf{n})$ as a vector function of $\mathbf{n}$, a unit normal to the plane, there is an ambiguity of sign which we resolve in the following usual manner. The plane divides the material into two parts, and $\mathbf{n}$ may be chosen (arbitrarily) so as to point towards either part. Let a definite choice for $\mathbf{n}$ be made; the two parts of the material may now be labelled "P-material" and "N-material", according as they lie on that side of the plane towards which $\mathbf{n}$ points or on the opposite side (P for positive, N for negative). We shall use the convention that $\mathbf{f} = \mathbf{f}(\mathbf{n})$ is the traction *which P-material exerts on N-material* (Fig. 3.1). It follows, in particular, that *the normal component of traction* $\mathbf{f}.\mathbf{n}$ *is positive for a tension* and negative for a compression.

It should perhaps be emphasized that, in this discussion of forces acting across a surface, the surface can be inside the material or on the boundary; in the latter case, there must be external forces exerted on the material, by the walls of an apparatus for example, which are equal and opposite to the forces exerted by the material. It should also be noted that the surface forces considered here are not of the type usually called surface tension, which act across a line in a boundary surface; the dimensions of surface tension are those of (force)/(length), while the dimensions of traction are those of (force)/(area).

The assumption that the limit of the ratio (surface force)/(area), as the area tends to zero, exists presupposes that the material can be treated as a continuum; if it is necessary to take account of the discontinuous nature of matter on a molecular scale, one presumes that it will always be possible to define the macroscopic quantity traction in

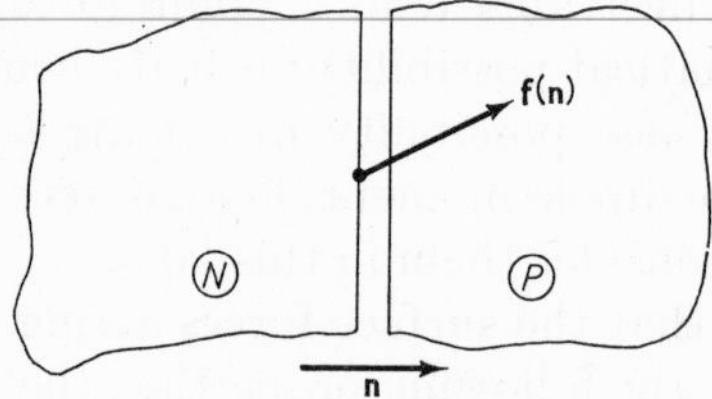

FIG. 3.1. Sign convention for traction.

terms of a suitable space- and time-average over certain microscopic variables throughout a "physically infinitesimal volume element", i.e. a region large enough to contain a very great number of molecules but small enough (on a macroscopic scale) to ensure that the traction can be regarded as constant over the region. A familiar example is furnished by the definition of pressure in a gas.

The totality of tractions $\mathbf{f}(\mathbf{n})$ for planes of all possible orientations $\mathbf{n}$ is called the *stress*, or state of stress, in the material. The stress is said to be *uniform*, or homogeneous, if it is the same throughout the material, i.e. if, for all $\mathbf{n}$, $\mathbf{f}(\mathbf{n})$ is independent of position in the material. In a uniform state of stress, therefore, the traction is the same at all particles in a given material plane, and in every parallel plane.

In a uniform state of stress, the body forces must be zero, or, more precisely, must have zero resultant and can therefore be taken to be zero without loss of generality; for the body forces (including inertial forces) acting on any parallelepiped of material must have a resultant that is equal and opposite to the resultant of the surface forces exerted by the material outside the parallelepiped; but because the areas of opposite faces are equal, the tractions on opposite faces are equal and opposite, and therefore have zero resultant force.

When the stress is uniform, this argument applies whether the parallelepiped is finite or infinitesimally small. When the stress is non-uniform, a similar argument applied to an infinitesimally small parallelepiped (usually a cube) leads to three conclusions. First, the tractions across any two opposite faces are still equal in magnitude, to the lowest order of approximation, because the surface forces are proportional to the area of the faces while the body forces are proportional to the volume; thus the surface forces must "be in equilibrium amongst themselves" whether body forces are present or not. It is therefore profitable to deal first with the problem of describing stress under conditions of uniform stress in the absence of body forces, for such a description can then be applied to each infinitesimally small material element under general conditions of non-uniform stress when body forces are present. Second, the difference in magnitude of surface forces acting across opposite faces is an infinitesimal of the same order as the body force, and hence the equations arising from the conditions of "translational equilibrium" of the material element relate the body forces to the spatial gradients of traction. Third, the conditions of "rotational equilibrium" in the absence of external body couples imply that there are certain relations between the values of the tractions acting across planes of different orientations at any given point (see below).

A state of uniform stress is determined when the tractions across any three planes whose normals are not coplanar (i.e. not parallel to a plane) are given, for the traction across any other plane can be calculated from the conditions for the equilibrium of a tetrahedron whose faces are parallel to that plane and to the three given planes. It is natural, in view of the description of strain given in Chapter 2, to use the faces of the basic parallelepiped whose edges are embedded vectors $\mathbf{e}_i$ as the reference planes across which the tractions are specified; this is done below, first for the case in which the parallelepiped is a unit cube, and then for a general parallelepiped.

This use of a parallelepiped whose faces are material planes is a departure from established practice, for most published treatments take reference planes to be fixed in space, but it is in fact more natural and leads to the definition of stress components whose values are not altered if the material is given any rigid rotation or translation relative to a set of axes fixed in space. Such stress components can therefore be used, along with the shape variables γ_{ij} or γ^{ij}, in a rheological equation of state which will automatically have a significance independent of any rigid motion of the material relative to axes fixed in space. This is a great convenience when one is considering possible forms of rheological equations of state (Oldroyd, 1950a), in particular for materials for which the stress depends on finite strain history; for then the large rotations inherent, for example, in steady shear flow are taken care of. The advantage largely disappears, however, in classical theories of elasticity and hydrodynamics where the relevant strain history is infinitesimally small and the rotations are usually infinitesimally small. Stress components referred to planes or axes fixed in space can of course be used, provided that certain extra terms are included where necessary to subtract unwanted changes arising from rigid-body motions. However, when time derivatives or time integrals of stress are involved (e.g. in certain equations for elastic liquids or visco-elastic solids), the increased complication of the extra terms can be considerable (Chapter 12).

Stress Components in an Orthonormal Basis

To describe a uniform state of stress in a material of given shape, we first introduce an arbitrary orthonormal set of embedded base vectors $\mathbf{e}_i$; the basic parallelepiped is therefore a unit cube.

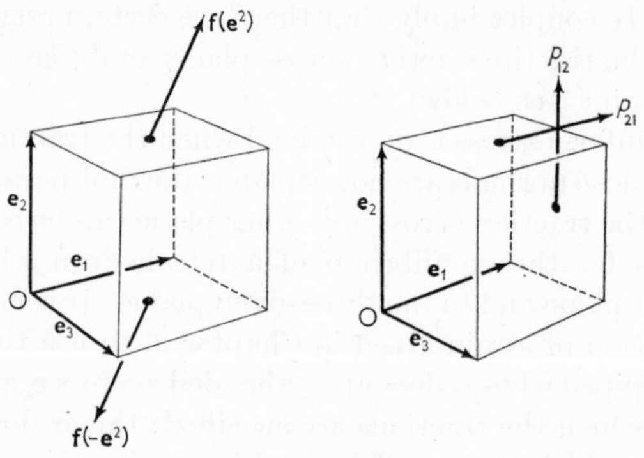

FIG. 3.2.

Let us first consider any pair of opposite faces of the cube, say those having a unit normal $\mathbf{n} = \mathbf{e}^2$ ($= \mathbf{e}_2$, since the basis is self-reciprocal). For the upper face (Fig. 3.2), external material is P-material with respect to the normal $\mathbf{e}^2$ and therefore exerts a traction $\mathbf{f}(\mathbf{e}^2)$ on the cube. Since this traction is the same at all points of the face, the resultant surface force will act at the centre of the face and will also be equal to $\mathbf{f}(\mathbf{e}^2)$, since the face has unit area. For the lower face, using the same normal $\mathbf{e}^2$, external material is N-material and therefore exerts at the centre of the face a force $\mathbf{f}(-\mathbf{e}^2) = -\mathbf{f}(\mathbf{e}^2)$ on the cube. The forces exerted on opposite faces of the cube are thus equal in magnitude and opposite in direction and are therefore equivalent to a couple; a similar statement is evidently true for the forces exerted on the other two pairs of faces. All the forces exerted on the cube are therefore equivalent to a couple, which must be zero; the consequences of this will be given below.

As stated above, the traction acting across any plane of given normal $\mathbf{n}$ can be calculated from the tractions across three orthogonal faces of the cube. The appropriate calculation will be given in detail below for the general case using a parallelepiped, and need not be given here for the cube. The state of stress is therefore determined by the three tractions $\mathbf{f}(\mathbf{e}^i) \equiv \mathbf{f}^i$ $(i = 1, 2, 3)$; it is natural to express each of these vectors as a linear combination of the base vectors $\mathbf{e}_k$, by equations of the form

$$\mathbf{f}^i \equiv \mathbf{f}(\mathbf{e}^i) = \sum_{k=1}^{3} p_{ik}\mathbf{e}_k \qquad (i = 1, 2, 3). \tag{3.1}$$

The stress is therefore determined by the coefficients p_{ik}, which are called *cartesian stress components*. Taking the scalar product of each side of this equation with $\mathbf{e}^j$ and using (1.16), we see that

$$\mathbf{f}^i . \mathbf{e}^j = p_{ij} = \begin{pmatrix} p_{11} & p_{12} & p_{13} \\ p_{21} & p_{22} & p_{23} \\ p_{31} & p_{32} & p_{33} \end{pmatrix}. \tag{3.2}$$

It should be noted that in this array rows and columns have a different significance: for the elements in row i are components of the traction acting across the face of normal $\mathbf{e}^i$, while the elements in column j are the jth components of all three tractions.

We can now consider the condition that there must be no resultant couple acting on the cube. Taking moments about the edge $\mathbf{e}_3$ (Fig. 3.2), we find that $p_{12} = p_{21}$, because other stress components give forces which either have zero moment about the edge $\mathbf{e}_3$ or have moments which cancel one another when opposite faces of the cube are considered; similarly, by taking moments about the edges $\mathbf{e}_1$ and $\mathbf{e}_2$ in turn, we find that $p_{23} = p_{32}$ and $p_{31} = p_{13}$. These results may be expressed in the form

$$p_{ij} = p_{ji} \qquad (i, j = 1, 2, 3), \tag{3.3}$$

showing that the stress components p_{ij} are symmetric. These conditions reduce the number of independent stress components from nine to six. There are no other restrictions, and thus any set of quantities satisfying the symmetry condition (3.3) can represent a state of stress; for the appropriate tractions on the cube faces will be given by (3.1), and the traction across any oblique plane can then be calculated.

The elements p_{11}, p_{22}, p_{33} along the main diagonal of (3.2) are called *normal stress components*, since they represent the components of tractions resolved along the normals to the faces; the off-diagonal elements are called *tangential* or *shear stress components*.

There are three simple states of stress of particular importance.

In a liquid which has been at rest for a sufficient time, there is no tangential component of traction on any plane and the normal component of traction, $-p_0$ say, is the same for all planes. In this state of *hydrostatic pressure*, or isotropic stress, the cartesian stress components in any orthonormal basis evidently have the following values:

$$p_{ij} = \begin{pmatrix} -p_0 & 0 & 0 \\ 0 & -p_0 & 0 \\ 0 & 0 & -p_0 \end{pmatrix}. \tag{3.4}$$

p_0 is positive for a pressure, negative for a tension. The two parts of this definition are not independent, for the tangential components must be zero if the normal components on all planes are equal, as we shall show below, using stress components referred to a general basis.

In a state of *simple tension*, which is used for example in the determination of Young's modulus by elongation of an elastic filament, the traction across one plane is normal to that plane and of magnitude T, say, while the traction across planes perpendicular to this plane is zero. The cartesian stress components referred to an orthonormal basis which has $\mathbf{e}^1$ as the normal to the plane across which the traction T acts are evidently

$$p_{ij} = \begin{pmatrix} T & 0 & 0 \\ 0 & 0 & 0 \\ 0 & 0 & 0 \end{pmatrix}. \tag{3.5}$$

In a state of *shear stress* of magnitude σ, which is equivalent to that used for example in the determination of the shear or rigidity modulus of an elastic solid, an orthonormal basis may be chosen so that the only non-zero components of traction on planes of normals $\mathbf{e}^i$ are tangential components $p_{12} = p_{21} = \sigma$, i.e. we have

$$p_{ij} = \begin{pmatrix} 0 & \sigma & 0 \\ \sigma & 0 & 0 \\ 0 & 0 & 0 \end{pmatrix}. \tag{3.6}$$

For each of these three states of stress, the forces exerted on the faces of a unit cube by material outside it are illustrated in Fig. 3.3.

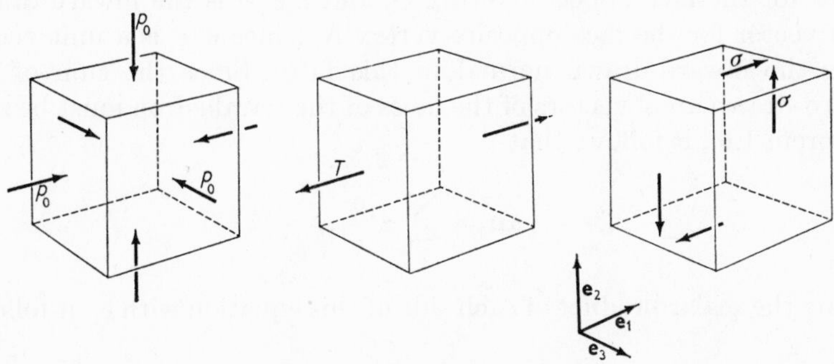

FIG. 3.3. Forces on a unit cube in states of hydrostatic pressure P_0, simple tension T and shear stress σ.

Stress Components in a General Basis

We now extend the above analysis by taking an arbitrary set of base vectors $\mathbf{e}_i$ (not necessarily orthonormal) drawn from any given particle O of a body, and show how to express the traction across any given plane in terms of components of the tractions which act across the faces of the basic parallelepiped.

Theorem. *The traction* $\mathbf{f} = \mathbf{f}(\mathbf{n})$ *acting across an arbitrary plane, whose unit normal drawn from the origin* O *to the plane is* $\mathbf{n} = \sum_i l_i \mathbf{e}^i$, *is given in terms of the tractions* $\mathbf{f}^i$ *acting across planes of normals* $\mathbf{e}^i$ *by the equation*

$$\mathbf{f} = \sum_i \sum_j \pi^{ij} l_i \mathbf{e}_j, \tag{3.7}$$

where

$$\pi^{ij} = e^i \mathbf{f}^i . \mathbf{e}^j. \tag{3.8}$$

The quantities π^{ij}, defined by (3.8), will be called the *stress components relative to*, or in, *the basis* $\mathbf{e}_i$. We may note at once that when the basis is orthonormal, $e^i = 1$ and hence $\pi^{ij} = p_{ij}$, by (3.2). When the basis is not orthonormal, the extra factor e^i in (3.8) arises from the fact that the faces of the basic parallelepiped have different areas (cf. (3.10) below).

Proof. Let the given plane, of normal $\mathbf{n}$, meet the edges $\mathbf{e}_i$ of the basic parallelepiped in particles A_i (Fig. 2.2), and consider the equilibrium of the tetrahedron $OA_1A_2A_3$.

We first derive a relation between the areas of the faces of this tetrahedron. Let α be the area of the face opposite vertex O, and α^i the area of the face opposite vertex A_i. Then $\alpha\mathbf{n}$ is the outward-drawn areal vector for the face opposite vertex O, and $\alpha^i\mathbf{e}^i/e^i$ is the inward-drawn areal vector for the face opposite vertex A_i (since $\mathbf{e}^i/e^i$ is a unit vector along the inward-drawn normal to this face). Since the sum of the inward-drawn areal vectors of the faces of the tetrahedron must be zero (Theorem 1.6), it follows that

$$(3.9) \qquad \alpha\mathbf{n} = \sum_j \alpha^j \frac{\mathbf{e}^j}{e^j}.$$

Taking the scalar product of each side of this equation with $\mathbf{e}_i$, it follows that

$$(3.10) \qquad \alpha^i = \alpha e^i l_i \qquad \text{by (1.16), (2.20).}$$

This is the relation required in the proof.

The forces exerted by material outside the tetrahedron on material inside consist of $\alpha\mathbf{f}$ across the face opposite vertex O and $-\alpha^i\mathbf{f}^i$ across faces opposite vertices A_i; there being no body forces, it follows that for the equilibrium of the tetrahedron we must have

$$\alpha\mathbf{f} = \sum_i \alpha^i \mathbf{f}^i.$$

On substituting for α^i from (3.10), this becomes

$$(3.11) \qquad \mathbf{f} = \sum_i e^i l_i \mathbf{f}^i.$$

But we have the identity (for any vector $\mathbf{r}$)

$$(3.12) \qquad \mathbf{r} = \sum_j \mathbf{r}.\mathbf{e}^j \mathbf{e}_j \qquad \text{(Examples 1, No. 4),}$$

and when this is used with $\mathbf{r} = \mathbf{f}^i$, (3.11) becomes

$$\mathbf{f} = \sum_i \sum_j e^i l_i \mathbf{f}^i.\mathbf{e}^j \mathbf{e}_j,$$

$$= \sum_i \sum_j \pi^{ij} l_i \mathbf{e}_j \qquad \text{by (3.8),}$$

which proves the theorem.

It is evident that the stress components π^{ij} determine the state of stress completely, for the traction across any given plane can be calculated, from (3.7), when they are given.

Of the nine quantities π^{ij}, only six are independent, for they satisfy the symmetry condition

$$\pi^{ij} = \pi^{ji} \qquad (i, j = 1, 2, 3), \tag{3.13}$$

similar to (3.3). The proof of this result, which, like the proof of (3.3), depends on the fact that the resultant couple acting on the basic parallelepiped is zero, is left as an exercise for the reader (Examples 3, No. 3).

The following equations, for the particular cases in which the basis is orthonormal or orthogonal, will often be used in later chapters:

$$\pi^{ij} = p_{ij} \qquad \text{(orthonormal basis)}; \tag{3.14}$$

$$\left.\begin{aligned} \pi^{ij} &= e^i e^j p_{ij} \\ p_{ij} &= e_i e_j \pi^{ij} \end{aligned}\right\} \text{(orthogonal basis)}. \tag{3.15}$$

Of these equations, (3.14) has already been proved, from (3.2) and (3.8). In equations (3.15), the quantities p_{ij} (which, since the basis $\mathbf{e}_i$ is not orthonormal, require definition) are used to denote the cartesian stress components relative to the basis $\mathbf{e}_i/e_i$, which is evidently orthonormal, and therefore $p_{ij} = \mathbf{f}^i . \mathbf{e}^j/e^j$, which follows from (3.2) when $\mathbf{e}^j$ is replaced by $\mathbf{e}^j/e^j$. The first of equations (3.15) now follows at once from (3.8). Since the basis $\mathbf{e}_i$ is orthogonal, $\mathbf{e}^i$ and $\mathbf{e}_i$ are parallel (for any given i) and therefore the equation $\mathbf{e}^i . \mathbf{e}_i = 1$ (1.16) implies that

$$e^i e_i = 1 \qquad (i = 1, 2, 3). \tag{3.16}$$

With this result, the second of equations (3.15) follows from the first.

Although the above description of stress has been made using a basis which was stated to be embedded in the material under consideration, no use has yet been made of this property; in fact, only one state of the material has so far been considered, and the distinction between vectors fixed in space and vectors fixed in the body of course becomes real only when more than one state of the body (i.e. more than one configuration in space) is considered. The stress components π^{ij} or p_{ij}, defined above, can therefore be regarded as relating to a basis fixed in space or embedded in the body.

We now consider a moving body. It is convenient first to consider the case in which the body moves rigidly, and yet exists in a state of stress, which may arise, for example, from some previous strain. The question arises as to what we mean by a *constant stress* in a moving body. *When the body is moving rigidly* (e.g. a stretched elastic filament rotating at constant elongation, and therefore at constant tension), the stress is said to be constant if the traction across any given material plane has constant components relative to any set of base vectors fixed in the material. In this case, π^{ij} or p_{ij}, as defined by (3.8) or (3.2), will be constant if the basis $\mathbf{e}_i$ is embedded in the material, but will vary during the rotation if the basis $\mathbf{e}_i$ is fixed in space.

In order to have a constant state of stress described by constant stress components π^{ij}, we shall therefore take the base vectors $\mathbf{e}_i$ to be embedded in the material.

It now follows from (3.8) that in any non-rigid motion the stress components π^{ij} can vary, not only because the traction components may vary but also because the lengths and mutual inclinations of the base vectors $\mathbf{e}^i$ vary; in particular, constancy of the components π^{ij} does not imply constancy of the traction across a given plane, as we shall see in Chapter 4, where the rubberlike solid is a case in point (cf. also Examples 3, No. 5).

At first sight, this may appear to introduce a complication in the description of stress. However this does not prove to be inconvenient in practice, and in fact it may be that this complication is inherent in the description of stress in a material whose shape is changing. (It may not be possible, for example, to give any useful meaning to the phrase "constant stress in a material whose shape is changing".) (See Appendix 1.)

In any case, it is evident from the definition (3.8) that, for any continuous motion of a material (whether rigid or not), if the material is in a given shape and a given state of stress at time t, then *the stress components π^{ij} have definite values at time t which are not affected if the motion is varied by any rigid-body motion whatever*; for although the vectors $\mathbf{f}^i$, $\mathbf{e}^j$ would be affected, their scalar products (and the magnitude e^i) would not.

We now derive certain results, relating to the normal components of traction, which are required in later chapters in the particular methods which will be used for deriving certain rheological equations of state.

The traction $\mathbf{f}$ acting across any given plane of unit normal $\mathbf{n}$ may be resolved into two components, one parallel to the plane and one normal to the plane. The normal component is given by the equation

$$\mathbf{f}.\mathbf{n} = \sum_i \sum_j \pi^{ij} l_i l_j, \tag{3.17}$$

which is obtained by taking the scalar product of both sides of (3.7) with $\mathbf{n}$ and using (2.20), which defines l_i.

We have stated above, when considering a state of hydrostatic pressure, that if the normal components of traction on all planes are equal then the tangential traction on every plane is zero, thus the state of stress is determined. The following theorem represents a generalization of this result.

(3.18) **Theorem.** *The state of stress in a material is completely determined if the components of traction normal to six suitably chosen planes are given.*

It is reasonable to expect that if the state of stress can be determined by specifying values of normal components of traction then the values for six suitably chosen planes should suffice; for we know that a state of stress is determined by components π^{ij}, six of which are independent.

Proof. By (2.21) and Theorem (1.27), Corollaries 2 and 3, it follows that the quantities $\pi^{ij} = \pi^{ji}$ are determined if the values of the expression on the right-hand side of (3.17) are given for six suitably chosen sets of values of the quantities l_i; one choice of six sets of values is given by (1.32) when the basis is orthonormal. It follows that π^{ij}, and hence also the state of stress, is determined when the values of the normal component of traction, $\mathbf{f}.\mathbf{n}$, are given for six suitably chosen planes.

Corollary. If the values of the component of traction normal to six suitably chosen planes are each equal to $-p_0$, *then*

$$\pi^{ij} = -p_0\gamma^{ij}, \tag{3.19}$$

and the state of stress is a hydrostatic pressure of magnitude p_0.

Proof. By (2.21) and (3.17), we have

$$\sum_i \sum_j (\pi^{ij}+p_0\gamma^{ij})\, l_i l_j = \mathbf{f}.\mathbf{n}+p_0 = 0,$$

for six suitably chosen sets of values of l_i satisfying (1.29). It follows from Theorem (1.27) that

$$\pi^{ij}+p_0\gamma^{ij} = 0,$$

which proves (3.19). On substituting this expression for π^{ij} in (3.7), it follows that the traction $\mathbf{f}$ on any plane, of unit normal $\mathbf{n}$, is given by the equation

$$\begin{aligned} \mathbf{f} &= -\sum_i \sum_j p_0\gamma^{ij} l_i \mathbf{e}_j \\ &= -\sum_i p_0 \mathbf{n}.\mathbf{e}_i \mathbf{e}^i \qquad \text{by (1.20), (2.20),} \\ &= -p_0\mathbf{n}, \qquad \text{by Examples 1, No. 4, with } \mathbf{r} = \mathbf{n}. \end{aligned}$$

Thus the traction on every plane is parallel to the normal and represents a pressure of magnitude p_0; there is therefore no tangential component of traction on any plane, and the state of stress is a hydrostatic pressure, according to the definition given earlier.

It is sometimes convenient to consider the superposition, in a given state, of two or more states of stress. If π^{ij} and π'^{ij} are the stress components for any two states of stress when the material has a given shape, and $\mathbf{f}$ and $\mathbf{f}'$ are the corresponding tractions across any given plane, then, since (3.7) is linear in $\mathbf{f}$ and π^{ij}, it follows that

(3.20) $$\mathbf{f}+\mathbf{f}' = \sum_i \sum_j (\pi^{ij}+\pi'^{ij})\, l_i \mathbf{e}_j,$$

But the vector sum $\mathbf{f}+\mathbf{f}'$ represents the resultant of the two tractions $\mathbf{f}$ and $\mathbf{f}'$, and therefore the sum $\pi^{ij}+\pi'^{ij}$ represents the stress components in the state of stress resulting from the superposition of the two states π^{ij}, π'^{ij}.

In dealing with incompressible materials, we shall make frequent use of this result in the case in which one of the two states of stress is a hydrostatic pressure p_0; the corresponding quantities

(3.21) $$\pi^{ij}+p_0\gamma^{ij} \equiv \Pi^{ij}$$

have been called components of the *extra stress*. When the basis is orthonormal, these components may be written in the form

$$\pi^{ij}+p_0\gamma^{ij} = \begin{pmatrix} p_{11}+p_0 & p_{12} & p_{13} \\ p_{21} & p_{22}+p_0 & p_{23} \\ p_{31} & p_{32} & p_{33}+p_0 \end{pmatrix},$$

because of (2.62), (3.14).

The State of Stress in an Isotropic Material in Shear

We now consider a simple shear $t_0 \to t$ in a material which is isotropic in the sense that insofar as the rheological properties are concerned all directions in the material are equivalent. Let us further suppose that the stress in state t is determined, either completely or to within an additive hydrostatic pressure, by the strain $t_0 \to t$.

It can be seen from Fig. 3.4 that simple shear is symmetric with respect to a rotation of axes about $\mathbf{e}_3$ through 180° relative to the material, in the sense that the description of simple shear using axes $\mathbf{e}_1$, $\mathbf{e}_2$, $\mathbf{e}_3$ as shown is identical to the description using a second set of axes $\mathbf{e}'_1$, $\mathbf{e}'_2$, $\mathbf{e}'_3$, where

(3.22) $$\mathbf{e}'_1 = -\mathbf{e}_1, \quad \mathbf{e}'_2 = -\mathbf{e}_2, \quad \mathbf{e}'_3 = \mathbf{e}_3.$$

Since the material is isotropic, and therefore possesses no preferred directions, and the stress is determined by the shear $t_0 \to t$, it follows that the stress must possess the same property of symmetry as the shear. This means that the stress must have the same description relative to the two sets of base vectors $\mathbf{e}_i$, $\mathbf{e}'_i$, i.e. that

(3.23) $$p_{ij} = p'_{ij}$$

where p_{ij} are the cartesian stress components relative to the basis $\mathbf{e}_i$, and p'_{ij} those relative to $\mathbf{e}'_i$.

Using a prime to denote quantities associated with the basis $\mathbf{e}'_i$, (3.23) and (3.2) imply that

$$\mathbf{f}^i.\mathbf{e}^j = \mathbf{f}'^i.\mathbf{e}'^j, \tag{3.24}$$

where $\mathbf{f}^i = \mathbf{f}(\mathbf{e}^i)$ and $\mathbf{f}'^i = \mathbf{f}(\mathbf{e}'^i)$.

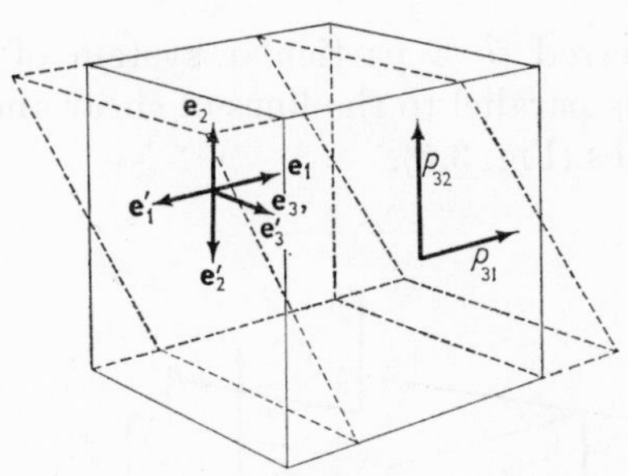

FIG. 3.4.

From (1.15), (3.22), and the fact that the basis $\mathbf{e}_i$ is orthonormal, we have $\mathbf{e}'^1 = \mathbf{e}'_2 \wedge \mathbf{e}'_3 = (-\mathbf{e}_2) \wedge \mathbf{e}_3 = -\mathbf{e}^1$, etc., i.e.

$$\begin{cases} \mathbf{e}'^1 = -\mathbf{e}^1, \\ \mathbf{e}'^2 = -\mathbf{e}^2, \\ \mathbf{e}'^3 = \mathbf{e}^3. \end{cases} \tag{3.25}$$

Hence, in particular, $\mathbf{f}'^3 = \mathbf{f}(\mathbf{e}'^3) = \mathbf{f}(\mathbf{e}^3) = \mathbf{f}^3$, and equations (3.24) for $i = 3, j = 1, 2$ become

$$\mathbf{f}^3.\mathbf{e}^1 = \mathbf{f}^3.(-\mathbf{e}^1) = -\mathbf{f}^3.\mathbf{e}^1,$$

$$\mathbf{f}^3.\mathbf{e}^2 = \mathbf{f}^3.(-\mathbf{e}^2) = -\mathbf{f}^3.\mathbf{e}^2,$$

which can be satisfied only if $\mathbf{f}^3.\mathbf{e}^1 = \mathbf{f}^3.\mathbf{e}^2 = 0$. By (3.2) and (3.3), it follows that

$$\begin{cases} p_{31} = p_{13} = 0, \\ p_{32} = p_{23} = 0. \end{cases} \tag{3.26}$$

It is easy to verify that this exhausts the information obtainable from (3.23), for the equations obtained with other values for i and j contain terms which involve products of two minus signs or none and are satisfied identically.

It follows therefore that the most general possible state of stress for an isotropic material in simple shear is that represented by the cartesian stress components

$$p_{ij} = \begin{pmatrix} p_{11} & p_{12} & 0 \\ p_{21} & p_{22} & 0 \\ 0 & 0 & p_{33} \end{pmatrix} \tag{3.27}$$

when these are referred to a particular system of orthonormal base vectors in which $\mathbf{e}_i$ is parallel to the lines of shear and $\mathbf{e}_2 = \mathbf{e}^2$ is normal to the shearing planes (Fig. 3.5).

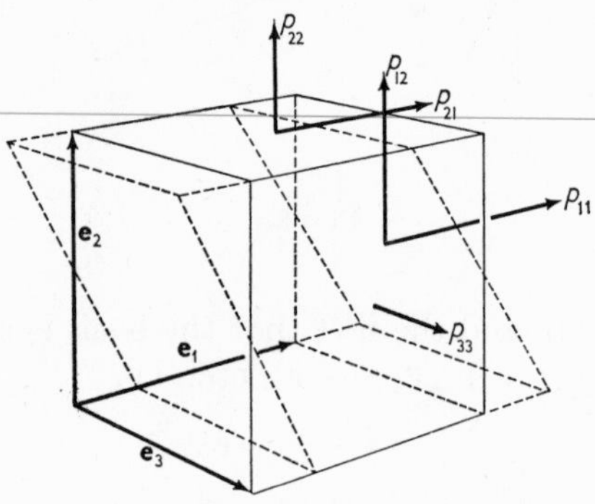

FIG. 3.5.

In an incompressible material, the state of stress is determined by the strain or strain history only to within an additive hydrostatic pressure, and therefore the absolute value of any one normal component of stress is of no rheological significance. The values of the differences of normal stress components are, however, not altered by the addition of any hydrostatic pressure, and presumably depend on the rheological properties of the material. It follows, therefore, that there are only three independent stress quantities of rheological significance, namely two differences of normal components and one tangential component:

$$p_{22}-p_{33}, \quad p_{11}-p_{22}, \quad p_{21}; \tag{3.28}$$

the third difference $p_{11}-p_{33}$ of normal components is the sum of these two differences, and the other non-zero tangential component p_{12} is equal to p_{21}, by (3.3).

In the foregoing argument, it is assumed that the stress (or extra stress) in state t is determined by the shape of the material in two states t_0, t related by a simple shear; the argument is therefore applicable to any isotropic perfectly elastic solid (defined in Chapter 4).

It is easy to see, however, that the argument can be extended so as to apply to any isotropic material for which the stress (or extra stress) in a state t is determined by the shape of the material in any number of states provided these are all related to the state t by simple shears with common shearing planes and common lines of shear; for the whole of such a strain history will have, in state t, the same symmetry (with respect to a 180° rotation about $\mathbf{e}_3$) as that possessed by a single simple shear $t_0 \rightarrow t$.

It follows therefore that (3.27) represents the most general state of stress possible in any isotropic material (elastic liquid or viscoelastic solid, as defined in Chapter 4) in a state of steady shear flow or in any non-steady *uni-directional* shear flow.

The normal stress differences, $p_{11}-p_{22}$ and $p_{22}-p_{33}$, which are both zero in materials considered in classical theories of elasticity and hydrodynamics, can have non-zero values for polymer systems (Chapter 10) and are at present the object of an increasing amount of investigation.

The measurement of the normal stress differences (3.28), which is discussed in Chapter 9, involves the use of shear or shear flow with curved lines of shear and curved shearing surfaces and therefore requires an extension of the above argument to non-uniform states of stress and strain. The above argument is due to Weissenberg (cf. Russell, 1946), who has given the necessary extension for the case of shear flow between a cone and plate in relative rotation (cf. Roberts, 1952). Further extensions, applicable to other systems of experimental interest, have been given by Coleman and Noll (1959a). Poynting (1909, 1912) appears to have been the first to suggest that unequal normal stress components might arise in *finite* shear of an elastic solid; in classical theories confined to infinitesimally small strains, the normal stress components in shear are equal to one another.

Examples 3

1. In any state of uniform stress, a plane across which there is no tangential component of traction is called a *principal plane*; any line normal to a principal plane is called a *principal axis*, and the normal component of traction on a principal plane is called a *principal value* of stress, or principal stress.

(i) Show that in any uniform state of stress the equations which determine a principal axis $\mathbf{n} = \sum_i l_i \mathbf{e}^i$ may be written in the form

$$\sum_i (\pi^{ij} - \sigma\gamma^{ij})\, l_i = 0 \qquad (j = 1, 2, 3),$$

where π^{ij} are the stress components and σ is the corresponding principal value of stress.

(ii) Deduce that there are in general three principal values of stress, and that (when these are all different) the three corresponding principal axes are mutually orthogonal.

2. Determine the principal axes and principal values of stress for the state of stress (3.27) appropriate to an isotropic material in steady shear flow. Show that two principal axes lie in the plane of $\mathbf{e}_1$, $\mathbf{e}_2$ (Fig. 3.5) and that one of these principal axes lies in the positive quadrant (defined by $\mathbf{e}_1$, $\mathbf{e}_2$) making an angle χ' with $\mathbf{e}_1$, where

$$2 \cot 2\chi' = \frac{p_{11} - p_{22}}{p_{21}},$$

and that the corresponding principal value of stress is equal to

$$\tfrac{1}{2}(p_{11} + p_{22}) + p_{21} \operatorname{cosec} 2\chi'.$$

Show that the difference of principal values of stress corresponding to the two principal axes in the plane of $\mathbf{e}_1$ and $\mathbf{e}_2$ is equal to

$$2 p_{21} \operatorname{cosec} 2\chi'.$$

3. By considering the surface forces exerted on the basic parallelepiped and taking moments about the particle at the centre of this parallelepiped (or otherwise), prove that

$$\sum_i e^i \mathbf{f}^i \wedge \mathbf{e}_i = 0.$$

Deduce that $\pi^{ij} = \pi^{ji}$. (The moment about a point O of a force $\mathbf{f}$ whose line of action passes through a point P is a vector $\mathbf{r} \wedge \mathbf{f}$, where $\mathbf{r} = \overrightarrow{\mathrm{OP}}$.)

4. Show that the rate of working of the external surface forces on the material in the basic parallelepiped is

$$\frac{1}{2\rho} \sum_i \sum_j \pi^{ij} \frac{d\gamma_{ij}}{dt}$$

per unit mass, where ρ is the density of the material.

5. Prove that, if h is the separation of any given pair of parallel material planes of unit normal $\mathbf{n} = \sum l_i \mathbf{e}^i$, the rate of change of the normal component of traction on these planes satisfies the equation

$$h^2 \frac{d}{dt}\left(\frac{\mathbf{f}.\mathbf{n}}{h^2}\right) = \sum_i \sum_j \frac{d\pi^{ij}}{dt} l_i l_j.$$

(This result gives a direct interpretation of the time derivative $d\pi^{ij}/dt$.)

6. Prove that, in any uniform state of stress, the sum of the normal components of traction on each of a set of three mutually orthogonal planes has the same value for every such set.

Deduce that the value of the expression $\sum_i \sum_j \pi^{ij} \gamma_{ij}$ is independent of the choice of base vectors.

Show that the value of the expression $\sum_i \sum_j \pi^{ij} \gamma^{ij}$ is dependent on the choice of base vectors.

7. In a given state of stress, $\mathbf{f}.\mathbf{n}$ is the component of traction normal to an arbitrary plane, of unit normal $\mathbf{n}$. The "polar diagram" of the quantity $(\mathbf{f}.\mathbf{n})^{-1/2}$ is defined as the locus, as $\mathbf{n}$ varies, of the point P, where $\overrightarrow{\mathrm{OP}} = (\mathbf{f}.\mathbf{n})^{-1/2}\mathbf{n}$ and O is a given particle; when $\mathbf{f}.\mathbf{n} \leqslant 0$, P is not defined.

Show that the equation of this polar diagram is

$$\sum_i \sum_j \pi^{ij} x_i x_j = 1$$

where π^{ij} are the stress components and x_i the coordinates of P relative to any set of base vectors $\mathbf{e}^i$ (i.e. $\overrightarrow{\mathrm{OP}} = \sum_i x_i \mathbf{e}^i$).

If the basis is orthonormal and coincides with the principal axes of stress, show that the stress components and the equation for the polar diagram take the forms

$$\pi^{ij} = \begin{pmatrix} \sigma_a & 0 & 0 \\ 0 & \sigma_b & 0 \\ 0 & 0 & \sigma_c \end{pmatrix}, \quad \sigma_a(x_1)^2 + \sigma_b(x_2)^2 + \sigma_c(x_3)^2 = 1,$$

where σ_a, σ_b, σ_c are the principal values of stress.

This polar diagram is known as the "stress quadric".

8. In any state of stress for which $\det \pi^{ij} \neq 0$, the polar diagram of the traction is defined as the locus, as $\mathbf{n}$ varies, of the point P, where $\overrightarrow{OP} = \mathbf{f}$, the traction across a plane of normal $\mathbf{n}$, and O is any given particle. If x^i are the coordinates of P relative to a basis $\mathbf{e}_i$ (i.e. $\overrightarrow{OP} = \sum_i x^i \mathbf{e}_i$), show that the equation of this polar diagram may be written in the form

$$\sum_i \sum_m \sum_k \sum_j \bar{\pi}_{mi} \gamma^{mk} \bar{\pi}_{kj} x^i x^j = 1,$$

where $\bar{\pi}_{ij}$, the quantities "reciprocal" to π^{ij}, are defined by the equations

$$\sum_j \bar{\pi}_{ij} \pi^{jk} = \delta_{ik} \qquad (i, k = 1, 2, 3).$$

Show that, when the basis is orthonormal and coincides with the principal axes of stress, the equation for the polar diagram takes the form

$$\left(\frac{x^1}{\sigma_a}\right)^2 + \left(\frac{x^2}{\sigma_b}\right)^2 + \left(\frac{x^3}{\sigma_c}\right)^2 = 1, \quad \text{and that} \quad \bar{\pi}_{ij} = \begin{pmatrix} \sigma_a^{-1} & 0 & 0 \\ 0 & \sigma_b^{-1} & 0 \\ 0 & 0 & \sigma_c^{-1} \end{pmatrix},$$

where σ_a, σ_b, σ_c are the principal values of stress.

This polar diagram is known as the "stress ellipsoid", or "reciprocal stress ellipsoid".

CHAPTER 4

The Rubberlike Solid

In the preceding chapters we have seen that, relative to any set of base of vectors embedded in a given material, the shape and stress in any state may be uniquely and completely described by the values assigned to the variables γ^{ij} (or γ_{ij}) and π^{ij}. We are now in a position to consider what different forms of relation between these variables may be required to describe the rheological behaviour of various materials of interest, notably polymer solids and liquids.

Since the values of γ^{ij} and π^{ij} depend also on the choice of base vectors, whereas the rheological behaviour does not, it will be necessary to ensure that the relations between γ^{ij} and π^{ij} have a significance which is independent of the choice of base vectors. This imposes a real restriction on the possible forms of rheological equations of state (cf. Examples 4, No. 5). General rules for the immediate recognition of admissible equations are stated in Chapter 8 and proved in Chapter 12 by methods which lie outside the scope of the rest of this book. In the present chapter and the following two chapters, we reach the same goal by a different route: we use certain elementary methods which automatically lead to admissible equations for some important particular idealized materials, viz. the rubberlike elastic solid (this chapter), the Newtonian viscous liquid (Chapter 5), and a particular elastic liquid (Chapter 6). These examples together give sufficient illustration of the main points at issue.

Terminology

It is first necessary to say what we shall mean by the terms solid, liquid, elastic, viscous, and incompressible, without embarking on the difficult project of classifying all the conceivable types of rheological behaviour—a project that has received some attention in the literature (Weissenberg, 1931; Noll, 1958).

To simplify the wording, we shall take the temperature to be constant throughout; the materials will of course be treated as continuous.

(4.1) A material will be called *incompressible* if

(i) the volume of each material element is constant, and

(ii) the shape of no material element can be altered by the superposition of any hydrostatic pressure (positive or negative).

These conditions are to apply whether the material is at rest or undergoing any strain history whatever. Condition (i) is a very good approximation to the truth for polymer solutions (and liquids generally); for polymer solids in the rubberlike state; but not of course for gases, which we exclude from our consideration. Condition (ii) may require justification.

We shall confine our attention to materials which are incompressible, unless the contrary is stated (e.g. in Chapter 8), and which are such that *the stress in any state t is determined to within an arbitrary additive hydrostatic pressure p by the strain history.*

It follows therefore that the rheological equations of state must be expressible in the form

$$(4.2) \qquad \pi^{ij}(t) = -p\gamma^{ij}(t) + \mathscr{F}^{ij}\left\{\gamma^{rs}(t') \quad \begin{matrix}\text{for } r, s = 1, 2, 3 \\ \text{and all } t' \leqslant t\end{matrix}\right\} (i, j = 1, 2, 3).$$

Here, the generalized "functional" symbol $\mathscr{F}^{ij}$ must at this stage be allowed to encompass not only algebraic combinations of the values of the variables γ^{ij} at various times but also their time derivatives and time integrals, and the time itself may occur explicitly. The coefficients involved can include scalar constants representing elastic moduli, relaxation times, viscosity, and possibly other material constants having no familiar classical analogue. It is the form of these equations, embodied in the symbol $\mathscr{F}^{ij}$, which will vary from one material to another.

The materials will be supposed *homogeneous* in the sense that the relations (4.2) are independent of position in the material, and therefore do not contain particle coordinates ξ^i.

If a material is anisotropic in the sense that not all material lines are equivalent with respect to rheological behaviour, then the coefficients involved in $\mathscr{F}^{ij}$ could embody certain vectors parallel to material lines along the preferred or special directions in the material. We shall consider materials which are *isotropic* in the sense that there are no such special directions in the material. The term anisotropic is sometimes used in rheology in a rather different sense (Weissenberg, 1935) to describe the fact that a flowing material (which may be isotropic in the above sense) can exhibit anisotropic behaviour in regard to the relation between small changes in the given state of flow and the associated small changes of stress; such "anisotropy", however, may be regarded as induced by the flow, rather than inherent in the material.

(4.3) A material will be called an *elastic solid*, or a solid, if

(i) there is a unique equilibrium shape, $\gamma^{ij}(t_0)$ say, at zero stress, and

(ii) when the material is held in any shape γ^{ij} other than $\gamma^{ij}(t_0)$, the stress attains a non-isotropic equilibrium state which is determined to within an arbitrary additive hydrostatic pressure by the given shape γ^{ij}.

It should be noted that the symbol t_0 in this context is a label for a particular shape, the "stress-free shape $\gamma^{ij}(t_0)$", and does not denote an instant of time.

(4.4) A solid will be called *perfectly elastic*, or ideally elastic, if the equilibrium shape in (i) *and* the equilibrium extra stress in (ii) are attained *instantaneously*; if either the shape in (i) or the extra stress in (ii) or both take finite times to attain equilibrium, the solid will be called *visco-elastic*, non-ideally elastic, or imperfectly elastic.

We should expect therefore that for a perfectly elastic solid the equations (4.2) will involve the shape variables $\gamma^{ij}(t)$ and $\gamma^{ij}(t_0)$ but neither time derivatives nor time integrals nor values of the shape variables appropriate to states other than the current state t and the stress-free state t_0, to which the material must return as soon as the stress is made isotropic. Time derivatives and time integrals of shape variables would be expected to introduce delay into such a return, and may therefore occur in the equations for a viscoelastic solid.

(4.5) A material will be called a *liquid* if, when it is held in any constant shape, the stress always attains an equilibrium state which is isotropic (or zero). This implies that a liquid at rest cannot support a shear stress.

A liquid is called *non-viscous*, inviscid, or ideal, if the stress is always isotropic whatever the state of flow or flow history may be, i.e. if the liquid can never sustain a shear stress. A *viscous* liquid can sustain a shear stress, or non-isotropic stress, in flow.

(4.6) A liquid will be called *purely viscous* or *inelastic* if, following any flow history,

(i) the stress becomes *instantaneously* isotropic (or zero) as soon as the liquid is held in any constant shape, and

(ii) the liquid remains at constant shape as soon as the stress is made instantaneously isotropic (or zero).

If either or both of these conditions are not satisfied, the liquid will be called *elastic*, or *viscoelastic*. If (i) is not satisfied, the liquid exhibits the phenomenon of *stress relaxation*. If (ii) is not satisfied, the liquid exhibits the phenomenon of *elastic recovery*.

The terms solid and liquid, as defined above, are mutually exclusive; for a solid can have only one equilibrium shape at zero stress, while a liquid can have any equilibrium shape at zero stress. It is to be expected therefore that the rheological equations of state (4.2) for a liquid will not contain shape variables (such as $\gamma^{ij}(t_0)$ for an elastic solid) referring to any unique state of permanent rheological significance; for a purely viscous liquid, the first time derivative $d\gamma^{ij}/dt$ may be expected to occur, in addition to the variables γ^{ij} themselves, while for elastic liquids higher time derivatives and time integrals may occur.

The foregoing discussion rests to some extent on the work of Oldroyd (1950a, b).

Derivation of Rheological Equations of State

We shall now derive the rheological equations of state for a particular hypothetical elastic solid, using a method which automatically ensures that the equations have a form and significance which is not dependent on the choice of base vectors.

Hypothesis. Let there be an incompressible material for which, in any state t, the component of traction $\mathbf{f}$ normal to an arbitrary material plane of unit normal $\mathbf{n}$ is given in terms of the separation h of that plane from any parallel material plane by an equation of the form

$$\mathbf{f}.\mathbf{n} = \mu_0 \frac{h^2 - h_0^2}{h_0^2} - p_0, \tag{4.7}$$

where h_0 is the value of h in a particular state t_0, μ_0 is a positive constant, and p_0 may depend on t but not on $\mathbf{n}$.

This hypothesis (a particular case of a hypothesis due to Weissenberg (1949)) evidently represents one possible generalization of an elementary fact of experience, namely, that if a tensile stress be applied to a material such as rubber, the material lines in the direction of the tension increase in length and parallel material planes normal to the direction of the tension increase in separation. The normal component of traction, according to (4.7), is clearly an increasing function of the separation ratio h/h_0; while any increasing function would be *a priori* permissible, the particular one chosen (in view of (2.29)) makes the subsequent mathematics easier and does in fact represent a case of considerable interest in the field of polymers, as we shall presently see.

In the state t_0, we have $h = h_0$ and hence, from (4.7), $\mathbf{f}.\mathbf{n} = -p_0$. Thus the normal component of traction has the same value on every material plane, and therefore the stress is isotropic, by Theorem (3.18), Corollary.

The question now arises as to whether the hypothesis is self-consistent. We have seen that the normal components of traction when specified on each of six suitably chosen planes serve to determine the state of stress completely; the normal components on every other plane are therefore determined. The hypothesis, however, specifies the normal component of traction (to within an additive constant $-p_0$) on every plane, and we have to show that the values so specified do represent a possible state of stress. (Cf. Examples 3, No. 7, for a geometric illustration of the restrictions on the possible values of normal components of traction.) This point will be covered in the course of the following argument.

According to Theorems (2.36) and (3.18), the specifying of separation ratio values and normal component of traction values on a sufficient number of planes determines the states of strain and stress completely; we would therefore expect that the hypothesis is sufficient to determine the stress–strain relations of the material for any type of strain $t_0 \to t$, showing that the hypothetical material is rheologically well-defined. We now show that this is in fact the case by deriving the stress–strain relations in terms of the variables π^{ij}, γ^{ij} for an arbitrary state t and *for an arbitrary basis of embedded vectors* $\mathbf{e}_i$.

Equations (2.29) and (3.17) give expressions for $(h^2 - h_0^2)/h_0^2$ and $\mathbf{f}.\mathbf{n}$ in terms of the quantities l_i which define the orientation of the normal $\mathbf{n}$; by using the fact that the quantities l_i satisfy the restriction (2.21), we can express the term in p_0 in a similar form. Thus (4.7) is equivalent to the following equation:

$$(4.8) \qquad \sum_i \sum_j \pi^{ij} l_i l_j = \mu_0 \sum_i \sum_j \{\gamma^{ij}(t_0) - \gamma^{ij}\} l_i l_j - p_0 \sum_i \sum_j \gamma^{ij} l_i l_j,$$

where π^{ij}, γ^{ij} and l_i refer to the state t. Since by hypothesis this equation is valid for all values of l_i subject to the condition (2.21), it follows from Theorem (1.27), on collecting all the terms in (4.8) together, that the coefficient of $l_i\, l_j$ must be zero, i.e. that

$$(4.9) \qquad \pi^{ij} + p_0 \gamma^{ij} = \mu_0\{\gamma^{ij}(t_0) - \gamma^{ij}\} \qquad (i, j = 1, 2, 3).$$

The condition of incompressibility implies that the volume will be constant whatever the stress may be; by (1.22), this may be expressed in the form

$$(4.10) \qquad \det \gamma^{ij} = \det \gamma^{ij}(t_0) \qquad (\text{for all } \pi^{ij}).$$

Equations (4.9) and (4.10) are the rheological equations of state for the hypothetical material.

From these equations, we show that *the material is an ideally elastic solid*, in the sense in which these terms are defined above. For, in the first place, if the stress is zero, then $\pi^{ij} = 0$ and (4.9) implies that

$$(4.11) \qquad \gamma^{ij} = \frac{\mu_0}{p_0 + \mu_0} \gamma^{ij}(t_0).$$

Hence $\qquad \det \gamma^{ij} = \left(\frac{\mu_0}{p_0 + \mu_0}\right)^3 \det \gamma^{ij}(t_0) \qquad$ (cf. (1.37)),

and therefore $\qquad \mu_0/(p_0 + \mu_0) = 1, \qquad$ by (4.10).

Thus $\gamma^{ij} = \gamma^{ij}(t_0)$, by (4.11), showing that the material has a unique shape $\gamma^{ij}(t_0)$ when the stress is zero, so that (4.3)(i) is satisfied. Further, if the material is held in any given shape $\gamma^{ij} \neq \gamma^{ij}(t_0)$, then it is clear from the argument just given that γ^{ij} cannot be a multiple of $\gamma^{ij}(t_0)$; hence π^{ij}, which according to (4.9) is determined, to within an additive isotropic stress $p_0\gamma^{ij}$, by γ^{ij}, cannot be a multiple of γ^{ij} and the stress is therefore non-isotropic; thus (4.3)(ii) is satisfied, and the material is therefore an elastic solid. It is also clear from the form of (4.9) that, in the above argument, the shape $\gamma^{ij}(t_0)$ is attained as soon as the stress is made zero, and that the extra stress $\pi^{ij} + p_0\gamma^{ij}$ is attained as soon as the material has shape γ^{ij}; both the conditions (4.4) are therefore satisfied, and the solid is perfectly elastic.

The solid is *isotropic*, because equation (4.7), which defines the material rheologically, contains no reference to any particular material line or material plane. The solid is *homogeneous*, because μ_0 in (4.7) does not depend on position in the material.

The form of the rheological equations of state (4.9), (4.10) is independent of the choice of base vectors; for the equations have been derived, using an arbitrary set of embedded base vectors, from an equation (4.7) which contains no reference to any set of base vectors. If $\bar{\pi}^{ij}$ and $\bar{\gamma}^{ij}$ denote stress components and shape variables defined relative to any other set of embedded base vectors $\bar{\mathbf{e}}_i$, then (4.7) will lead to the rheological equations of state

$$\begin{aligned} \bar{\pi}^{ij} + p_0\,\bar{\gamma}^{ij} &= \mu_0\{\bar{\gamma}^{ij}(t_0) - \bar{\gamma}^{ij}\}, \\ \det \bar{\gamma}^{ij} &= \det \bar{\gamma}^{ij}(t_0), \end{aligned}$$

which have the same form as (4.9) in regard to stress components and shape variables, and the same value of the constant μ_0, which, as we shall show, is the shear modulus of the solid. This comparatively simple example has been written out in full to illustrate what is meant in this context by saying that two sets of equations "have the same form".

The argument leading from the hypothesis (4.7) to the rheological equations of state (4.9), (4.10) can easily be seen to be reversible, and it follows from this that the hypothesis is self-consistent. Any given values of the six independent quantities $\pi^{ij} = \pi^{ji}$ represent a possible state of stress, and the corresponding values of γ^{ij} and p_0 are determined by (4.9) and (4.10); the normal components of traction then satisfy (4.7), which does therefore represent a possible relation for any state of stress.

We may note that, regarding the rheological equations of state (4.9) and (4.10) as given, a specification of stress π^{ij} serves to determine both γ^{ij} and p_0, whereas a specification of γ^{ij} (consistent with (4.10)) determines

π^{ij} but not p_0. Here and elsewhere we regard the shape of the solid in the stress-free state as given, along with the modulus μ_0, so that $\gamma^{ij}(t_0)$ are given constants whose values are known as soon as the embedded base vectors $\mathbf{e}_i$ are chosen.

It is evident that the rheological equations of state (4.9) can be written in the simpler form

$$\pi^{ij} + p\gamma^{ij} = \mu_0 \gamma^{ij}(t_0), \tag{4.12}$$

where $p = p_0 + \mu_0$. The original form (4.9) serves to emphasize the dependence of the extra stress $\pi^{ij} + p_0\gamma^{ij}$ on the strain $t_0 \to t$.

We thus have the rather curious result that the extra stress is constant. However, as remarked in Chapter 3, this does not mean that the traction across a given material plane is constant; it is clear from (3.7) that the traction $\mathbf{f}$ across a plane of constant orientation (and therefore constant l_i) can vary during strain because of the variation of the base vectors $\mathbf{e}_i$ (even when p is constant).

We now evaluate the tractions across suitable planes for the main types of strain.

The General Uniform Strain

Since the solid is perfectly elastic, we can obtain a complete picture of its properties by considering the tractions required to deform the solid from the stress-free state t_0 to a single arbitrary state t; intervening states are of no significance. The most general uniform deformation $t_0 \to t$ involves a strain which is determined by the values of the three principal elongation ratios and by the directions in the material of the principal axes of strain.

Following the treatment of the general uniform strain given in Chapter 2, let us take a set of embedded base vectors $\mathbf{e}_i$, *orthonormal in the stress-free state* t_0, coinciding with the principal axes of the strain $t_0 \to t$ (Fig. 2.3). The lengths e_i of the base vectors in state t are then equal to the principal elongation ratios (2.39), and the values of the shape variables γ^{ij}, $\gamma^{ij}(t_0)$ are given by (2.45), (2.46).

With these values for the shape variables, the rheological equations of state (4.12) take the form

$$\pi^{ij} + p\begin{pmatrix} e_1^{-2} & 0 & 0 \\ 0 & e_2^{-2} & 0 \\ 0 & 0 & e_3^{-2} \end{pmatrix} = \mu_0 \begin{pmatrix} 1 & 0 & 0 \\ 0 & 1 & 0 \\ 0 & 0 & 1 \end{pmatrix},$$

where, in this and in similar contexts, it is understood that π^{ij} stands for the array of numbers π^{ij}.

The required components of traction in state t are equal to the cartesian stress components p_{ij}, defined in terms of the orthonormal basis $\mathbf{e}_i/e_i$; since the basis $\mathbf{e}_i$ is orthogonal in state t, p_{ij} is given in terms of π^{ij} by (3.15), so that $p_{11} = (e_1)^2\pi^{11}$, etc., and hence

$$(4.13)\qquad p_{ij} = -p\begin{pmatrix}1 & 0 & 0\\ 0 & 1 & 0\\ 0 & 0 & 1\end{pmatrix} + \mu_0\begin{pmatrix}(e_1)^2 & 0 & 0\\ 0 & (e_2)^2 & 0\\ 0 & 0 & (e_3)^2\end{pmatrix}.$$

Thus $p_{ij} = 0$ when $i \neq j$, which shows that there is no tangential component of traction on any plane perpendicular to a base vector. Such planes are therefore principal planes of stress, according to the definition given in Examples 3, No. 1.

It follows that the principal axes of stress in state t coincide with the principal axes of the strain $t_0 \to t$, where t_0 denotes the stress-free state. This is in fact a property of every *isotropic* perfectly elastic solid, as we shall prove in Chapter 8.

The principal values of stress, p_{ii}, are given by the equations

$$(4.14)\qquad p_{ii} = -p + \mu_0(e_i)^2 \qquad (i = 1, 2, 3),$$

and are not completely determined by the principal elongation ratios e_i owing to the hydrostatic pressure term, whose magnitude at this stage is arbitrary.

If, for example, we specify that the traction across planes perpendicular to $\mathbf{e}_3$ shall be zero, i.e. that

$$(4.15)\qquad p_{33} = 0,$$

then $p = \mu_0(e_3)^2$, from the third of equations (4.14), so that the hydrostatic pressure term is determined, and hence

$$(4.16)\qquad \begin{cases} p_{11} = \mu_0[(e_1)^2 - (e_3)^2] \\ p_{22} = \mu_0[(e_2)^2 - (e_3)^2], \end{cases}$$

where

$$(4.17)\qquad e_3 = (e_1 e_2)^{-1},$$

by the constant volume condition (2.48).

Simple Elongation at Constant Volume

Simple elongation, in the direction $\mathbf{e}_1$ say, at constant volume is a particular case of the general uniform strain just considered. If there is zero traction across planes which are parallel to the direction of elongation, so that

$$(4.18)\qquad p_{22} = p_{33} = 0,$$

then (4.16) becomes

$$p_{11} = \mu_0[(e_1)^2 - (e_1)^{-1}], \tag{4.19}$$

because $e_2 = e_3 = (e_1)^{-1/2}$, by (2.49).

This gives the traction component p_{11}, which is equal to the tension per unit area of cross-section in state t, in terms of e_1, the ratio of final and initial lengths. Hence for Young's modulus E we have

$$E \equiv \frac{p_{11}}{e_1 - 1} = \mu_0\left(1 + e_1 + \frac{1}{e_1}\right), \tag{4.20}$$

if we agree to apply the definition beyond the region of infinitesimally small strains (i.e. $e_1 - 1$ infinitesimally small, in this case) in which the term "Young's modulus" is usually used.

For the particular elastic solid defined by (4.7), Young's modulus is thus an increasing function of elongation ratio, and is not a constant. For the limiting value, E_0, of Young's modulus at small elongations, it follows from (4.20) that

$$E_0 \equiv \lim_{e_1 \to 1} E = 3\mu_0, \tag{4.21}$$

in agreement with the classical relation for an incompressible isotropic elastic solid of shear modulus μ_0.

For Poisson's ratio σ, we have

$$\sigma \equiv -\frac{e_1\, de_2}{e_2\, de_1} = \frac{1}{2}, \tag{4.22}$$

since $e_2 = (e_1)^{-1/2}$, by (2.49). This is a consequence of the constancy of volume coupled with the relation $e_2 = e_3$.

Simple Shear

We now consider the case in which the uniform strain $t_0 \to t$ is a simple shear of magnitude s. Following the treatment of simple shear given in Chapter 2, we take a set of base vectors, *orthonormal in state t*, with $\mathbf{e}_1$ along a line of shear and $\mathbf{e}^2$ normal to the shearing planes (Fig. 2.4). The base vectors $\mathbf{e}_1$, $\mathbf{e}_2$ do not coincide with principal axes of the strain $t_0 \to t$.

Since the basis is now orthonormal in the state t in which the components of traction are to be calculated, we have $p_{ij} = \pi^{ij}$, by (3.14), and hence the rheological equation of state (4.9) gives the result

$$p_{ij} = -p_0 \begin{pmatrix} 1 & 0 & 0 \\ 0 & 1 & 0 \\ 0 & 0 & 1 \end{pmatrix} + \mu_0 \begin{pmatrix} s^2 & s & 0 \\ s & 0 & 0 \\ 0 & 0 & 0 \end{pmatrix}, \tag{4.23}$$

when the appropriate values for the shape variables are substituted from (2.62) and (2.66).

This verifies that there is no tangential component of traction across planes normal to $\mathbf{e}_3$ (cf. (3.26)), which is therefore a principal axis of stress.

The differences of normal stress components are given by the equations

$$\begin{cases} p_{11} - p_{22} = \mu_0 s^2, \\ p_{22} - p_{33} = 0, \end{cases} \tag{4.24}$$

and the shear stress by

$$p_{21} = \mu_0 s, \tag{4.25}$$

which proves the statement made earlier that μ_0 is equal to the shear modulus, and also shows that the shear modulus is constant.

In comparing the results that the shear modulus is constant and Young's modulus is not, it should be noted that there is an arbitrariness inherent in the definition of moduli when finite strains are involved which disappears when the strains are infinitesimally small. If we regard a modulus as some ratio of "stress to strain" which is to characterize the response of an elastic solid to a particular type of strain, then there is no reason why the particular ratio $p_{11}/(e_1 - 1)$ used to define Young's modulus in (4.20) should be preferred to, say,

$$\frac{p_{11}}{\frac{1}{2}(e_1^2 - 1)} \quad \text{or} \quad \frac{p_{11}}{\frac{1}{3}[(e_1)^2 - (e_1)^{-1}]},$$

both of which have the same limit as the chosen ratio when $e_1 \to 1$. The last of these ratios is constant for the particular elastic solid considered above. Again, there is no reason for considering the particular ratio p_{21}/s, rather than p_{21}/s^3, say, as the shear modulus. Having made the point, however, we shall for definiteness keep to the definitions given in (4.20) and (4.25).

Perhaps the main point of interest with the present elastic solid lies in the fact that *one difference of normal stress components in shear is not zero* (4.24). Remembering the sign convention for stress components, it follows from (4.24) that the material has a "tension along the lines of shear", i.e. that on planes normal to the lines of shear there is a *tensile* normal component of traction, if the normal component of traction on the shearing planes is taken (arbitrarily) as defining the reference level of pressure. This depends on the fact that the shear modulus μ_0 must be taken to be positive for any real material. Since $p_{11}-p_{22}$ depends on the square of s, a reversal of the direction of shear does not change the value (or sign) of $p_{11}-p_{22}$; this is also a result to be expected from the symmetry of shear.

From (4.24) and (4.25), the material constant μ_0 can be eliminated, and the interesting equation

$$\frac{p_{11}-p_{22}}{p_{21}} = s \tag{4.26}$$

obtained. This equation is in fact valid for any isotropic perfectly elastic solid, as we shall show in Chapter 8. It shows that in any such material the occurrence of unequal normal stress components in shear is essentially a "finite strain effect"; for when s is small, $p_{11}-p_{22}$ is small compared to the shear stress.

Two of the principal axes of stress lie in the plane of $\mathbf{e}_1$ and $\mathbf{e}_2$, making angles χ', $\chi'+(\pi/2)$, say, with $\mathbf{e}_1$. From the result of Examples 3, No. 2, and equation (4.26), it follows that the orientation of the principal axes of stress is related to the magnitude s of the shear strain by the equation

$$2\cot 2\chi' = s = \frac{p_{11}-p_{22}}{p_{21}}. \tag{4.27}$$

From this equation, we see that

$$\chi' \to \frac{\pi}{4}\left(\text{or} \frac{\pi}{4}+\frac{\pi}{2}\right) \quad \text{as } s \to 0. \tag{4.28}$$

As s increases from zero, the first value of χ' decreases from $\pi/4$ to zero.

It follows that (in comparison with the shear stress) appreciable values of the normal stress difference $p_{11}-p_{22}$ are associated with orientations of an axis of the stress (or strain) ellipsoid appreciably different from the value $\pi/4$ appropriate to infinitesimally small strains. It also follows, from (2.67) and (4.27), that

$$\chi' = \chi, \tag{4.29}$$

verifying that the principal axes of stress and of strain coincide.

The Kinetic Theory of Rubberlike Elasticity

In order to explain the elastic properties of rubber and other polymers in the "rubberlike state", a molecular theory, known as the kinetic or statistical theory, has been developed by a number of authors; a full account of the theory and the relevant experimental data has been given by Treloar (1958).

The kinetic theory describes an isotropic incompressible perfectly elastic solid, and leads to relations between principal values of stress and principal elongation ratios which are identical with the corresponding relations (4.14) derived above for the material defined by the hypothesis (4.7). (In Treloar's equations (4.19a), the symbols t_i, λ_i, G, p correspond to p_{ii}, e_i, μ_0, $-p$ in our equation (4.14).) Since these relations are derived for a general uniform strain (at constant volume), it follows that the material defined by (4.7) is identical with that described by the kinetic theory and may therefore be called a *rubberlike solid*.

We shall now give a brief outline of the kinetic theory, leading to an expression for the free energy as a function of principal values of strain; from this function, we shall derive the rheological equations of state in the form (4.12), primarily as an illustration of method using the quantities π^{ij}, γ^{ij}.

We make this "molecular" break in our hitherto purely "continuum" arguments for several reasons. The kinetic theory is of fundamental importance in polymer rheology and gives such a good description of a variety of experimental data (Chapter 10) that there is little doubt that the theory is based on the correct mechanism of deformation in the rubberlike state and that the significant discrepancies between theory and experiment which do exist will lead to no more than minor revisions of the theory. As a successful molecular theory of macroscopic properties of a condensed phase, the theory must be classed as a remarkable development in classical physics.

Moreover, the kinetic theory and its extension to rubberlike liquids (Chapter 6) appears to be the only molecular theory for polymer systems (and perhaps also for any systems) which has been developed to the extent of yielding complete rheological equations of state in a form suitable for application to any type of strain history and not restricted to small strains or small rates of strain. As we shall see in Chapter 8, the variety of conceivable forms for rheological equations of state for isotropic elastic liquids and solids, other than perfectly elastic solids, is so great that it is unlikely that the correct equations for any given material can be determined from the results of experiment alone; any molecular theory which affords a reason for preferring one form of equation to another can therefore be of use.

The observed properties of rubber (in the rubberlike state), on which the kinetic theory is based, may be summarized as follows. A knowledge of the terms polymer, rubber, chain molecule, and rubberlike state (which are defined in Chapter 10) will be assumed.

Elasticity. A rubber filament will return to within a few per cent of its original (stress-free) length after being elongated to five or ten times this length.

Incompressibility. The bulk (or compressibility) modulus (about 2×10^{10} dynes/cm^2) is that of a liquid. The shear modulus (about 4×10^6 dynes/cm^2) is some 5000 times smaller, and is some 200,000 times smaller than the shear modulus for a typical hard solid.

Entropy. The tension in a stretched rubber filament, for extensions in the range 30–300%, is mostly due to the difference of entropy between stretched and unstretched states; the difference of internal energy is comparatively small and arises from the very small change of volume which occurs on extension. The tension *increases* with increase of temperature when a filament is held at constant extension. Calculated changes of internal energy for extension *at constant volume* are negligibly small.

It is perhaps the fact that entropy changes outweigh internal energy changes in the deformation of rubber that is primarily responsible for the simplification necessary to develop a realistic and tractable molecular theory for a condensed phase; for this fact supports the hypothesis that for deformations at constant volume the effects of secondary forces between polymer molecules are unimportant. The original thermodynamic analysis (Gee, 1946) of the data (Anthony, Caston and Guth, 1942) on which this fact, or conclusion, is based has recently been questioned (Khasanovitch, 1959; Ciferri, 1961) and a modified analysis applied to new data indicates that internal energy changes may not in fact be negligible and may contribute as much as 10% of the tension for elongations at constant volume (Crespi and Flisi, 1963). This is a matter of current investigation which is not taken account of in the following theory.

The above properties of rubber coupled with known features of the long-chain structure of a rubber molecule lead to the following picture of the structure of rubber on which the kinetic theory is based.

A sample of rubber consists of an assembly of very long chain molecules linked together at a few points so as to form a three-dimensional network extending throughout the sample. A given molecule may be linked to the network at two or more points, but between successive points of linkage there will be a long, highly kinked length of chain molecule containing many "links" (repeating units); the number of links in such a "segment" of a chain molecule "effectively" linked to the network will be different for different segments of that or of other chain molecules. There may also be some chain molecules which are linked to the network at only one point or at no point. The points or regions of cross-linkage between chain molecules may be chemical bonds or physical entanglements.

Apart from the points of cross-linkage, the interactions between chain molecules are weak secondary forces comparable to those between molecules of low molecular weight in a typical liquid; the chain molecules have sufficient freedom to undergo rapid thermal motion of considerable amplitude so that the segment of a chain molecule between any two cross-links can pass rapidly through all (or almost all) of its large number (or high number density) of available configurations.

In any given chain molecule, there are a large number of bonds (along the main chain) about which free rotation is possible; there are therefore a large number of configurations of equal potential energy. A free chain molecule would spend most of its time in highly kinked configurations (where the configuration density is highest) with the distance between its ends only a fraction (say $\frac{1}{10}$) of the corresponding distance when the molecule is fully extended without bond distortion.

Changes of volume and changes of shape at constant volume involve two distinct mechanisms. Change of volume involves a change in the average separation of neighbouring molecules and a consequent change in potential energy associated with the weak secondary forces of interaction; the compressibility modulus is therefore comparable to that of a liquid. Change of shape at constant volume, on the other hand, involves a change in the number of configurations of equal potential energy available to the network and hence involves a change of configurational entropy without change of internal energy; the shear modulus may therefore be very different in value compared to the compressibility modulus, and does in fact turn out to be of the right order of magnitude and to be determined by the concentration of chain segments in the network, irrespective of the detailed chemical structure of the chain molecule.

The high extensibility arises from the fact that the distance between the ends of each segment of chain in the network can be changed by a large factor (say up to 10), owing to the highly kinked configurations, without breaking any bonds. The tension in a stretched filament arises from the thermal motion of the chains in the network, which have been constrained to occupy configurations remote from the average configurations appropriate to the network in the stress-free state. When the tension is removed, the filament returns to its original shape, which is governed by the network structure, or "connectivity". The return is rapid because the secondary forces between molecules are weak.

According to this model, it is to be expected that the stress (at thermodynamic equilibrium) in any state t can be calculated from the change of configurational entropy which the network undergoes when the material is deformed from its stress-free state t_0, if we restrict ourselves to deformations at constant volume. For this purpose, it is convenient to express the change of entropy in terms of variables describing the shape of the material, regarded as a continuous material.

The most satisfactory calculation of this type appears to be that of James and Guth (James, 1947), which is based on the following assumptions, appropriate to a so-called "Gaussian network".

(i) The chain molecules are formed from freely-jointed rigid straight links each of length l; when the ends of any chain segment in the network occupy fixed positions of separation r, the number density of configurations (of equal energy) available to that segment is a Gaussian function

$$\kappa \exp\left(-\frac{3r^2}{2nl^2}\right) \tag{4.30}$$

of the separation r, where n is the number of links in the segment, and κ is a constant whose value is immaterial.

(ii) When a sample of rubber is given a uniform deformation, those points of the network which correspond to the bounding surface of the sample move as if they were "fixed in the surface", i.e. as if they were particles of the fictitious continuous material which is to represent the sample.

(iii) The volume is constant (at constant temperature).

When the sample is in a given shape, the boundary points of the network occupy fixed positions, and the number of configurations available to the network can be conveniently regarded as the product of two factors:

(a) the number of configurations available when the network junctions occupy specified positions;

(b) the number of configurations available to the network junctions.

The network entropy will be a sum of entropies arising from these two factors.

The calculations of James and Guth lead to the following conclusions.

(1) The time-average positions of all points of the network share in the same uniform deformation as the boundary points, and may

therefore be identified with particles of the fictitious continuous material. (The time average is over a large number of thermal fluctuations.)

(2) The entropy contribution from "junction fluctuations" (i.e. from (b) above) is independent of the shape of the sample, and does not contribute to the stress.

(3) The change of network entropy S (per unit volume of material) in a uniform deformation $t_0 \to t$ arises from (a) above and may be expressed in the form

$$(4.31) \qquad S(t)-S(t_0) = -\tfrac{1}{2}kcN_0\{(e_1)^2+(e_2)^2+(e_3)^2-3\}$$

where e_i are the principal elongation ratios for the strain $t_0 \to t$, k is Boltzmann's constant, and cN_0 is a constant whose value depends on the detailed structure of the network.

Calculations of the value of this constant appear to be less reliable than those establishing the *form* of (4.31), which is not dependent on the detailed structure of the network; but it seems to be generally agreed that for some structures one may take N_0 to be the concentration of effective network junctions, with c a number whose value is about unity ($c \doteqdot 1$, James and Guth, 1947; $c = 2$, Wall, 1942).

In obtaining (4.31), with equal coefficients for $(e_1)^2$, $(e_2)^2$, and $(e_3)^2$, James introduces a further assumption that the network is isotropic on the average in the unstressed state t_0. This assumption is unnecessary, however, for Lodge (1960c) has shown that the material corresponding to a Gaussian network is necessarily an *isotropic* perfectly elastic solid. The elasticity is perfect because it is assumed that the thermal motion of network chains is so rapid, compared with rates at which the shape of the material is changed in any experiment, that the time taken to reach thermodynamic equilibrium in a given shape is negligible.

To obtain the rheological equations of state from the expression (4.31) for the entropy, we first re-write this expression in the form

$$(4.32) \qquad S(t)-S(t_0) = -\tfrac{1}{2}kcN_0\left\{\sum_i \sum_j \gamma^{ij}(t_0)\,\gamma_{ij}(t)-3\right\},$$

where the shape variables γ_{ij}, γ^{ij} are defined using any chosen set of base vectors embedded in the continuous material (cf. Examples 2, No. 7). We assume that the temperature T and the shape variables γ_{ij} form a complete (but not independent) set of thermodynamic variables of state, i.e. that values assigned to these variables suffice to determine an equilibrium state completely.

In any change from one equilibrium state to another at constant temperature, the work done by the external tractions on unit volume of material must equal the increase in Helmholtz free energy F. When the deformation involved is infinitesimal in the sense that the corresponding changes $d\gamma_{ij}$ in the shape variables are infinitesimally small, the work done, dW, may be expressed in terms of the stress components π^{ij} as follows:

$$dW = \tfrac{1}{2} \sum_i \sum_j \pi^{ij} \, d\gamma_{ij}. \tag{4.33}$$

This result follows from Examples 3, No. 4. Since

$$F = U - TS, \tag{4.34}$$

and the internal energy U is constant, it follows that $dW = dF = -TdS$, and hence that

$$\sum_i \sum_j \pi^{ij} \, d\gamma_{ij} = kTcN_0 \sum_i \sum_j \gamma^{ij}(t_0) \, d\gamma_{ij}, \tag{4.35}$$

from (4.32) and (4.33).

Since the volume is constant, we have $\det \gamma_{ij} =$ constant, and hence

$$\sum_i \sum_j \gamma^{ij} \, d\gamma_{ij} = 0, \tag{4.36}$$

by Examples 2, No. 6. We allow for this restriction on the values of $d\gamma_{ij}$, by means of a Lagrange multiplier, p.

Adding (4.36), multiplied by an arbitrary number p, to (4.35), we obtain an equation which may be written in the form

$$\sum_i \sum_j A^{ij} \, d\gamma_{ij} = 0, \tag{4.37}$$

where for brevity we have written

$$A^{ij} \equiv \pi^{ij} + p\gamma^{ij} - kTcN_0 \gamma^{ij}(t_0). \tag{4.38}$$

Since $A^{ij} = A^{ji}$, we may write (4.37) in the form

$$A^{11} d\gamma_{11} + A^{22} d\gamma_{22} + A^{33} d\gamma_{33} + 2(A^{23} d\gamma_{23} + A^{31} d\gamma_{31} + A^{12} d\gamma_{12}) = 0. \tag{4.39}$$

The six differentials in this equation are subject only to a single condition (4.36), which we may regard as determining any one differential, $d\gamma_{11}$ say, in terms of the other five. We may choose the value of the Lagrange multiplier p so that the coefficient of $d\gamma_{11}$ in (4.39) is zero; in the resulting equation, the five differentials can be given arbitrary values, and therefore the coefficient of each of them must be zero. Hence all coefficients in (4.39) must be zero, which means that

$$\pi^{ij}+p\gamma^{ij} = kTcN_0\gamma^{ij}(t_0) \qquad (i,j = 1,2,3). \tag{4.40}$$

These are the rheological equations of state, relative to an arbitrary embedded basis, for a rubberlike solid whose molecular network is Gaussian. The properties of any such material are therefore determined by a single material constant

$$\mu_0 = kTcN_0, \tag{4.41}$$

whose value is determined essentially by N_0, the number of effective network junctions in unit volume of the material. By comparison of equations (4.12) and (4.40), we see that μ_0 is the shear modulus, and that the rubberlike solid is identical with the material defined by hypothesis (4.7).

A discussion of the validity of the kinetic theory and its various modifications has been given by Treloar (1958), together with an account of the equally important parallel theory of birefringence, which is outside the scope of the present book. A brief account of the main experimental data in relation to the kinetic theory is given in Chapter 10 of the present book.

Composite Networks and Permanent Set

According to the above model, a rubberlike solid has a unique shape at zero stress because the long-chain molecules are cross-linked so as to form a network. If there were no cross-links, or insufficient cross-links for the formation of a network extending throughout the sample, it would be expected that individual chain molecules could slide past one another without restriction when the material is deformed, and that, when the stress is removed, the material would not return to its original shape; there may in practice be what might be termed a partial recovery (e.g. a filament elongated to say seven times its original length may "recover" to say twice its original length owing to the presence of temporary cross-links). Such behaviour is observed in uncross-linked polymer systems, which may therefore be described as elastic liquids in the sense of the definitions (4.5), (4.6). A possible set of rheological equations of state for such systems is derived in Chapter 6. As an introduction to these equations, we end the present chapter by considering briefly a development of the kinetic theory which has been given for rubberlike solids having networks prepared in a special way.

Let us consider a rubberlike material which has in unit volume

N_0 cross-links, introduced in a stress-free state t_0;

N_1 cross-links, introduced in a state t_1.

For definiteness, let us suppose that the N_0 cross-links were introduced first, the material then being subjected to a stress necessary to bring it into a different state t_1, where the second set of cross-links were introduced. The question arises as to what are the elastic properties of such a material, containing what will be called a *composite network*.

Assuming that the network is Gaussian, it follows from the kinetic theory that the material must be an isotropic perfectly elastic solid with rheological equations of state of the form

$$\pi^{ij} + p\gamma^{ij} = \mu_2 \gamma^{ij}(t_2) \tag{4.42}$$

where the modulus μ_2 and the stress-free shape $\gamma^{ij}(t_2)$ are to be determined; for the theory applies to a Gaussian network irrespective of the manner in which its cross-links are introduced (Lodge, 1960).

The problem therefore reduces to the determination of the modulus μ_2 and the stress-free shape $\gamma^{ij}(t_2)$ in terms of the given numbers of cross-links N_0, N_1 and the shapes $\gamma^{ij}(t_0)$, $\gamma^{ij}(t_1)$ of the material when they were introduced.

If we start with a material in which only the N_0 cross-links are present and which therefore has a stress-free shape $\gamma^{ij}(t_0)$, then the introduction of the second set of cross-links in a stressed state t_1 may be said to give rise to *permanent set*, i.e. to a change from one stress-free shape, $\gamma^{ij}(t_0)$, to another, $\gamma^{ij}(t_2)$.

In order to avoid intricate calculations necessary to determine $\gamma^{ij}(t_2)$, we consider a simple and not unreasonable postulate that the composite network behaves as if it were two independent networks, one having N_0 cross-links and stress-free shape $\gamma^{ij}(t_0)$, and the other N_1 cross-links and stress-free shape $\gamma^{ij}(t_1)$. This "two-network" hypothesis is due to Tobolsky, Andrews and Hanson (1946), and gives results which are in fact consistent with the results of certain more detailed (and less arbitrary) arguments developed by Berry, Scanlan and Watson (1956) and by Flory (1960).

Interpreting the hypothesis to mean that the entropies

$$\left\{\begin{aligned} S_0(t) &= S_0(t_0) - \tfrac{1}{2}kcN_0\left\{\sum_i \sum_j \gamma^{ij}(t_0)\,\gamma_{ij}(t) - 3\right\}, \\ S_1(t) &= S_1(t_1) - \tfrac{1}{2}kcN_1\left\{\sum_i \sum_j \gamma^{ij}(t_1)\,\gamma_{ij}(t) - 3\right\}, \end{aligned}\right. \tag{4.43}$$

for the two networks are additive, i.e. that the entropy for the composite network is given by

$$(4.44)\quad \begin{cases} S(t) = S_0(t)+S_1(t) \\ \quad = S_0(t_0)+S_1(t_1)- \\ \qquad -\frac{1}{2}kc\left\{\sum_i \sum_j [N_0\gamma^{ij}(t_0)+N_1\gamma^{ij}(t_1)]\gamma_{ij}(t)-3(N_0+N_1)\right\}, \end{cases}$$

it is clear that (4.44) is of the same form in the variables $\gamma_{ij}(t)$ as (4.32), and hence that (4.44) will lead to an equation of the form (4.42) in which

$$(4.45)\qquad \mu_2\gamma^{ij}(t_2) = kTc\{N_0\gamma^{ij}(t_0)+N_1\gamma^{ij}(t_1)\}.$$

This equation, with the constant volume condition

$$(4.46)\qquad \det\gamma^{ij}(t_2) = \det\gamma^{ij}(t_0) = \det\gamma^{ij}(t_1),$$

suffices to determine μ_2 and $\gamma^{ij}(t_2)$, and therefore is the solution of the problem according to the two-network hypothesis.

Although the values of $\gamma^{ij}(t_2)$ are thus determined, we should, strictly speaking, ask whether they do in fact determine a shape of the material. The question has not arisen before, because we have always considered values of the quantities γ^{ij} *defined* as scalar products of given base vectors. In (4.45), the quantities $\gamma^{ij}(t_0)$ and $\gamma^{ij}(t_1)$ on the right-hand side are so defined, but the quantities $\gamma^{ij}(t_2)$ are defined by this equation; the question arises therefore whether the quantities $\gamma^{ij}(t_2)$ so defined can be treated as shape variables in the sense that base vectors $\mathbf{e}^i$ can be found such that $\gamma^{ij}(t_2) = \mathbf{e}^i.\mathbf{e}^j$. This question is dealt with in Examples 4, Nos. 1 to 4, where necessary and sufficient conditions for a set of quantities $\gamma^{ij} = \gamma^{ji}$ to be shape variables are stated, and from which it follows in particular that the quantities $\gamma^{ij}(t_2)$ do define a shape.

To investigate the implications of (4.45), it is natural to calculate the state of permanent set t_2 for different types of deformation $t_0 \rightarrow t_1$. When the deformation $t_0 \rightarrow t_1$ is a simple elongation, it is found that the permanent set deformation $t_0 \rightarrow t_2$ is also a simple elongation with the same direction of elongation and a smaller elongation ratio, as one might expect.

When the deformation $t_0 \rightarrow t_1$ is a pure shear (2.57), in which there is no elongation of lines parallel to a base vector $\mathbf{e}_3$ say, then we have the rather unexpected result that the permanent set deformation $t_0 \to t_2$ involves an elongation of these lines (Neubert and Saunders, 1958), as the following calculation shows.

Let us take a set of base vectors $\mathbf{e}_1$, $\mathbf{e}_2$, $\mathbf{e}_3$, orthonormal in state t_0, and coinciding with the principal axes for the pure shear $t_0 \to t_1$, whose corresponding principal elongation ratios are λ, λ^{-1}, 1 (Fig. 4.1). Then, from (2.59) and (2.60), with e_1, t replaced by λ, t_1, we have

$$\gamma^{ij}(t_0) = \begin{pmatrix} 1 & 0 & 0 \\ 0 & 1 & 0 \\ 0 & 0 & 1 \end{pmatrix}, \quad \gamma^{ij}(t_1) = \begin{pmatrix} \lambda^{-2} & 0 & 0 \\ 0 & \lambda^2 & 0 \\ 0 & 0 & 1 \end{pmatrix}.$$

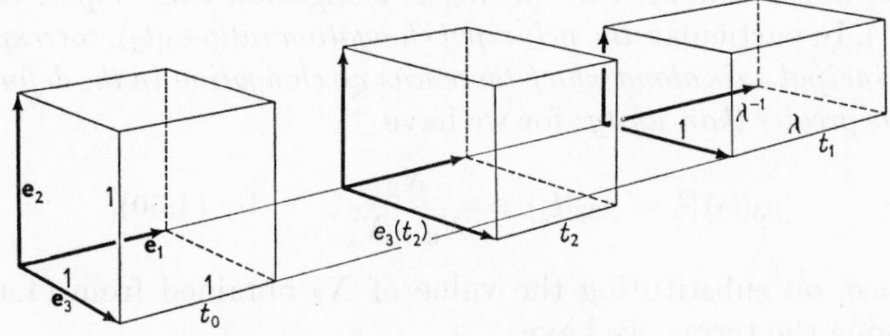

FIG. 4.1. Permanent set $t_0 \to t_2$ for rubber cross-linked in states t_0 and t_1 related by pure shear.

With these expressions, equation (4.45) becomes

$$N_2 \gamma^{ij}(t_2) = \begin{pmatrix} N_0 + N_1\lambda^{-2} & 0 & 0 \\ 0 & N_0 + N_1\lambda^2 & 0 \\ 0 & 0 & N_0 + N_1 \end{pmatrix}, \tag{4.47}$$

where

$$N_2 \equiv \frac{\mu_2}{kTc}. \tag{4.48}$$

From (4.47), using the constant volume condition (4.46) and remembering (1.37), we obtain the equation

$$(N_2)^3 = (N_0 + N_1\lambda^{-2})(N_0 + N_1\lambda^2)(N_0 + N_1), \tag{4.49}$$

which determines N_2, and hence also the modulus μ_2.

To obtain the values of $\gamma_{ij}(t_2)$, it is simplest to use (1.23), evaluating the cofactors of elements in $\det \gamma^{ij}(t_2)$ using (4.47). The result is

$$\gamma_{ij}(t_0) = \begin{pmatrix} 1 & 0 & 0 \\ 0 & 1 & 0 \\ 0 & 0 & 1 \end{pmatrix}, \quad \gamma_{ij}(t_2) = \begin{pmatrix} \dfrac{N_2}{N_0+N_1\lambda^{-2}} & 0 & 0 \\ 0 & \dfrac{N_2}{N_0+N_1\lambda^2} & 0 \\ 0 & 0 & \dfrac{N_2}{N_0+N_1} \end{pmatrix}. \tag{4.50}$$

This shows that, when the deformation $t_0 \to t_1$ is a pure shear, the permanent set deformation $t_0 \to t_2$ is a general uniform strain with the same principal axes, and with no principal elongation ratio equal to unity (Fig. 4.1). In particular, *the principal elongation ratio* $e_3(t_2)$, *corresponding to the principal axis along which there was no elongation in the deformation* $t_0 \to t_1$, *is greater than unity*; for we have

$$[e_3(t_2)]^2 = \gamma_{33}(t_2) = \frac{N_2}{N_0+N_1}, \qquad \text{by (4.50)},$$

and hence, on substituting the value of N_2 obtained from (4.49) and rearranging the terms, we have

$$[e_3(t_2)]^6 = 1+\frac{N_0 N_1}{N_0+N_1}\left(\lambda-\frac{1}{\lambda}\right)^2, \tag{4.51}$$

showing that $e_3(t_2) > 1$ when $N_0 N_1 \neq 0$, $\lambda \neq 1$.

Examples 4

1. If $\gamma_{ij} = \gamma_{ji}$ be any six given numbers, prove that a necessary and sufficient set of conditions that the quadratic form

$$Q = \sum_i \sum_j \gamma_{ij}\,\xi^i \xi^j$$

be *positive definite* (i.e. that $Q > 0$ for all values of ξ^i other than $\xi^1 = \xi^2 = \xi^3 = 0$) is

$$\gamma_{11} > 0; \quad \begin{vmatrix} \gamma_{11} & \gamma_{12} \\ \gamma_{21} & \gamma_{22} \end{vmatrix} > 0; \quad \begin{vmatrix} \gamma_{11} & \gamma_{12} & \gamma_{13} \\ \gamma_{21} & \gamma_{22} & \gamma_{23} \\ \gamma_{31} & \gamma_{32} & \gamma_{33} \end{vmatrix} > 0.$$

2. If $\gamma_{ij} = \gamma_{ji}$ be any six given numbers, prove that a necessary and sufficient condition that the equations

$$\mathbf{e}_i \cdot \mathbf{e}_j = \gamma_{ij} \qquad (i,j = 1,2,3)$$

have a real solution for the unknown vectors $\mathbf{e}_i$ such that these vectors are linearly independent is that the form Q (defined in No. 1 above) be positive definite.

3. Relative to a given system of embedded base vectors $\mathbf{e}_i$, the shape of a material in two states t_0, t_1 is determined by the values of $\gamma_{ij}(t_0)$ and $\gamma_{ij}(t_1)$, where $\gamma_{ij} = \mathbf{e}_i . \mathbf{e}_j$. The values of a set of quantities $\gamma_{ij}(t_2)$ are *defined* by the equations

$$\gamma_{ij}(t_2) = C_0 \gamma_{ij}(t_0) + C_1 \gamma_{ij}(t_1),$$

where C_0, C_1 are positive constants. Prove that the quantities $\gamma_{ij}(t_2)$ can define a shape relative to the same basis, and that this shape is uniquely determined if it is given that the basis is right-handed in all three states t_0, t_1, t_2.

4. If $\sum\sum \gamma_{ij} \xi^i \xi^j$ is positive definite and $\gamma_{ij} = \gamma_{ji}$, prove that $\sum\sum \gamma^{ij} \eta_i \eta_j$ is positive definite, where γ^{ij} are defined in terms of γ_{ij} by (1.21); show also that the converse is true.

Deduce from No. 3 above that the result obtained from No. 3 by writing γ^{ij} for γ_{ij} throughout is true. (This proves that $\gamma^{ij}(t_2)$, defined by (4.45), defines a shape, as stated in the text.)

5. Show that

$$\pi^{ij} + p\gamma^{ij} = \mu_0 \gamma_{ij}(t_0)$$

is not a possible form for the rheological equations of state of a material.

(Calculate the tractions in state t for a pure strain $t_0 \rightarrow t$ of elongation ratios λ_a, λ_b, λ_c, by two methods: using (i) a basis orthonormal in state t_0, and (ii) a basis orthonormal in state t, verifying that the results are different.)

CHAPTER 5

The Newtonian Liquid

The simplest liquid is the ideal, or non-viscous, incompressible liquid defined in Chapter 4; for this liquid, the stress is always isotropic, and so the rheological equations of state may be written in the form

$$(5.1) \qquad \begin{cases} \pi^{ij} = -p\gamma^{ij}, \\ \det \gamma^{ij} = \text{constant}. \end{cases}$$

A large part of classical hydrodynamics is concerned with the flow of such liquids in complicated circumstances.

In the present chapter we deal with the next simplest liquid; this is known as the Newtonian, or Stokesian, liquid and is purely viscous and incompressible. Following a procedure similar to that of Chapter 4, we first derive rheological equations of state for this liquid, and then apply them to obtain the state of stress in the simplest states of flow.

Derivation of Rheological Equations of State

To obtain rheological equations of state in a form which is independent of the choice of base vectors used to define π^{ij} and γ^{ij}, we start from the following hypothesis, which contains no reference to any set of base vectors.

(5.2) *Hypothesis.* Let there be an incompressible material for which, at any time t, the component of traction $\mathbf{f}$ normal to an arbitrary material plane, of unit normal $\mathbf{n}$, is given in terms of the separation h of that plane from any parallel material plane by an equation of the form

$$(5.3) \qquad \mathbf{f}.\mathbf{n} = 2\eta \frac{1}{h}\frac{dh}{dt} - p,$$

where η is a positive constant and p is independent of $\mathbf{n}$.

From our intuitive picture of a viscous liquid, the hypothesis is reasonable in that it expresses $\mathbf{f}.\mathbf{n}+p$ as an increasing function of the rate of change of separation per unit separation; the term p is included to allow for the effect of incompressibility. The hypothesis is the simplest possible in that this function is linear and that tangential components of stress and the rate of change of relative tangential displacement of parallel planes do not occur explicitly in (5.3). The hypothesis is sufficient to determine the rheological properties of the material, as we shall now show.

Following the procedure adopted in Chapter 4, we use (3.17) and (2.21) to express $\mathbf{f}.\mathbf{n}$ and "p" in terms of π^{ij}, γ^{ij} and l_i. From (2.27) with $n = 1$, we have

$$\sum_i \sum_j \frac{d\gamma^{ij}}{dt} l_i l_j = h^2 \frac{d}{dt}\left(\frac{1}{h^2}\right) = -\frac{2}{h}\frac{dh}{dt}.$$

Hence (5.3) is equivalent to the equation

$$\sum_i \sum_j \left\{\pi^{ij} + p\gamma^{ij} + \eta \frac{d\gamma^{ij}}{dt}\right\} l_i l_j = 0$$

in which the quantities $l_i\, l_j$ refer to the current state t and can be given arbitrary values subject only to the condition (2.21). The coefficient of $l_i\, l_j$ is symmetric in i and j and must vanish, by Theorem (1.27). Hence

$$\text{(5.4)} \qquad \pi^{ij} + p\gamma^{ij} = -\eta \frac{d\gamma^{ij}}{dt} \qquad (i,j = 1,2,3).$$

This is the rheological equation of state of the material defined by hypothesis (5.2). The condition of incompressibility

$$\text{(5.5)} \qquad \frac{d}{dt}(\det \gamma^{ij}) = 0$$

may be written in the equivalent form

$$\text{(5.6)} \qquad \sum_i \sum_j \gamma_{ji} \frac{d\gamma^{ij}}{dt} = 0,$$

by Examples 2, No. 6.

Since the above argument is plainly reversible, i.e. (5.3) could be deduced from (5.4), it follows that the hypothesis (5.2) is self-consistent, since a set of stress components can always be found such that normal components of traction on all planes satisfy the postulated relation (5.3).

To see what type of material these equations represent, we note that, whatever the previous flow history may be, (i) if the material be held at constant shape, so that $d\gamma^{ij}/dt = 0$, then $\pi^{ij} = -p\gamma^{ij}$, by (5.4), i.e. the stress becomes isotropic instantaneously; and (ii) if the stress be instantaneously made zero and kept zero, so that $\pi^{ij} = 0$, then

$$\frac{d\gamma^{ij}}{dt} = -\frac{p}{\eta}\gamma^{ij}. \tag{5.7}$$

Substituting this expression for $d\gamma^{ij}/dt$ into the incompressibility condition (5.6), we have

$$0 = \sum_i \sum_j \gamma_{ji} \frac{d\gamma^{ij}}{dt} = -\frac{p}{\eta} \sum_i \sum_j \gamma_{ji}\gamma^{ij}$$

$$= -\frac{p}{\eta} \sum_j \delta_j \quad \text{by (1.21)}$$

$$= -\frac{3p}{\eta}, \quad \text{by (1.13).}$$

Hence $p = 0$, and therefore, by (5.7), $d\gamma^{ij}/dt = 0$, showing that the shape becomes constant instantaneously.

The material is therefore a viscous inelastic liquid in the sense of the definition (4.6). It is also isotropic and homogeneous, since all material lines are equivalent as far as (5.3) is concerned.

We now calculate the stress components which are required to maintain this liquid in the two most important types of flow—shear flow and elongational flow.

Steady Shear Flow

The state of steady shear flow has been defined in Chapter 2 and described in terms of base vectors $\mathbf{e}_i$ which are instantaneously orthonormal in the current state t; $\mathbf{e}_1$ is parallel to the direction of shear and $\mathbf{e}_2$ is instantaneously normal to the shearing planes. At time t, the cartesian stress components are given by (3.14), and the quantities γ^{ij}, $d\gamma^{ij}/dt$ by (2.62) and (2.73); from the rheological equation of state (5.4), we therefore have the result

$$p_{ij} = -p\begin{pmatrix} 1 & 0 & 0 \\ 0 & 1 & 0 \\ 0 & 0 & 1 \end{pmatrix} + \begin{pmatrix} 0 & \eta G & 0 \\ \eta G & 0 & 0 \\ 0 & 0 & 0 \end{pmatrix} \tag{5.8}$$

where G is the shear rate. From this result, it follows that the non-zero stress components are given by the equations

$$(5.9) \qquad \begin{cases} p_{11}-p_{22} = 0, \\ p_{22}-p_{33} = 0, \end{cases}$$

$$(5.10) \qquad p_{21} = p_{12} = \eta G,$$

showing that the normal stress components are equal to one another, and that the tangential stress component is proportional to the shear rate.

In a liquid in steady shear flow, the ratio of tangential stress component to shear rate is called the *viscosity* of the liquid, at least when this ratio has a value which does not vary with time. For the liquid represented by the equation (5.4), the coefficient η is therefore equal to the viscosity.

Liquids for which p_{21} is proportional to G, i.e. for which the viscosity is independent of shear rate, are usually called "*Newtonian*", although it is perhaps preferable to restrict the use of this term to incompressible liquids having a rheological equation of state of the particular form (5.4). Such a liquid is also called "Stokesian", after Stokes who first extended Newton's hypothesis concerning shear flow in a viscous liquid so as to obtain equations equivalent to (5.4) and therefore applicable to any type of flow. When (5.4) is generalized so as to be applicable to non-uniform flow and is combined with the "stress equations of motion" (which relate the spatial gradient of stress and the body forces), the so-called "Navier–Stokes" equations (or their equivalent in the present notation) are obtained; these form the basis of much of the work of classical hydrodynamics of viscous flow.

It should, perhaps, be emphasized that the equality of normal stress components in shear flow is as much a characteristic feature of the Newtonian liquid as is the constancy of viscosity. In Chapter 6 we shall consider a liquid for which the normal stress components in shear flow are not all equal, although the viscosity is independent of shear rate. For such a liquid in particular and for polymer solutions in general, the familiar determination of viscosity must be supplemented by the less familiar but equally important measurement of normal stress differences, if the properties in steady shear flow are to be completely determined. The principles underlying certain methods of measuring such normal stress differences are outlined in Chapter 9, as this is considered to be one of the most important recent fields of development in polymer rheology and, indeed, in the physical properties of liquids; for such methods, when combined with a determination of viscosity, represent the first direct determination of the complete state of stress in any liquid in a known state of flow.

When the viscosity varies with shear rate, some writers use the term "apparent viscosity" and some the terms "anomalous" or "structure" viscosity. We shall, however, simply use the term "viscosity" (which is no more apparent when dependent on shear rate) as above to denote the ratio of tangential stress and shear rate in steady shear flow. It does, however, seem desirable to stipulate that the tangential stress should reach a constant value in steady shear flow before one refers to this ratio as the viscosity of the material; otherwise one could say that an ideally elastic solid had a viscosity (equal to the ratio of tangential stress to shear rate in a steadily increasing simple shear), which would conflict with the notion that a purely viscous material can do no mechanical work (cf. Examples 5, No. 1).

Steady Elongational Flow

Steady elongational flow has been defined in Chapter 2 and described in terms of a basis $\mathbf{e}_i$ which is orthonormal in an arbitrary state t_0 and orthogonal (but not orthonormal) in the current state t; $\mathbf{e}_1$ is parallel to the direction of elongation.

The cartesian stress components p_{ij} in the current state t may be obtained from π^{ij} by using (3.15); π^{ij} may be obtained from the rheological equation of state (5.4) by substituting the values for γ^{ij} and $d\gamma^{ij}/dt$ given in (2.52), (2.53), and (2.54) (with $n = 1$). The following result is obtained:

$$(5.11) \qquad p_{ij} = \begin{pmatrix} -p & 0 & 0 \\ 0 & -p & 0 \\ 0 & 0 & -p \end{pmatrix} + \begin{pmatrix} 2\eta\bar{G} & 0 & 0 \\ 0 & -\eta\bar{G} & 0 \\ 0 & 0 & -\eta\bar{G} \end{pmatrix};$$

$\bar{G}$ is the elongation rate defined by (2.51).

If we consider, for example, a cylindrical liquid filament with generators parallel to $\mathbf{e}_1$ and sides free from traction, then

$$0 = p_{22} = -p-\eta\bar{G} \qquad \text{by (5.11);}$$

with this value for p, we obtain the following expression for the normal component of traction on planes normal to the generators:

$$(5.12) \qquad p_{11} = 3\eta\bar{G}.$$

In the steady elongational flow of a liquid, the ratio

$$\frac{p_{11}}{\bar{G}} \equiv \bar{\eta} \tag{5.13}$$

is called the "*elongational viscosity*", the "coefficient of viscous traction", or the "Trouton viscosity", after Trouton (1906) who derived the relation (5.12) and made the appropriate measurements on very viscous materials.

Thus, *for a Newtonian liquid, the elongational viscosity is three times the viscosity* and is independent of the elongation rate. This relation is analogous to the relation between Young's modulus and shear modulus for an isotropic incompressible elastic solid in the region of infinitesimally small strains, as the treatment of the rubberlike solid in Chapter 4 illustrates (4.21), (4.25). There is, in fact, a useful analogy which can be drawn between the rubberlike solid and the Newtonian liquid which is not confined to any particular type of strain; the present formalism is particularly well suited to demonstrating this analogy, which is of some importance in relation to subsequent treatments of elastic liquids.

A Solid–Liquid Analogy

From the definition of a derivative, we have

$$\frac{d\gamma^{ij}}{dt} = \lim_{\tau\to 0}\frac{\gamma^{ij}(t+\tau)-\gamma^{ij}(t)}{\tau}$$

$$= -\lim_{\delta t\to 0}\frac{\gamma^{ij}(t-\delta t)-\gamma^{ij}(t)}{\delta t}, \quad \text{on putting } \tau = -\delta t.$$

The rheological equation of state (5.4) for a Newtonian liquid may therefore be written in the equivalent form

$$\pi^{ij}(t)+p\gamma^{ij}(t) = \lim_{\delta t\to 0}\frac{\eta}{\delta t}\{\gamma^{ij}(t-\delta t)-\gamma^{ij}(t)\}. \tag{5.14}$$

If we compare this equation with the corresponding equation for a rubberlike solid, namely

$$\pi^{ij}(t)+p_0\gamma^{ij}(t) = \mu_0\{\gamma^{ij}(t_0)-\gamma^{ij}(t)\}, \tag{4.9}$$

we see that there is a similarity of form and that the stress-free state t_0 corresponds to a state $t-\delta t$ infinitesimally close to the current state, while the shear modulus μ_0 corresponds to the ratio $\lim(\eta/\delta t)$. The difference between p and p_0 is unimportant.

It follows that the Newtonian liquid can be regarded as a rubberlike "solid" with an infinitely large shear modulus and a variable stress-free state infinitesimally close to the current state. This is an illustration of an idea first advanced by Maxwell (1868), and usually expressed by the phrase "a viscous liquid may be regarded as a relaxing elastic solid". Maxwell's formulation of this idea was given in simplified terms which require generalization if they are to be applied to actual materials; one such generalization has been given by Hencky (1929), who used relations between stress and finite strain different from the corresponding relations (4.9) used above.

Examples 5

1. Prove that in any state of flow the rate of working of the external tractions on a cubical element of a Newtonian liquid (defined by (5.4)) is positive or zero, and that the value zero occurs if and only if the liquid is moving as a rigid body.

2. Prove that in oscillatory shear flow (cf. (2.80) with $G = 0$), the tangential stress component p_{21} in a Newtonian liquid is 90 degrees out of phase with the motion.

3. With any given material plane of unit normal $\mathbf{n} = \sum_i l_i \mathbf{e}^i$ we may associate a vector $\mathbf{u} = \sum_i \sum_j \dot{\gamma}^{ij} l_i \mathbf{e}_j$, where the dot denotes differentiation with respect to time. By considering the sum of the square magnitudes of $\mathbf{u}$ for any three orthogonal planes, prove that $\sum_i \sum_j \sum_k \sum_m \dot{\gamma}^{ij} \dot{\gamma}^{km} \gamma_{jk} \gamma_{im}$ has a value which is independent of the choice of base vectors and is positive or zero; prove that the value zero occurs if and only if the material is moving rigidly.

Deduce that the result of Example No. 1 above is valid for the material in an arbitrary parallelepiped.

4. Prove that the isotropic pressure p in the equation (5.4) for a Newtonian liquid is given in terms of the stress components π^{ij} by the equation

$$p = -\tfrac{1}{3} \sum_i \sum_j \gamma_{ij} \pi^{ij},$$

and find the corresponding equation in cartesian components p_{ij}.

5. Show that the rheological equation of state (5.4) for a Newtonian liquid can be expressed in the alternative form

$$\pi_{ij} + p\gamma_{ij} = \eta \frac{d\gamma_{ij}}{dt},$$

where

$$\pi_{ij} = \sum_{l} \sum_{m} \gamma_{il} \gamma_{jm} \pi^{lm}.$$

CHAPTER 6

A Rubberlike Liquid

We have now reached a stage where we can derive a possible rheological equation of state for an elastic liquid; this is the main object of the present book.

We seek equations for a liquid which will in some sense combine properties of the rubberlike solid and the Newtonian liquid; out of a great variety of possible equations for elastic liquids, it is reasonable to expect that such an equation, if obtainable, might have relevance for the description of liquid polymer systems, such as concentrated solutions or molten polymers. We choose a simple way of combining the rubberlike and Newtonian properties, since our main purpose is to illustrate the points involved and the methods used; it turns out, however, that the particular equations developed do give a description of most of the main rheological properties of concentrated polymer solutions which is at least qualitatively correct.

The equations are derived in this chapter, and applied to problems involving steady shear flow, steady elongational flow, and stress relaxation following steady shear flow; problems involving elastic recovery are treated in Chapter 7. The present chapter ends with an outline of a molecular theory for concentrated polymer solutions which yields the same rheological equations of state as those developed below. More elaborate rheological equations of state for elastic liquids are given in Chapter 8.

Derivation of Rheological Equations of State

Comparing hypotheses (4.7) and (5.3), which defined the rubberlike solid and the Newtonian liquid, we see that the equations (4.7) for the solid contain a reference to a unique state t_0 (the stress-free state), and that no such state is involved in the equations (5.3) for the liquid; this difference is just what we should expect in view of the definitions (4.3) and (4.5) of solid and liquid and of the remarks following the definition (4.6). To obtain an equation for a "rubberlike liquid", therefore, we must modify equation (4.7) so as to eliminate any reference to a unique state such as t_0.

From the solid–liquid analogy considered in Chapter 5, it can be seen that such an elimination, if effected by replacing t_0 by $t-\delta t$ (where t is the current time), leads to the Newtonian liquid; we therefore require a different method of eliminating t_0 if we are to get an equation for a liquid of a different type. The following hypothesis evidently represents one such method. It is obtained from the hypothesis (4.7) for the rubberlike solid by replacing t_0 by t', μ_0 by a function of $t-t'$, and by integrating the term involving separation ratios over the time interval $-\infty < t' \leqslant t$.

(6.1) *Hypothesis.* Let there be an incompressible material for which, at any time t, the component of traction $\mathbf{f}$ normal to an arbitrary material plane, of unit normal $\mathbf{n}$, is given by an equation of the form

$$\mathbf{f}.\mathbf{n} = \int\limits_{t'=-\infty}^{t} \mu(t-t')\frac{h^2-h'^2}{h'^2}dt' - p_0, \tag{6.2}$$

where h, h' denote the values at times t, t' ($t \geqslant t'$) of the separation of the plane from any parallel material plane; μ, a positive decreasing function of the time interval $t-t'$, is independent of $\mathbf{n}$ and p_0 is independent of $\mathbf{n}$.

According to this hypothesis, the value of $\mathbf{f}.\mathbf{n}+p_0$ at any given instant t depends on the *history* of changes of separation ratio h, i.e. on the values of $(h^2-h'^2)/h'^2$ at all previous times t'; in view of the molecular relaxation processes which are to be expected in a liquid, it is reasonable to suppose that the older states will have less importance than the more recent states and hence that the "memory function" μ will be a decreasing function of time interval, as postulated.

We shall in fact require that μ should decrease sufficiently rapidly to secure the convergence of the integrals

$$\mu_r \equiv \int\limits_{t'=-\infty}^{t} \mu(t-t')\,(t-t')^r\,dt' \tag{6.3}$$

$$= \int\limits_0^{\infty} \mu(\tau)\,\tau^r\,d\tau \qquad (r = 0, 1, 2),$$

which will occur in problems involving steady shear flow; the second form here is obtained by means of the transformation

$$t' \rightarrow \tau = t-t', \tag{6.4}$$

and shows that the μ_r are constants. (Note that r is a suffix in μ_r and a power in τ^r.)

A reasonable form for the memory function, which we shall sometimes use, is that represented by the equation

$$\mu(\tau) = \sum_{s=1}^{m} a_s \exp\frac{-\tau}{\tau_s} \qquad (a_s \geqslant 0, \tau_s > 0), \tag{6.5}$$

i.e. a sum of exponential functions with non-negative coefficients and negative exponents which may be taken to be unequal without loss of generality. In this case, the integrals (6.3) converge and have the values

$$\mu_r = r! \sum_{s=1}^{m} a_s(\tau_s)^{r+1}. \tag{6.6}$$

If, in particular, there is only one term in the sum (6.5), say that corresponding to $s = 1$, then (6.5) may be written in the form

$$\mu(\tau) = \frac{\mu_0}{\tau_1}\exp\frac{-\tau}{\tau_1}, \tag{6.7}$$

because $a_1\tau_1 = \mu_0$, by (6.6) with $r = 0$.

To obtain the rheological equations of state for the material defined by hypothesis (6.1), we use (3.17) and (2.21) to express $\mathbf{f}.\mathbf{n}$ and the term in p_0 in terms of l_i, which define the direction of the unit normal $\mathbf{n}$ at time t relative to the usual embedded vectors $\mathbf{e}_i$. The factor $(h^2 - h'^2)/h'^2$ in the integrand of (6.2) may be similarly expressed by means of (2.29) with t_0 replaced by t'. We then obtain from (6.2) the equation

$$\sum_i \sum_j (\pi^{ij} + p_0\gamma^{ij})\, l_i l_j = \sum_i \sum_j \int_{t'=-\infty}^{t} \mu(t-t')\,\{\gamma^{ij}(t') - \gamma^{ij}\}\,dt'\, l_i l_j.$$

Here the factor $l_i l_j$ depends on t but not on t' and may therefore be taken outside the integral. In the resulting equation, l_i may be given any values consistent with the condition (2.21), since, by hypothesis, (6.2) holds for unit normals $\mathbf{n}$ of all orientations. The coefficient of $l_i l_j$, being symmetric in i and j, must therefore vanish, by Theorem (1.27), and hence we obtain the following rheological equation of state:

$$\pi^{ij} + p_0\gamma^{ij} = \int_{t'=-\infty}^{t} \mu(t-t')\,\{\gamma^{ij}(t') - \gamma^{ij}\}\,dt'. \tag{6.8}$$

This may be written in the alternative form

$$\begin{cases} \pi^{ij} + p\gamma^{ij} = \displaystyle\int_{t'=-\infty}^{t} \mu(t-t')\,\gamma^{ij}(t')\,dt' \qquad (i,j = 1,2,3), \\ \det \gamma^{ij} = \text{constant}, \end{cases} \tag{6.9}$$

if we collect together the terms in γ^{ij}, write $p \equiv p_0 + \int_{-\infty}^{0} \mu\,dt'$, and include the incompressibility condition.

The rheological equations of state (6.9) are the basis of the calculations in this chapter and in the next chapter.

It is easy to see that the above argument is reversible, and therefore the hypothesis (6.1) and the equations (6.9) are equivalent to one another. It follows, in particular, that the hypothesis (6.1) is self-consistent and contains sufficient information to determine the rheological properties of the material concerned; for any given flow history at constant volume is consistent with (6.1) and (6.9), and (6.9) determine the values of the extra stress components $\pi^{ij} + p\gamma^{ij}$ at any time t when the previous flow history is specified; the corresponding values of $\mathbf{f}.\mathbf{n} + p_0$ satisfy (6.1), which is therefore a possible statement about normal components of traction on planes of all orientations.

Proof that the Material (6.1) is an Elastic Liquid

We shall now prove that the material defined by the hypothesis (6.1) is an elastic liquid in the sense of the definitions (4.5) and (4.6). To do this, we allow the material to have an arbitrary flow history up to an instant t_1 and hold the material at constant shape from this instant on; we then show that, provided the stress was finite at t_1, the stress ultimately becomes isotropic.

To investigate the behaviour of the stress components π^{ij} for times $t > t_1$, it is convenient to divide the range of integration in the integral occurring in the rheological equations of state (6.9) into two parts, $(-\infty, t_1)$ and (t_1, t). For the contribution from the second part, $\gamma^{ij}(t')$ is constant and can be taken outside the integral:

$$\int_{t_1}^{t} \mu(t-t')\,\gamma^{ij}(t')\,dt' = \gamma^{ij}(t) \int_{t_1}^{t} \mu(t-t')\,dt';$$

this term thus represents an isotropic contribution to the stress at time t and can be absorbed into the existing term $p\gamma^{ij}(t)$ by redefining p.

We then obtain the equation

$$\pi^{ij}(t) + p\gamma^{ij}(t) = \int_{-\infty}^{t_1} \mu(t-t')\,\gamma^{ij}(t')\,dt' \qquad (t \geqslant t_1). \tag{6.10}$$

In Appendix 2, it is shown that the integral on the right-hand side of this equation tends to zero as t increases, i.e. that

$$\int_{-\infty}^{t_1} \mu(t-t')\,\gamma^{ij}(t')\,dt' \to 0 \quad \text{as } t \to \infty, \tag{6.11}$$

provided that the integral is finite when $t = t_1$, that

$$\mu(t) \to 0 \quad \text{as } t \to \infty, \tag{6.12}$$

and that

$$\int_a^b |\gamma^{ij}(t')|\, dt' \tag{6.13}$$

is finite for all finite values of a, b such that $-\infty < a < b < t_1$.

The first of these conditions is satisfied if the stress is finite at $t = t_1$ (cf. (6.10) with $t = t_1$); this imposes a restriction on the flow history, as we shall see below when we consider steady elongational flow. The second condition, (6.12), is satisfied by virtue of our previous assumption that μ decreases fast enough to ensure convergence of the integrals (6.3). The third condition, (6.13), is a mild condition which will be satisfied in practice because $\gamma^{ij}(t')$ will be bounded in any *finite* interval ($a \leqslant t' \leqslant b$) and will either be continuous or will have finite discontinuities which will not impair the integrability of $|\gamma^{ij}(t')|$; it is in fact only by taking a flow history over an infinite interval that $\gamma^{ij}(t')$ can become unbounded.

If μ is an exponential function (6.7), then

$$\mu(t-t') = \left(\exp\frac{t_1-t}{\tau_1}\right)\mu(t_1-t'), \tag{6.14}$$

and hence the integral on the right-hand side of (6.10) becomes

$$\left(\exp\frac{t_1-t}{\tau_1}\right)\int_{-\infty}^{t_1} \mu(t_1-t')\,\gamma^{ij}(t')\,dt', \tag{6.15}$$

which obviously tends to zero as t increases, provided only that the integral is finite at $t = t_1$; this argument is evidently immediately extensible to cover the case when μ is a sum of a finite number of exponential functions of the form (6.5). The point of the proof given in the appendix is to include cases in which μ may not be expressible as a finite sum of exponential functions.

Since the integral on the right-hand side of (6.10) tends to zero as t increases, it follows that

$$\pi^{ij}(t) \to -p\gamma^{ij}(t),$$

i.e. that the stress becomes isotropic. The material is therefore a liquid, according to the definition (4.5).

Further, as can be seen from (6.15), the stress does not in general become isotropic instantaneously, and therefore the liquid is elastic, according to the definition (4.6).

It is, however, possible to find a limiting form for the memory function μ which does make the stress become isotropic instantaneously, i.e. which makes the integral in (6.10) zero as soon as t exceeds t_1. It can be seen that this will be the case if

$$\mu(t-t') = 0 \quad \text{for } t > t'$$

and $\mu(t-t')$ has a suitable singularity at $t = t'$. In this case, the material behaves like a purely viscous liquid insofar as there is no stress relaxation. It is in fact possible to derive the rheological equations of state for a Newtonian liquid as a limiting case of (6.8), as the following non-rigorous argument indicates.

By means of the change of variable $t' \to \tau = t-t'$, equations (6.8) may be written in the form

$$\pi^{ij}(t)+p_0\gamma^{ij}(t) = \int_0^\infty \mu(\tau)\,[\gamma^{ij}(t-\tau)-\gamma^{ij}(t)]\,d\tau. \tag{6.16}$$

Let us restrict our attention to flow histories for which the Taylor expansion

$$\gamma^{ij}(t-\tau) = \gamma^{ij}(t)-\tau\frac{d\gamma^{ij}(t)}{dt}+\frac{\tau^2}{2!}\frac{d^2\gamma^{ij}(t)}{dt^2}-\dots \tag{6.17}$$

is valid for all values of $\tau \geqslant 0$ for any given value of t.

On substituting this expansion in (6.16) and using (6.3), we obtain the equation

$$\pi^{ij}+p_0\gamma^{ij} = -\mu_1\frac{d\gamma^{ij}}{dt}+\frac{\mu_2}{2!}\frac{d^2\gamma^{ij}}{dt^2}-\frac{\mu_3}{3!}\frac{d^3\gamma^{ij}}{dt^3}+\dots, \tag{6.18}$$

where the argument t is understood throughout.

It is possible to regard this equation as a rheological equation of state in its own right; but it is not equivalent to the rheological equation of state (6.8) from which it has been derived, for the material defined by (6.18) can exhibit no stress relaxation: because as soon as the shape is held constant, all the time derivatives on the right-hand side of (6.18) vanish and so the stress becomes isotropic instantaneously. The reason for this non-equivalence of (6.8) and (6.18) lies in the assumption that the Taylor expansion (6.17) is valid; for this imposes a restriction on the admissible flow histories which would exclude, for example, the type of discontinuous changes in time derivatives of γ^{ij} which are involved when the shape is kept constant in a stress relaxation experiment.

It can be seen that (6.18) represents a Newtonian liquid if all terms, other than the first, on the right-hand side are negligible; for the equation is then of the form (5.4) with the viscosity $\eta = \mu_1$. We consider two distinct ways in which this limiting case can arise.

The first case is that in which the flow is so slow that $d^2\gamma^{ij}/dt^2$ and all higher order time derivatives are negligible in comparison with $d\gamma^{ij}/dt$. We shall see below what this involves when we consider the particular case of steady shear flow.

The second case is that in which the material is such that $\mu_2, \mu_3, \ldots$ are all negligible compared with μ_1. For example, let us consider the following particular form for the memory function:

$$\mu(\tau) = \begin{cases} 0 & 0 < \delta < \tau, \\ \kappa\delta^{-2} & 0 \leqslant \tau \leqslant \delta, \end{cases} \tag{6.19}$$

where κ and δ are positive constants.

From (6.3), we find that in this case

$$\mu_1 = \frac{\kappa}{2}, \quad \mu_2 = \frac{\kappa}{3}\delta, \quad \mu_3 = \frac{\kappa}{4}\delta^2, \ldots, \tag{6.20}$$

and hence, on taking δ to be small enough, we can make $\mu_2, \mu_3, \ldots$ negligibly small compared with μ_1. (A more detailed argument may be necessary to show that the first term on the right-hand side of (6.18) then dominates the sum of all the others if these are infinitely many.)

We have thus shown that for a general form of memory function the material defined by (6.1) is an elastic liquid, and that for suitable slow flows the limiting behaviour is that of a Newtonian liquid of viscosity μ_1. In Chapter 7, we shall go to the other extreme and show that for very rapid deformations the behaviour is that of a rubberlike solid.

This completes the general discussion of the elastic liquid defined by (6.1) or (6.9). We shall now apply the rheological equations of state (6.8) or (6.9) to obtain the behaviour of the liquid in shear flow and in elongational flow.

Steady Shear Flow

The shape variables γ^{ij} are given by (2.70) for steady shear flow of shear rate G, the basis being chosen so as to be orthonormal at time t, to have $\mathbf{e}_1$ parallel to the lines of shear, and $\mathbf{e}^2$ normal to the shearing planes. With these values for γ^{ij}, the rheological equations of state (6.8) take the form

$$\pi^{ij} + p_0\gamma^{ij} = \int_0^\infty \mu(\tau) \begin{pmatrix} G^2\tau^2 & G\tau & 0 \\ G\tau & 0 & 0 \\ 0 & 0 & 0 \end{pmatrix} d\tau$$

when the variable of integration is changed from t' to $\tau = t - t'$, and it is assumed that the state of steady shear flow has continued throughout the period $-\infty < t' \leqslant t$.

Since the basis is orthonormal at time t, we have $p_{ij} = \pi^{ij}$, by (3.14), and $\gamma^{ij} = \delta_{ij}$; the integrals in the above equation are of the form (6.3) with $r = 1, 2$, and hence we obtain the equation

$$(6.21) \qquad p_{ij} = \begin{pmatrix} -p_0 & 0 & 0 \\ 0 & -p_0 & 0 \\ 0 & 0 & -p_0 \end{pmatrix} + \begin{pmatrix} \mu_2 G^2 & \mu_1 G & 0 \\ \mu_1 G & 0 & 0 \\ 0 & 0 & 0 \end{pmatrix}$$

which implies that

$$(6.22) \qquad \begin{cases} p_{11} - p_{22} = \mu_2 G^2 \\ p_{22} - p_{33} = 0 \end{cases}$$

and that

$$(6.23) \qquad p_{21} = p_{12} = \mu_1 G.$$

The cartesian stress components p_{ij}, referred to the shearing planes and to planes instantaneously perpendicular to the lines of shear, are therefore independent of time; one difference of normal stress components is zero, but the other is not. The sign is such that, if the traction p_{22} normal to the shearing planes be taken to be zero, *there is a tensile component p_{11} normal to planes normal to the lines of shear.*

For the viscosity η, defined by the equation

$$(6.24) \qquad \eta \equiv \frac{p_{21}}{G}$$

when the state of shear flow is steady in the sense that both p_{21} and G are independent of time, we have, from (6.23),

$$(6.25) \qquad \eta = \mu_1 = \int_0^\infty \mu(\tau)\,\tau\,d\tau.$$

The viscosity is therefore independent of shear rate, but the liquid does not behave like a Newtonian liquid in steady shear flow because the normal stress difference $p_{11} - p_{22}$ is not zero.

We can now see that the criterion for "Newtonian behaviour" of this particular elastic liquid in steady shear flow is

$$(6.26) \qquad G \ll \frac{\mu_1}{\mu_2},$$

for, when the flow is slow in this sense, it follows from (6.22) and (6.23) that

$$p_{11}-p_{22} \ll p_{21}. \tag{6.27}$$

In this connection, it is instructive to return to (6.18), which was mentioned above in connection with the limiting case of slow flow. For steady *shear* flow, $d^3\gamma^{ij}/dt^3$ and all higher order time derivatives of γ^{ij} are zero (2.72); the condition (6.26) above is therefore sufficient to ensure that $d\gamma^{ij}/dt$ is the only term of significance on the right-hand side of (6.18), which is therefore of the form (5.4), the rheological equation of state for a Newtonian liquid.

Relaxation of Stress on Cessation of Steady Shear Flow

We shall now suppose that a steady shear flow is imposed for an infinite length of time, or for a time long enough for the stress components to reach their constant values (6.22), (6.23); that the flow is suddenly stopped at an instant $t=t_1$; and that no further flow takes place. We know that the stress will ultimately become isotropic; we now calculate the time variation of $p_{11}-p_{22}$ and p_{21} during this period of stress relaxation.

To calculate the stress π^{ij} at time $t > t_1$, we use the rheological equation of state in the form (6.8). Since by hypothesis there is no change of shape for $t > t_1$, the basis $\mathbf{e}_i$, orthonormal at t_1, will be orthonormal for all $t > t_1$. We can use the expressions (2.70) previously derived for $\gamma^{ij}(t')$ and $\gamma^{ij}(t)$ in two states t', t related by a simple shear of angle ϵ if we take

$$s = \tan\epsilon = \begin{cases} G(t_1-t') & (t' \leqslant t_1) \\ 0 & (t' > t_1). \end{cases} \tag{6.28}$$

It follows that, for $t \geqslant t_1$,

$$\gamma^{ij}(t')-\gamma^{ij}(t) = \begin{cases} \begin{pmatrix} G^2(t_1-t')^2 & G(t_1-t') & 0 \\ G(t_1-t') & 0 & 0 \\ 0 & 0 & 0 \end{pmatrix} & (t' \leqslant t_1) \\ \\ 0 & (t' > t_1), \end{cases} \tag{6.29}$$

since $\gamma^{ij}(t) = \gamma^{ij}(t_1)$.

There is therefore no contribution to the integral in (6.8) from the part of the range of integration for which $t_1 \leqslant t' \leqslant t$, and hence (6.8) becomes

$$(6.30) \quad \pi^{ij}(t) + p_0\gamma^{ij}(t) = \int_{t'=-\infty}^{t_1} \mu(t-t')\,dt' \begin{pmatrix} G^2(t_1-t')^2 & G(t_1-t') & 0 \\ G(t_1-t') & 0 & 0 \\ 0 & 0 & 0 \end{pmatrix}.$$

From this equation and (3.14) it follows that the cartesian stress components at time t are given by the equations

$$(6.31) \quad \begin{cases} p_{11}-p_{22} = G^2 I_2(t-t_1) \\ p_{22}-p_{33} = 0 \\ p_{21}=p_{12} = GI_1(t-t_1), \end{cases}$$

where

$$(6.32) \quad I_r(t-t_1) = \int_{\tau=t-t_1}^{\infty} \mu(\tau)\,[\tau-(t-t_1)]^r d\tau \qquad (r = 1, 2).$$

The last expression is obtained by using the change of variable

$$t' \to \tau = t-t'.$$

It can be seen that, for a general form of memory function μ, $p_{11}-p_{22}$ and p_{21} have a different dependence on time. In fact, we can prove the following interesting result when the memory function is a sum of exponentials.

(6.33) *When the memory function μ is a sum of the form (6.5) containing at least two distinct exponential terms, the difference $p_{11}-p_{22}$ of normal stress components relaxes more slowly than the tangential stress component p_{21}. If μ is a single exponential function, then $p_{11}-p_{22}$ and p_{21} relax at the same rate* (Lodge, 1956).

Since $p_{11}-p_{22}$ and p_{21} in general have different values at the start of relaxation, it is necessary to say what is meant here by the statement that the two quantities relax at the same, or at a different, rate. For this purpose, it is convenient to introduce a constant β chosen so that $p_{11}-p_{22}$ and βp_{21} have the same value at the start of relaxation: i.e.

$$(6.34) \quad p_{11}-p_{22} = \beta p_{21} \qquad (t = t_1).$$

Thus

$$(6.35) \quad \beta = \frac{\mu_2}{\mu_1}G, \qquad \text{by (6.22), (6.23).}$$

We then say that $p_{11}-p_{22}$ relaxes more slowly than p_{21} if the difference $p_{11}-p_{22}-\beta p_{21}$ is positive for $t > t_1$; if $p_{11}-p_{22}-\beta p_{21}$ remains zero for $t > t_1$, we say that $p_{11}-p_{22}$ and p_{21} relax at the same rate.

Proof of (6.33). We have to consider the sign of $p_{11}-p_{22}-\beta p_{21}$. From (6.31) and (6.35), we have

$$p_{11}-p_{22}-\beta p_{21} = \frac{G^2}{\mu_1}(\mu_1 I_2 - \mu_2 I_1). \tag{6.36}$$

With μ given as a sum of exponentials (6.5), the quantities μ_1, μ_2 are given by (6.6) and the integrals I_1, I_2, defined by (6.32), may be evaluated; writing $t-t_1 = \tau$, we find that

$$I_r(\tau) = r!\sum_{\sigma=1}^{m} a_\sigma(\tau_\sigma)^{r+1}\exp\left(\frac{-\tau}{\tau_\sigma}\right) \qquad (r = 1, 2), \tag{6.37}$$

and hence

$$\begin{aligned}\mu_1 I_2 - \mu_2 I_1 &= 2\left\{\sum_s a_s\tau_s^2\sum_\sigma a_\sigma\tau_\sigma^3 - \sum_s a_s\tau_s^3\sum_\sigma a_\sigma\tau_\sigma^2\right\}\exp\left(\frac{-\tau}{\tau_\sigma}\right)\\ &= 2\sum_s\sum_\sigma a_s a_\sigma\tau_s^2\tau_\sigma^2(\tau_\sigma-\tau_s)\exp\left(\frac{-\tau}{\tau_\sigma}\right)\\ &= \sum_s\sum_\sigma a_s a_\sigma\tau_s^2\tau_\sigma^2(\tau_\sigma-\tau_s)\exp\left(\frac{-\tau}{\tau_\sigma}\right)\\ &\quad+\sum_\sigma\sum_s a_\sigma a_s\tau_\sigma^2\tau_s^2(\tau_s-\tau_\sigma)\exp\left(\frac{-\tau}{\tau_s}\right).\end{aligned}$$

The last step is taken by dividing the double sum into two equal parts and interchanging the summation suffixes in one of them. We can now see that

$$p_{11}-p_{22}-\beta p_{21} = \frac{G^2}{\mu_1}\sum_s\sum_\sigma a_s a_\sigma\tau_s^2\tau_\sigma^2(\tau_\sigma-\tau_s)\left\{\exp\left(\frac{-\tau}{\tau_\sigma}\right)-\exp\left(\frac{-\tau}{\tau_s}\right)\right\}. \tag{6.38}$$

Every term in this double sum is either positive or zero; for if the factor $\tau_\sigma-\tau_s > 0$, then the factor $\{\exp(-\tau/\tau_\sigma)-\exp(-\tau/\tau_s)\} > 0$, and their product is positive; if the first factor is negative, so also is the second, and their product is still positive; moreover, the remaining factors, $a_s a_\sigma \tau_s^2 \tau_\sigma^2$, are positive. Excluding the unimportant case $a_\sigma = 0$ (all σ) which would give $\mu = 0$, we see that every term in the sum is zero if and only if $\tau_\sigma-\tau_s = 0$ for all values of σ, s, i.e. if and only if $\tau_\sigma = \tau_1$ (for all σ), so that there is only one distinct exponential term in the sum (6.5).

Thus $p_{11}-p_{22}-\beta p_{21}$ is positive if there are two or more exponentials in the sum (6.5) and zero if there is only one, which proves the statement (6.33).

Oscillatory Shear Flow

For a sinusoidally varying shear flow of amplitude α and angular frequency ω, the magnitude s of the shear $t' \to t$ is given by (2.80) with $G = 0$, while $\gamma^{ij}(t') - \gamma^{ij}(t)$ is given by (2.66) (with $t_0 = t'$) relative to our usual shear flow basis $\mathbf{e}_i$ which is orthonormal in the current state t. According to (2.81), the material passes through its "central state" at times $t = 0, \pm\pi/\omega, \pm 2\pi/\omega, \ldots$, since at these times the absolute magnitude of the shear rate is a maximum.

From (3.14), (6.8), and (2.66), we obtain the following expressions for the non-zero cartesian stress components at the current time t:

$$(6.39)\quad \begin{cases} p_{11} - p_{22} = \displaystyle\int_{t'=-\infty}^{t} \mu(t-t')\, s^2\, dt' \\ p_{21} = p_{12} = \displaystyle\int_{t'=-\infty}^{t} \mu(t-t')\, s\, dt' \\ p_{22} - p_{33} = 0. \end{cases}$$

From (2.80) with $G = 0$, we have

$$(6.40)\quad \begin{cases} s = \alpha\{\sin\omega t(1-\cos\omega\tau) - \cos\omega t \sin\omega\tau\} \\ s^2 = \alpha^2\{1 - \cos 2\omega t\cos\omega\tau - \sin 2\omega t \sin\omega\tau\}\{1-\cos\omega\tau\}, \end{cases}$$

where $\tau = t - t'$. On substituting these expressions in (6.39), we finally obtain the following expressions for the cartesian stress components in oscillatory shear flow:

$$(6.41)\quad \begin{cases} p_{11} - p_{22} = \alpha^2\{A - B\cos 2\omega t - C\sin 2\omega t\} \\ p_{21} = \alpha\{A\cos\omega t - D\sin\omega t\}. \end{cases}$$

The coefficients A, B, C, D here are functions of the angular frequency ω and are defined in terms of the memory function μ by the equations

$$(6.42)\quad \begin{cases} A = \displaystyle\int_0^\infty \mu(\tau)(1-\cos\omega\tau)\, d\tau \\ B = \displaystyle\int_0^\infty \mu(\tau)(1-\cos\omega\tau)\cos\omega\tau\, d\tau \\ C = \displaystyle\int_0^\infty \mu(\tau)(1-\cos\omega\tau)\sin\omega\tau\, d\tau \\ D = \displaystyle\int_0^\infty \mu(\tau)\sin\omega\tau\, d\tau. \end{cases}$$

It is seen from this solution that *the normal stress difference* $p_{11}-p_{22}$ *varies at double the applied frequency* ω and is proportional to the square of the amplitude α; the tangential component p_{21} varies at the applied frequency and contains a term $\alpha A \cos \omega t$ which is out of phase with the shear motion (2.80).

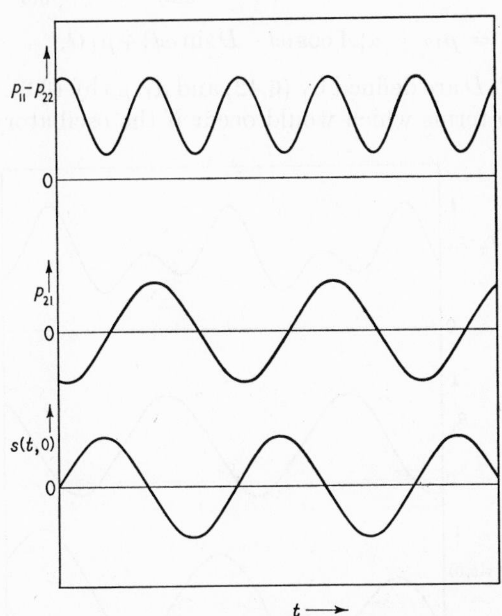

FIG. 6.1. Oscillatory shear in a rubberlike liquid. Normal stress difference $p_{11}-p_{22}$, shear stress p_{21}, and magnitude of shear strain $s(t, 0)$ as functions of time t. (From (2.80) and (6.41) with $G = 0$ and other constants chosen arbitrarily.)

It is noteworthy that the same coefficient A occurs in the out-of-phase part of p_{21} and in the constant term in $p_{11}-p_{22}$; from this it follows that

$$\frac{\text{average of } p_{11}-p_{22} \text{ over a period}}{\text{amplitude of out-of-phase part of } p_{21}} = \alpha; \tag{6.43}$$

this ratio is thus independent of frequency and of the memory function (Lodge, 1961b).

From (6.39), it can be seen that $p_{11}-p_{22}$ *is always positive*; thus, in a graph of $p_{11}-p_{22}$ against time, the "troughs" lie above the line $p_{11}-p_{22} = 0$ (Fig. 6.1).

For the case of an oscillatory shear flow of amplitude α and angular frequency ω superposed on a steady shear flow of shear rate G having the same shearing planes and direction of shear, the appropriate expression for s is given by (2.80), and a similar calculation leads to the following results for the non-zero cartesian stress components at time t:

$$(6.44)\quad \begin{cases} p_{11}-p_{22} = \alpha^2\{A-B\cos 2\omega t - C\sin 2\omega t\}+\mu_2 G^2 \\ \qquad\qquad + 2\alpha G\left\{\left(\mu_1-\dfrac{\partial D}{\partial \omega}\right)\cos\omega t - \dfrac{\partial A}{\partial \omega}\sin\omega t\right\}, \\ p_{21} = p_{12} = \alpha\{A\cos\omega t - D\sin\omega t\}+\mu_1 G, \end{cases}$$

where A, B, C, D are defined by (6.42) and μ_1, μ_2 by (6.3). It is seen that, in addition to terms which would occur if the oscillatory flow and the

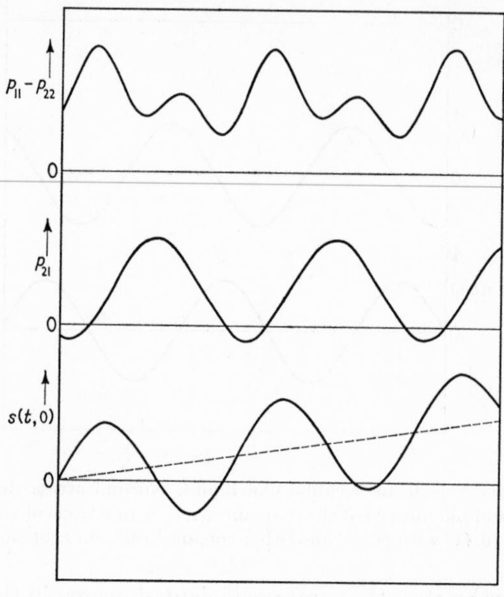

FIG. 6.2. Oscillatory shear superposed on steady shear flow in a rubberlike liquid. Normal stress difference $p_{11}-p_{22}$, shear stress p_{21}, and magnitude of shear strain $s(t, 0)$ as functions of time t. (From (2.80) and (6.44) with arbitrarily chosen values for the constants.)

steady flow took place separately, there is in the expression for the normal stress difference $p_{11}-p_{22}$ a term in αG which may be regarded as arising from an interaction between the two types of flow (Fig. 6.2).

Steady Elongational Flow

For steady elongational flow at an elongation rate $\bar{G}$, the value of $\gamma^{ij}(t)$ is given by (2.53) relative to a basis $\mathbf{e}_i$ which is orthonormal at an arbitrary instant t_0 and is orthogonal but not orthonormal at any other instant t; the vector $\mathbf{e}_1$ is parallel to the direction of elongation. Using (2.53) with $t = t'$, the rheological equation of state (6.9) becomes

$$\pi^{ij}(t) + p\gamma^{ij}(t) = \int_{t'=-\infty}^{t} \mu(t-t')\,dt' \begin{pmatrix} \exp 2\bar{G}(t_0 - t') & 0 & 0 \\ 0 & \exp \bar{G}(t' - t_0) & 0 \\ 0 & 0 & \exp \bar{G}(t' - t_0) \end{pmatrix}.$$

By (3.15), the cartesian stress components at time t are obtained by multiplication with $e_i\ e_j$, which in this case are given by (2.53); this removes the arbitrary time t_0 from the expression, and leads to the result

$$(6.45)\quad p_{ij} = \begin{pmatrix} -p & 0 & 0 \\ 0 & -p & 0 \\ 0 & 0 & -p \end{pmatrix} + \int_{t'=-\infty}^{t} \mu(t-t')\,dt' \begin{pmatrix} \exp 2\bar{G}(t - t') & 0 & 0 \\ 0 & \exp \bar{G}(t' - t) & 0 \\ 0 & 0 & \exp \bar{G}(t' - t) \end{pmatrix}.$$

Thus $p_{22} = p_{33}$, and we may take these to be zero without loss of generality; this corresponds to the case of a liquid filament elongating under the influence of a tensile traction p_{11} normal to planes perpendicular to the direction of elongation, there being no traction on the sides of the filament. This determines the value of p in (6.45), which then gives the following expression for p_{11}:

$$(6.46)\qquad p_{11} = \int_0^{\infty} \mu(\tau)\,\{e^{2\bar{G}\tau} - e^{-\bar{G}\tau}\}\,d\tau.$$

This is obtained by means of a change of variable $t' \to \tau = t - t'$, and shows, in particular, that p_{11} is independent of time.

The way in which p_{11} depends on $\bar{G}$ depends on the form of the memory function μ. It will be sufficient here to consider the simplest physically reasonable case and take μ to be an exponential function (6.7).

We then find that, provided

$$(6.47)\qquad \bar{G} < \frac{1}{2\tau_1},$$

the integrals in (6.46) converge and lead to the result

$$(6.48)\qquad p_{11} = 3\mu_0\,\tau_1\,\bar{G}(1 - 2\bar{G}\tau_1)^{-1}(1 + \bar{G}\tau_1)^{-1}.$$

Using (5.13), (6.6), and (6.25), this leads to the following relation between Trouton viscosity $\bar{\eta}$ and viscosity η:

(6.49) $$\bar{\eta} = 3\eta(1-2\bar{G}\tau_1)^{-1}(1+\bar{G}\tau_1)^{-1}.$$

The dependence of Trouton viscosity on elongation rate given by this equation is represented in Fig. 6.3. It is seen that at very low elongation rates, $\bar{\eta} = 3\eta$, as for a Newtonian liquid; for elongation rates approaching

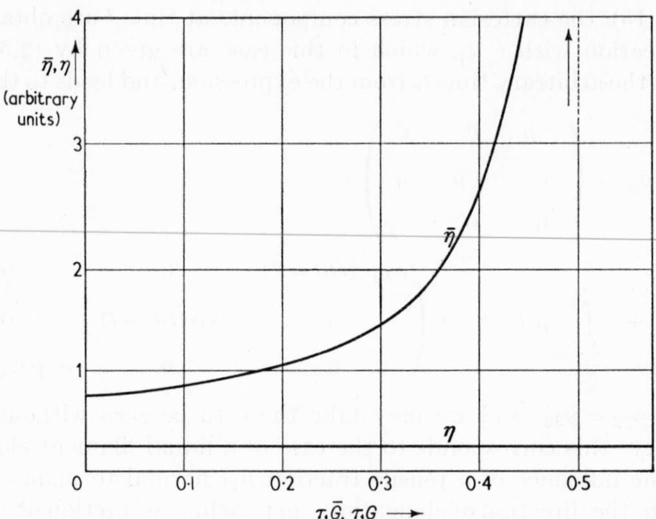

FIG. 6.3. Variation of Trouton viscosity $\bar{\eta}$ with elongation rate $\bar{G}$ and of viscosity η with shear rate G for a rubberlike liquid with memory function $\mu(\tau) = a_1 \exp(-\tau/\tau_1)$. (From (6.25) and (6.49).)

the value $1/2\tau_1$, $\bar{\eta}$ increases indefinitely. For higher elongation rates, the integral in (6.46) does not converge; this suggests that if one started to elongate the material from a state of rest the stress would increase indefinitely, and this can in fact be readily verified from the rheological equation of state.

It is also of interest to express the Trouton viscosity $\bar{\eta}$ as a function of the traction p_{11} instead of elongation rate; to do this, we eliminate $\bar{G}$ between (5.13) and (6.49) and solve the resulting quadratic equation for $\bar{\eta}$, choosing the positive sign for the square root because $\bar{\eta}$ is necessarily positive. We thus obtain the following equation

(6.50) $$2\frac{\bar{\eta}}{3\eta} = 1+\frac{\tau_1 p_{11}}{3\eta}+\left\{1+2\frac{\tau_1 p_{11}}{3\eta}+9\left(\frac{\tau_1 p_{11}}{3\eta}\right)^2\right\}^{1/2}.$$

The above analysis shows that the rubberlike liquid exhibits behaviour in steady elongational flow very different from that in steady shear flow; the elongational viscosity $\bar{\eta}$ increases rapidly with increase of elongation rate $\bar{G}$, whereas the viscosity η is independent of shear rate G. The resistance to flow ($\bar{\eta}$, η) thus depends markedly on the type of flow. It can be shown that differences of this type are not confined to the particular elastic liquid considered here; other types of elastic liquid will give viscosities which depend on shear rate, but the elongational viscosities will have different dependences on elongation rate.

The reason for these differences must lie in the geometrical differences between elongational flow and shear flow (Weissenberg, 1931, p. 9, attributes recognition of this fact to Hencky). We have already remarked, in the discussion following (2.68), that one such difference consists in the fact that all three principal axes of strain are constant in the material in elongational flow but only one principal axis of strain is constant in the material in shear flow. A second difference, in steady flow, consists in the fact that pairs of parallel material planes have separations which vary exponentially with time in elongational flow but less rapidly in shear flow, as the following calculation shows.

Let us consider, in particular, material planes which at time t are perpendicular to $\mathbf{e}_1$ (i.e. to the direction of elongation in elongational flow or to the direction of shear in shear flow). The coordinates η_i for such planes are of the form

$$\eta_i = (\eta_1, 0, 0), \tag{6.51}$$

and these coordinates are independent of time. By (2.23), it follows that the separation $h(t')$ of two such planes at time t' is given by

$$h(t') = \frac{1}{\eta_1}\{\gamma^{11}(t')\}^{-1/2}. \tag{6.52}$$

Using the expressions for $\gamma^{11}(t')$ obtained from (2.55) with $t = t'$ (for elongational flow) and from (2.70) (for shear flow), we then find the results

$$h(t') = \begin{cases} \dfrac{1}{\eta_1}\exp \bar{G}(t'-t_0) & \text{(elongational flow)} \\[2ex] \dfrac{1}{\eta_1}\{1+G^2(t-t')^2\}^{-1/2} \quad (t' < t) & \text{(shear flow).} \end{cases} \tag{6.53}$$

In both cases, the separation $h(t')$ increases with increase of t', but the increase is more rapid in the case of elongational flow. Such differences will be important for elastic liquids for which *a finite history* of h influences the current stress, but not for inelastic liquids for which only an infinitesimally small history (the rate-of-change of h) influences the current stress.

A Network Theory of Polymer Solutions

Rheological equations of state equivalent to (6.9) have been derived on the basis of a molecular theory for concentrated solutions of high polymers (Yamamoto and Inagaki, 1952; Lodge, 1954, 1956; Yamamoto, 1956) which differs only in detail from an earlier molecular theory of imperfectly elastic rubberlike solids due to Green and Tobolsky (1946). This in turn is an extension of the two-network hypothesis for composite networks (Tobolsky, Andrews and Hanson, 1946) already described in Chapter 4 above. In its simplest form, the theory for polymer solutions rests on certain assumptions which may be expressed as follows (Lodge, 1956).

(i) In a polymer solution at rest, at any instant enough long-chain molecules are linked together at a few points along their length by temporary physical entanglements so as to form a homogeneous network extending throughout the solution.

(ii) Due to the effects of thermal motion, entanglement junctions are continually being lost and new ones formed; at any instant t, the concentration of effective network junctions which were formed in a previous time interval t', $t'+dt'$ and still exist at time t is a function

$$N(t-t')\,dt' \tag{6.54}$$

which depends on the time interval $t-t'$ and not on t or t' separately.

(iii) In a flowing polymer solution, the network will deform and the associated change of configurational entropy will give rise to a non-isotropic contribution to the stress; it is assumed that all other possible non-isotropic contributions (e.g. from solvent viscosity and unattached chain molecules) to the stress are negligible.

To calculate the stress at any time t following an arbitrary flow history, it is further assumed that:

(iv) the network is at time t in thermodynamic equilibrium with regard to changes of network configuration subject to given time-average positions of the junctions; (the flow is thus regarded as involving a quasi-static deformation of the network, or the attainment of thermodynamic equilibrium in each state is infinitely rapid compared with times involved in the flow);

(v) the material is incompressible;

(vi) the extra stress $\pi^{ij}(t)+p\gamma^{ij}(t)$ is made up of a sum of contributions from all previous times t', the contribution from t' arising from chain molecules which joined the network in the interval $t', t'+dt'$ and are still part of the network at the current time t; the contribution from these chain molecules is that given by the kinetic theory of rubberlike elasticity for a network containing $N(t-t')dt'$ junctions per unit volume, and having stress-free and stressed states t' and t, respectively.

From this, it follows that the extra stress at time t is given by the following time integral:

$$(6.55) \qquad \pi^{ij}(t)+p\gamma^{ij}(t) = ckT \int_{t'=-\infty}^{t} N(t-t')\,\gamma^{ij}(t')\,dt';$$

this follows from the equations (4.12) and (4.41) for a rubberlike solid on replacing t_0 by t' and μ_0 by $ckTN(t-t')dt'$.

It is seen that (6.55) is identical to the rheological equation of state (6.9), which was derived from the hypothesis (6.1), if we put

$$(6.56) \qquad \mu(t-t') = ckTN(t-t')$$

and assume that

(vii) the "junction age distribution function" N is independent of flow history, i.e. that the network deformation has negligible effect on the processes of loss and formation of entanglement junctions.

Since the viscosity, according to (6.25) and (6.55), is proportional to the first moment of the junction age distribution function N, it is to be expected that an extension of the theory to allow for effects of flow history on N (and such effects will surely arise at large enough rates of strain) will lead to a value of viscosity which depends on shear rate. Yamamoto (1957, 1958) has shown that this is in fact the case.

It can now be seen that this theory is an extension of the two-network hypothesis for composite networks. According to the two-network hypothesis, the stress is calculated as a sum of contributions from two independent networks and the expression (4.42) for the extra stress contains two terms on the right-hand side, by (4.45). According to the theory for polymer solutions, the stress is calculated as a sum of contributions from an infinite number of independent networks, and the expression (6.55) for the extra stress accordingly contains an integral on the right-hand side.

The comments on the validity of the two-network hypothesis referred to in Chapter 4 are relevant to the question of the validity of the theory for polymer solutions, but the theory for polymer solutions involves the additional feature that network junctions are lost during deformation.

According to certain calculations, the two-network hypothesis (and therefore the theory for polymer solutions) is not valid in such circumstances (Scanlan and Watson, 1958; Flory, 1960), and the coefficients N_0, N_1 of the terms involving γ^{ij} in (4.45) must be given a different interpretation.

It is not appropriate here to give a detailed discussion of the question of the validity of the network theory of polymer solutions, but it should perhaps be remarked that the two most crucial points are the assumption that the stress is due to the deformation of a network (i), (iii), and the arbitrary assumption that the stress can be calculated as if the network were a superposition of independent networks (vi). In view of the latter assumption, it would be too much to expect quantitative validity for the theory. At the present stage of research, however, it is suggested that the value of a theory of this type lies rather in the indication that, as far as polymer solutions and possibly also polymer melts are concerned, out of the great variety of possible forms of rheological equations of state, it is in the first instance worth while concentrating attention on equations which involve stress–strain relations of the type encountered in the kinetic theory of rubberlike elasticity and which represent the dependence of stress on strain history by means of a single time integral. Further, the interpretation of the rheological equation of state (6.9) in terms of a relaxing network is of practical advantage in aiding the solution of certain problems, notably those concerning elastic recoil, which do not appear to have been tackled successfully otherwise.

Examples 6

1. The rubberlike liquid described by (6.8) is at constant shape up to an instant $t = t_1$ when a steady shear flow of shear rate G is imposed. Show that, in the usual notation, the cartesian stress components at any subsequent instant $t > t_1$ are given by the equations

$$p_{11}-p_{22} = G^2\{\mu_2 - I_2 - 2(t-t_1)\,I_1\},$$
$$p_{21} = G\{\mu_1 - I_1\},$$

where $I_r = I_r(t-t_1)$ and μ_r are defined by (6.32) and (6.3).

Show that $\beta p_{21} > p_{11}-p_{22}$, where β is given by (6.35), when μ is expressible as a sum of exponentials of the form (6.5) containing one or more terms. (This example shows that the transient behaviour at the start of shear flow is the reverse of the relaxation behaviour at the cessation of steady shear flow where p_{21} is concerned but not where $p_{11}-p_{22}$ is concerned owing to the term in I_1 which has no counterpart in the corresponding term (6.31) for relaxation.)

2. Show that, in the relaxation of stress at constant shape following the cessation of oscillatory shear flow, $p_{11}-p_{22}$ and p_{21} decrease steadily without oscillation when μ is given by (6.7).

3. When μ is given by (6.7) and the flow history is such that the extra stress

$$\Pi^{ij} \equiv \pi^{ij}+p\gamma^{ij}$$

is differentiable, show that the rheological equation of state (6.9) may be written in the form

$$\left(\tau_1\frac{d}{dt}+1\right)\Pi^{ij} = \tau_1\mu(0)\gamma^{ij}.$$

4. An incompressible liquid has a rheological equation of state of the form

$$\pi_{ij}+p\gamma_{ij} = -\int_{-\infty}^{t}\mu(t-t')\left[\gamma_{ij}(t')-\gamma_{ij}(t)\right]dt',$$

where
$$\pi_{ij} \equiv \sum_r\sum_s \gamma_{ir}\gamma_{js}\pi^{rs}$$

(cf. Examples 5, No. 5).

Calculate the cartesian stress components in steady shear flow, showing that the viscosity is the same as that for the rubberlike liquid (6.9) but that the differences of normal stress components are (in the usual notation) given by

$$\begin{cases} p_{11}-p_{33} = 0, \\ p_{22}-p_{33} = -G^2\mu_2, \end{cases}$$

where G is the shear rate and μ_2 is given by (6.3) with $r = 2$.

5. The rheological equation of state (6.9) is generalized by allowing the memory function to depend on the "flow invariant"

$$L_2(t) \equiv \sum_i\sum_j\sum_k\sum_m \dot{\gamma}^{ij}\dot{\gamma}^{km}\gamma_{jk}\gamma_{im}$$

(cf. Examples 5, No. 3), so that

$$\mu = \mu[t-t', L_2(t)].$$

Prove that in steady shear flow of shear rate G, $L_2 = 2G^2$, and hence that, in the usual notation for the cartesian stress components,

$$p_{11}-p_{22} = G^2\mu_2(G^2),$$

and
$$p_{21} = G\mu_1(G^2),$$

where
$$\mu_r(G^2) \equiv \int_{-\infty}^{t} \mu[t-t', 2G^2]\,(t-t')^r\,dt' \qquad (r = 1,2).$$

(This is one way of modifying the equations for a rubberlike liquid so as to give a liquid whose viscosity $\eta = \mu_1(G^2)$ depends on shear rate. Note that, if μ is a product of functions of the form $\mu = \mu'(t-t')\,\mu''[L_2(t)]$, then the factor μ'' is common to both the above expressions for stress components, and hence $(p_{11}-p_{22})/p_{21}$ is proportional to G as in the case of a rubberlike liquid.)

CHAPTER 7

Elastic Recoil in a Rubberlike Liquid

We now consider the characteristic and fundamental property of an elastic liquid, namely, the property of undergoing further changes of shape when the stress is made zero or isotropic at any instant following an arbitrary flow history. According to the definition (4.6) (ii), this is one of two properties which distinguish an elastic from an inelastic liquid. Since the further changes of shape are often in some sense the reverse of those which occurred during the flow history preceding stress removal, the term *elastic recovery* is used to describe the phenomenon; we shall see, however, that in the case in which the flow history is one of steady shear flow, the particular liquid considered in the last chapter "recovers" to a state (or states) which it has never been in before; to allow for this possibility, the term *elastic recoil* is perhaps preferable.

It will be seen that the problem of calculating elastic recoil for a liquid whose rheological equations of state are given is one which has no counterpart in the theory of perfectly elastic solids; for, whatever the strain, a perfectly elastic solid has a unique stress-free state to which it returns instantaneously when the stress is made zero. For an imperfectly elastic solid, there may be a problem of interest in calculating the sequence of states through which the return to the stress-free state is accomplished.

It is useful to distinguish between instantaneous, delayed, and ultimate recoveries (or recoils): *instantaneous recovery* is the strain which occurs immediately the stress is removed (or made isotropic) and may be described by a discontinuous change in the quantities γ^{ij} regarded as functions of time t; *delayed recovery* is the term used to describe any subsequent strains, which may usually be represented by continuous functions $\gamma^{ij}(t)$; and *ultimate recovery* stands for the strain measured from the state immediately preceding instantaneous recovery to the state to which the liquid finally tends at large values of time; thus ultimate recovery can be regarded as a "sum" of instantaneous recovery and total delayed recovery.

The concept "instantaneous recovery" represents an idealization in that the effects of inertia must be disregarded; it is nevertheless a very useful and not misleading idealization, for, on the one hand, some liquids do exhibit two extreme types of recovery—one very fast and one comparatively slow—and it seems to be a reasonable first approximation to treat the fast part as if it were instantaneous; and on the other hand, the rigorously-minded reader can, if he wishes, always envisage the behaviour of a volume element of vanishingly small dimensions for which the effects of inertia (being a body force) become negligible in comparison with effects relating to stress and strain (cf. Chapter 4).

It is also necessary to distinguish between two further types of recovery. Calculations described below suggest that, in certain experimental determinations of recovery, e.g. when the liquid is confined to the gap between rigid cylinders in relative rotation, the recovery observed when one cylinder is set free to rotate must be regarded as taking place under constraint; for in the absence of the cylinders the recovery could involve a change of liquid dimensions in directions perpendicular to the previous position of the cylinder walls. Accordingly, we shall (when necessary) use the term *free recovery* to denote what we have already called recovery (when there are no constraints), and the term *constrained recovery* otherwise. In constrained recovery, it is to be expected that some but not all stress components can be made zero instantaneously.

Calculations of recovery which involve finite strain appear to present rather more difficulty than, for example, calculations of stress when the flow history is given, although the form in which the rheological equations of state are given must have an influence on this point; in the case of the rubberlike liquid with equations of the form (6.9), the shape variables γ^{ij} appear in the integrand and therefore a recovery calculation (in which the stress is specified from some point on) must involve the solving of an integral equation for the unknowns γ^{ij}.

It is perhaps for this reason that recovery problems appear to have received little attention in the literature; in fact, the recovery calculations given below, based on the rubberlike-liquid equations of the last chapter, are the only calculations of finite recovery in a liquid, based on a suitably invariant rheological equation of state, known to the author.† Although these equations are among the simplest possible for describing elastic liquids, we shall see that they do give rise to several interesting and unexpected results, especially in relation to recovery following shear flow. Before using the equations to calculate recoveries following elongational and shear flows, we first establish certain relevant results which are valid for any flow history.

The Equivalent Rubberlike Solid

For the remainder of this chapter, we consider the rubberlike liquid defined by the rheological equations of state (6.9). As a guide to the

† A calculation of constrained shear recovery in an anistropic liquid has been made by J. L. Erickson (private communication).

solution of problems involving instantaneous recovery, it is helpful to consider first the network theory of polymer solutions which has led to these equations of state, as outlined at the end of Chapter 6.

According to this theory, one distinguishes between two types of molecular process which proceed at very different rates: (i) the process of loss and creation of junctions, which is slow (involving times of the order of, say, 0·01 seconds); and (ii) the process of change of network configurations when the time-average positions of junctions are specified, which is fast and is taken to be instantaneous. Moreover, at any instant in the course of an arbitrary flow history, the stress is determined by a network which is indistinguishable from the type of network supposed to exist in a rubberlike solid (and particularly in a rubberlike solid swollen with a low molecular weight solvent); we may call this the *equivalent rubberlike solid*. It is to be expected that the connectivity, the modulus, and the stress-free state for the equivalent rubberlike solid will (for a given polymer solution) depend on the flow history. It is clear that when the stress is instantaneously made zero or isotropic, the liquid will deform *instantaneously* (because the solvent viscosity is taken to be zero) to the stress-free state of the equivalent rubberlike solid at that instant. More generally, if at any instant in a (slow) flow history the liquid be subjected to arbitrary sufficiently rapid deformations it will for these deformations behave like a perfectly elastic solid of the rubberlike type. These expectations are embodied in the following statements, which will be proved on the basis of the rheological equations of state.

(7.1) *For sufficiently rapid deformations at any instant t_1 following an arbitrary flow history, the rubberlike liquid described by equation* (6.9) *with a continuous memory function μ has the same stress–strain relation as a rubberlike solid of stress-free state $\gamma^{ij}(t_1^*)$ and modulus μ_0^*, where*

(7.2) $$\mu_0^* \gamma^{ij}(t_1^*) = \int_{t'=-\infty}^{t_1} \mu(t_1-t')\,\gamma^{ij}(t')\,dt'$$

and

(7.3) $$\det \gamma^{ij}(t_1^*) = \det \gamma^{ij}(t_1).$$

In particular, if the stress be made zero or isotropic instantaneously at time t_1, the liquid will undergo the instantaneous deformation $\gamma^{ij}(t_1) \to \gamma^{ij}(t_1^*)$. The state $\gamma^{ij}(t_1^*)$ will be called the *instantaneously recoverable state* at time t_1.

The notation $\gamma^{ij}(t_1^*)$ calls for explanation. The shape variables γ^{ij} will usually be continuous functions of time except (in the present context) at the instant t_1, when the stress is instantaneously made zero or isotropic and there is in consequence a discontinuous change in γ^{ij}. At the time t_1, therefore, the variables γ^{ij} will have two distinct sets of values according as t_1 is approached from values of t less than or greater than t_1. We use $\gamma^{ij}(t_1)$ to denote the former values, and $\gamma^{ij}(t_1^*)$ to denote the latter values. Thus

$$\begin{cases} \gamma^{ij}(t_1) \equiv \lim_{\delta t \to 0} \gamma^{ij}(t_1 - \delta t) & (\delta t > 0), \\ \gamma^{ij}(t_1^*) \equiv \lim_{\delta t \to 0} \gamma^{ij}(t_1 + \delta t) & (\delta t > 0). \end{cases}$$

Since the discontinuous change is in the variables γ^{ij} and not in the variable t, it would perhaps be better to use the notation $\gamma^{ij*}(t_1)$ instead of $\gamma^{ij}(t_1^*)$; but the latter proves to be the more convenient, and will be adhered to.

The constant μ_0^* is called the *modulus* by analogy with the constant μ_0 in (4.12) which represents the shear modulus of the rubberlike solid.

Proof. We note first that (7.2) and (7.3) represent equations of which seven are independent; they are therefore sufficient to determine the quantities $\gamma^{ij}(t_1^*)$, μ_0^* of which seven are independent. Moreover, taking μ_0^* to be positive, we see that $\gamma^{ij}(t_1^*)$ is defined by (7.2) as a sum of terms each of which consists of the product of a positive coefficient and a quantity $\gamma^{ij}(t')$ which describes a shape of the material; it follows that the quantities $\gamma^{ij}(t_1^*)$ so defined do describe a possible shape of the material. (This follows from Examples 4, No. 4, which embodies a similar proposition for the particular case in which there are only two terms in the sum; the required extension to the case in which there are any number of terms in the sum can be readily seen to be valid.)

Let us now consider the flow history "$-\infty \to t_1 \to t$", where t is a label for any state attained "sufficiently rapidly" from the state $\gamma^{ij}(t_1)$ which itself terminates an arbitrary given flow history. The rheological equations of state (6.9), applicable by hypothesis to any flow history, may in particular be applied to the flow history $-\infty \to t_1 \to t$, and give the following expression for the stress in the state t:

$$\pi^{ij}(t) + p\gamma^{ij}(t) = \left(\int_{-\infty}^{t_1} + \int_{t_1}^{t} \right) \mu(t-t')\gamma^{ij}(t')\,dt'. \tag{7.4}$$

In the first of these integrals, we may replace $\mu(t-t')$ by $\mu(t_1-t')$, since μ is continuous (by hypothesis) and the difference between t and t_1 is infinitesimally small. The second integral is zero, because the range of integration is infinitesimally small and the integrand is bounded. It then follows that

$$\begin{aligned} \pi^{ij}(t) + p\gamma^{ij}(t) &= \int_{-\infty}^{t_1} \mu(t_1-t')\gamma^{ij}(t')\,dt' \\ &= \mu_0^*\gamma^{ij}(t_1^*), \qquad \text{by (7.2).} \end{aligned} \tag{7.5}$$

If μ_0^* is chosen to satisfy the constant volume condition (7.3), we see by comparing (7.5) with (4.12) that the stress at time t is given by an equation of the same form as the equation for a rubberlike solid of modulus μ_0^* and stress-free state $\gamma^{ij}(t_1^*)$, which proves the theorem.

Although the statement in the theorem that $\gamma^{ij}(t_1) \to \gamma^{ij}(t_1^*)$ represents the instantaneous recovery which occurs when the stress is made isotropic at time t_1 is included in the rest of the theorem which has just been proved, it is of sufficient importance to warrant a direct proof, which may be given as follows.

We are given any flow history during the interval $-\infty < t' \leqslant t_1$; at time t_1, the stress is made isotropic and the liquid undergoes an instantaneous deformation $\gamma^{ij}(t_1) \to \gamma^{ij}(t_1^*)$, where $\gamma^{ij}(t_1^*)$ is to be determined. Since the stress is isotropic in state t_1^*, it follows that

$$\pi^{ij}(t_1^*) = p^* \gamma^{ij}(t_1^*)$$

for some value of p^*, and hence the rheological equation of state (6.9) with $t = t_1^*$ becomes

$$(p^* + p)\gamma^{ij}(t_1^*) = \left\{ \int_{-\infty}^{t_1} + \int_{t_1}^{t_1^*} \right\} \mu(t_1^* - t')\gamma^{ij}(t')\,dt'.$$

In the first of these integrals, we may replace $\mu(t_1^* - t')$ by $\mu(t_1 - t')$, because μ is continuous and $t_1^* - t_1$ is infinitesimally small; the second integral is zero, because the range of integration is infinitesimally small and the integrand is bounded. Hence

$$(p^* + p)\gamma^{ij}(t_1^*) = \int_{-\infty}^{t_1} \mu(t_1 - t')\gamma^{ij}(t')\,dt',$$

which agrees with the equation (7.2) stated in the theorem if we write $p^* + p = \mu_0^*$ and use the constant volume condition (7.3) in conjunction with this equation to determine the value of μ_0^*. This proves the result. It was first published by Lodge (1958a) in a different formalism.

The foregoing result applies to instantaneous recovery. We complete our treatment of flow histories in general by proving the following result concerning delayed recovery.

(7.6) *If the stress is made isotropic at any instant t_1 following an arbitrary flow history, there is no delayed recovery when the memory function is a single exponential function of the form* (6.7) *and the rheological equation of state has the form* (6.9).

Proof. We are given an arbitrary flow history in the interval

$$-\infty < t' \leqslant t_1,$$

and from the instant t_1 onwards the stress is isotropic, i.e.

$$\pi^{ij}(t) = p_1 \gamma^{ij}(t) \qquad (t > t_1)$$

for some function p_1. The rheological equation of state (6.9) therefore becomes, when $t > t_1^*$,

$$(p_1 + p)\gamma^{ij}(t) = \left\{ \int_{-\infty}^{t_1} + \int_{t_1}^{t_1^*} + \int_{t_1^*}^{t} \right\} \mu(t-t')\gamma^{ij}(t')\,dt'.$$

In the first integral, we may write

$$\mu(t-t') = \mu(t_1 - t')\exp\frac{t_1 - t}{\tau_1}, \tag{7.7}$$

because of the particular form (6.7) for μ; the second integral is zero because the range of integration is infinitesimally small; hence the equation may be written in the form

$$(p_1 + p)\gamma^{ij}(t) = \mu_0^* \gamma^{ij}(t_1^*)\exp\frac{t_1 - t}{\tau_1} + \int_{t_1^*}^{t} \mu(t-t')\gamma^{ij}(t')\,dt';$$

we have here used (7.2).

This integral equation for the unknown functions $\gamma^{ij}(t)$ for $t_1^* < t$ (which represent the delayed recovery) is evidently satisfied by the solution

$$\gamma^{ij}(t) = \gamma^{ij}(t_1^*) \qquad (t > t_1^*) \tag{7.8}$$

where $\gamma^{ij}(t_1^*)$, μ_0^* are defined by (7.2) and (7.3); for this solution satisfies the incompressibility condition (7.3), and when substituted in the integral equation leads to the equation

$$p_1 + p = \mu_0^* \exp\frac{t_1 - t}{\tau_1} + \int_{t_1^*}^{t} \mu(t-t')\,dt'$$

when the common factor $\gamma^{ij}(t_1^*)$ is removed. But the quantity $p_1 + p$ is at our disposal and can therefore be taken to be given by this equation. The solution (7.8), however, implies that there is no delayed recovery, because $\gamma^{ij}(t_1^*)$ is the instantaneously recoverable state. This proves the statement (7.6).

It will be seen from the result (7.1) that, for the rubberlike liquid described by (6.9), the stress at any instant in an arbitrary flow history is a function of a finite strain, measured from the instantaneously recoverable state to the current state. The liquid is therefore a particular example of a class of materials considered by Weissenberg (1947), who first proposed that the stress in certain liquids may be a function of a finite ("recoverable") strain—an idea that represents one possible type of generalization to finite strains of Maxwell's idea that a liquid may be regarded as a relaxing solid (cf. also Hencky (1929)).

Instantaneous Recovery after Steady Elongational Flow

We now consider the case in which the rubberlike liquid (6.9) undergoes steady elongational flow throughout a time interval $-\infty < t' \leqslant t_1$; from t_1 onwards, the stress is isotropic. We require to calculate the instantaneous recovery which occurs at t_1.

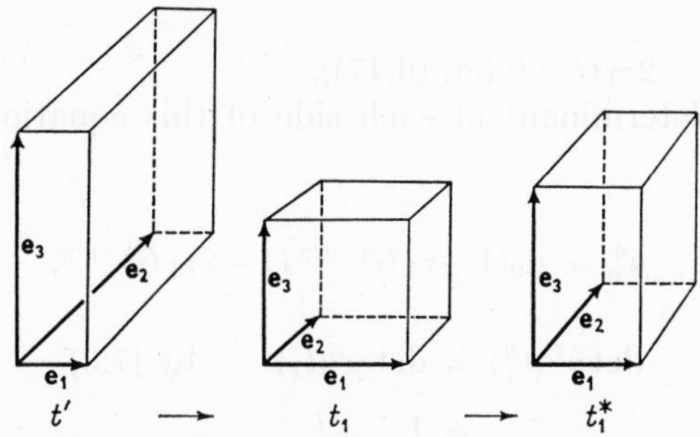

FIG. 7.1. Base vectors for steady elongational flow ($t' \to t_1$) and instantaneous recovery ($t_1 \to t_1^*$).

Since the material is isotropic and the flow history has complete rotational symmetry about any axis parallel to the direction of elongation, it is to be expected that the instantaneous recovery will possess the same symmetry and will involve a contraction of lines parallel to the previous direction of elongation together with an isotropic elongation of lines perpendicular to this direction; the problem therefore reduces to the calculation of the magnitude of this contraction, for a given value $\bar{G}$ of the rate of elongation in the steady flow before recovery.

According to (7.2), the instantaneously recoverable state $\gamma^{ij}(t_1^*)$ is given as an integral over the flow history during the period of steady elongational flow; the appropriate values for the quantities $\gamma^{ij}(t')$ in the integrand are therefore given by (2.53) with t, t_0 replaced by t', t_1, if we use a basis $\mathbf{e}_i$ which is *orthonormal in the state* t_1 and has $\mathbf{e}_1$ parallel to the direction of elongation (Fig. 7.1). We thus obtain the equation

$$\text{(7.9)} \quad \mu_0^* \gamma^{ij}(t_1^*) = \int_{-\infty}^{t_1} \mu(t_1-t') \begin{pmatrix} \exp 2\bar{G}(t_1-t') & 0 & 0 \\ 0 & \exp \bar{G}(t'-t_1) & 0 \\ 0 & 0 & \exp \bar{G}(t'-t_1) \end{pmatrix} dt'.$$

To evaluate the integrals occurring here, we shall consider the case in which the memory function is a single exponential function of the form (6.7); the integrations in (7.9) are then straightforward and yield the results

$$(7.10)\quad \mu_0^* \gamma^{ij}(t_1^*) = \begin{pmatrix} \dfrac{\mu_0}{1-2\tau_1 \bar{G}} & 0 & 0 \\ 0 & \dfrac{\mu_0}{1+\tau_1 \bar{G}} & 0 \\ 0 & 0 & \dfrac{\mu_0}{1+\tau_1 \bar{G}} \end{pmatrix},$$

provided that $1-2\tau_1 \bar{G} > 0$ (cf. (6.47)).

Taking the determinant of each side of this equation, we see that (by (1.37))

$$(7.11)\quad \mu_0^* = \mu_0 (1+\tau_1 \bar{G})^{-2/3} (1-2\tau_1 \bar{G})^{-1/3},$$

since

$$\begin{aligned} \det \gamma^{ij}(t_1^*) &= \det \gamma^{ij}(t_1) \qquad \text{by (7.3)} \\ &= 1, \end{aligned}$$

because the basis is orthonormal in state t_1.

Since the off-diagonal terms in (7.10) are zero, it follows that the basis is orthogonal in state t_1^*, as expected, and hence that

$$(7.12)\quad e_1(t_1^*) = \{\gamma^{11}(t_1^*)\}^{-1/2}.$$

Using (7.10), (7.11) and (7.12), we obtain finally the result

$$(7.13)\quad e_1(t_1^*) = \left(\frac{1-2\tau_1 \bar{G}}{1+\tau_1 \bar{G}}\right)^{1/3}.$$

Since $e_1(t_1) = 1$, $e_1(t_1^*)$ is the factor by which material lines parallel to the direction of elongation in the steady flow change in length instantaneously when the stress is made isotropic. It is seen from (7.13) that $e_1(t_1^*) < 1$, i.e. these lines decrease in length, as expected. The quantity $1/e_1(t_1^*)$, given by (7.13), is plotted as a function of elongation rate $\bar{G}$ in Fig. 7.2; it is seen that large instantaneous recovery is possible according to the present theory, a change of length by a factor 2 being obtained when the rate of elongation is $0{\cdot}4/\tau_1$.

The fact that $\gamma^{22}(t_1^*) = \gamma^{33}(t_1^*)$ in (7.10) shows that the change of length on recovery is the same for material lines parallel to $\mathbf{e}^2$ and parallel to e^3, showing that the recovery is of the type expected from the symmetry of the flow.

According to (7.11), the modulus μ_0^* of the equivalent rubberlike solid increases with increase of elongation rate $\bar{G}$; this is also represented in Fig. 7.2.

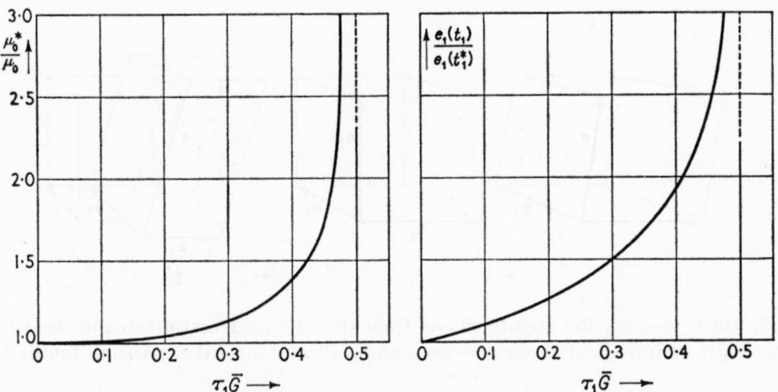

FIG. 7.2. Instantaneous recovery following steady elongational flow. Modulus μ_0^* and instantaneous change of length $e_1(t_1) \to e_1(t_1^*)$ as functions of elongation rate $\bar{G}$ for a rubberlike liquid with memory function

$$\mu(\tau) = \frac{\mu_0}{\tau_1}\exp\frac{-\tau}{\tau_1}.$$

(From equations (7.11), (7.13).)

Instantaneous Recovery after Steady Shear Flow

We now consider the case in which the liquid undergoes a steady shear flow of shear rate G throughout an interval $-\infty < t' \leqslant t_1$; at time t_1, the stress is made isotropic. We require to calculate the instantaneous recovery at time t_1.

It is convenient to use a basis $\mathbf{e}_i$ which is *orthonormal in the state* t_1 (immediately before recovery) and has $\mathbf{e}_1$ parallel to the direction of shear and $\mathbf{e}^2$ normal to the shearing planes, in agreement with our usual choice for shear flow (Fig. 7.3). Using the expression (2.70), with $t = t_1$, for $\gamma^{ij}(t')$, equation (7.2) for the instantaneously recoverable state $\gamma^{ij}(t_1^*)$ becomes

$$\mu_0^*\gamma^{ij}(t_1^*) = \int_{-\infty}^{t_1} \mu(t_1-t')\begin{pmatrix} 1+G^2(t_1-t')^2 & G(t_1-t') & 0 \\ G(t_1-t') & 1 & 0 \\ 0 & 0 & 1 \end{pmatrix} dt'.$$

On making the change of variable $t' \to \tau = t_1 - t'$, it is seen that the integrals occurring here are all of the form (6.3), and that we have in fact the equation

$$\mu_0^* \gamma^{ij}(t_1^*) = \begin{pmatrix} \mu_0 + \mu_2 G^2 & \mu_1 G & 0 \\ \mu_1 G & \mu_0 & 0 \\ 0 & 0 & \mu_0 \end{pmatrix}. \tag{7.14}$$

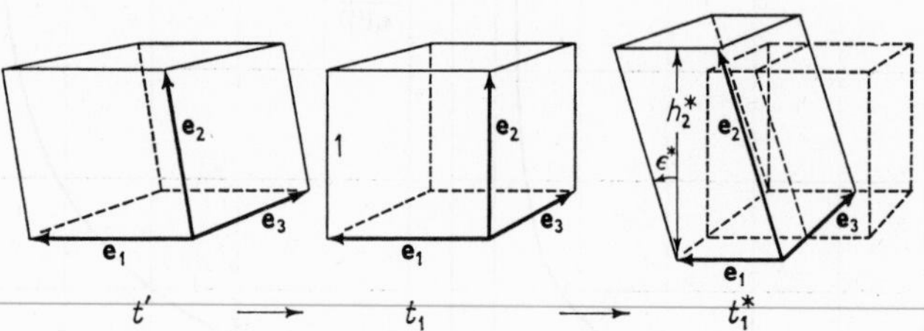

FIG. 7.3. Base vectors for steady shear flow ($t' \to t_1$) and instantaneous free recovery ($t_1 \to t_1^*$); definition of shear recovery angle ϵ^* and lateral expansion factor h_2^*.

Taking the determinant of each side of this equation, using (1.37), (7.3), and the fact that $\det \gamma^{ij}(t_1) = 1$ because the basis is orthonormal in state t_1, we obtain the following expression for the modulus μ_0^* of the equivalent rubberlike solid:

$$\mu_0^* = \mu_0 \left\{ 1 + \frac{\mu_0 \mu_2 - \mu_1^2}{\mu_0^2} G^2 \right\}^{1/3}. \tag{7.15}$$

It is convenient to introduce a positive quantity λ defined by the equation

$$\lambda^6 = 1 + \frac{\mu_0 \mu_2 - \mu_1^2}{\mu_0^2} G^2. \tag{7.16}$$

Using (7.15), equation (7.14) can now be written in the form

$$\gamma^{ij}(t_1^*) = \begin{pmatrix} \lambda^{-2}\left(1 + \frac{\mu_2}{\mu_0} G^2\right) & \lambda^{-2} \frac{\mu_1}{\mu_0} G & 0 \\ \lambda^{-2} \frac{\mu_1}{\mu_0} G & \lambda^{-2} & 0 \\ 0 & 0 & \lambda^{-2} \end{pmatrix}. \tag{7.17}$$

This defines the required instantaneously recoverable state. To see what this equation implies as to the shape in state t_1^* of the material which was a unit cube in state t_1 (Fig. 7.3), it is convenient (since $\mathbf{e}_i$ are embedded vectors but $\mathbf{e}^i$ are not) to use the equation

$$\mathbf{e}_i(t_1^*).\mathbf{e}_j(t_1^*) = \gamma_{ij}(t_1^*) = \begin{pmatrix} \lambda^{-4} & -\lambda^{-4}\frac{\mu_1}{\mu_0}G & 0 \\ -\lambda^{-4}\frac{\mu_1}{\mu_0}G & \lambda^{-4}\left(1+\frac{\mu_2}{\mu_0}G^2\right) & 0 \\ 0 & 0 & \lambda^2 \end{pmatrix}, \tag{7.18}$$

which can be obtained immediately from the cofactors of elements in (7.17), using (1.23), (7.16), and the fact that $\det\gamma^{ij}(t_1^*) = \det\gamma^{ij}(t_1) = 1$, since the basis $\mathbf{e}_i$ is orthonormal in state t_1.

Writing $\mathbf{e}_i(t_1^*) = \mathbf{e}_i^*$ for brevity, we see from (7.18) that

$$e_1^* = \lambda^{-2}, \quad e_3^* = \lambda. \tag{7.19}$$

We shall prove below that (when $G > 0$)

$$\lambda > 1. \tag{7.20}$$

Remembering that $e_i(t_1) = 1$ since the basis is orthonormal in state t_1, it follows from (7.19) that lines parallel to the direction of shear decrease in length (during the instantaneous recovery) by a factor λ^{-2} and that lines parallel to the direction $\mathbf{e}_3$ increase in length by a factor λ.

Furthermore, (7.18) shows that $\mathbf{e}_3^*.\mathbf{e}_2^* = \mathbf{e}_3^*.\mathbf{e}_1^* = 0$, showing that $\mathbf{e}_3^*$ is perpendicular to $\mathbf{e}_2^*$ and $\mathbf{e}_1^*$. The position in space of the vector $\mathbf{e}_3^*$ is arbitrary, and for convenience of comparison we may take its origin and line of action to coincide with those of $\mathbf{e}_3(t_1)$; the orientation of the material about the line representing $\mathbf{e}_3^*$ is now arbitrary, and we may assign this orientation so that $\mathbf{e}_1^*$ has the direction of $\mathbf{e}_1(t_1)$ (cf. Fig. 7.3). The remaining vector $\mathbf{e}_2^*$ must lie with $\mathbf{e}_1^*$ in a plane perpendicular to $\mathbf{e}_3^*$; if $\mathbf{e}_2^*$ makes an angle $\epsilon^* + \frac{1}{2}\pi$ with $\mathbf{e}_1^*$, then from (7.18) we have

$$e_1^* e_2^* \cos\left(\frac{\pi}{2}+\epsilon^*\right) = \gamma_{12}(t_1^*) = -\lambda^{-4}\frac{\mu_1}{\mu_0}G,$$

and

$$e_2^* = [\gamma_{22}(t_1^*)]^{1/2} = \lambda^{-2}\left(1+\frac{\mu_2}{\mu_0}G^2\right)^{1/2}. \tag{7.21}$$

Using (7.19), we therefore have the result

$$\sin\epsilon^* = \frac{\mu_1 G}{(\mu_0^2+\mu_0\mu_2 G^2)^{1/2}}. \tag{7.22}$$

Finally, since the area of the base of the parallelepiped is $e_1^* e_3^* = \lambda^{-1}$, and the volume is 1, the height h_2^* must be λ. Collecting these results together, we see that, for a rubberlike liquid described by the equations (6.9), *the instantaneous recovery following a steady shear flow can be resolved into* (i) *a shear of angle* ϵ^* *given by* (7.22); (ii) *a contraction of lines parallel to the direction of shear flow by a factor* λ^{-2}, *where* λ *is given by* (7.16); *and* (iii) *an increase in separation by a factor* λ *of each pair of parallel material planes parallel to the direction of shear in the steady shear flow*. The instantaneous recovery is illustrated in Fig. 7.3. These results are due to Lodge (1958a).

Proof of (*7.20*). It remains to prove our statement that $\lambda > 1$ when $G > 0$. From the definition (7.16) of λ, it is clear that this statement is equivalent to the statement

$$\mu_0 \mu_2 - \mu_1^2 > 0, \tag{7.23}$$

which we shall now prove.

From the definition (6.3), we have

$$\begin{aligned}\mu_0 \mu_2 - \mu_1^2 &= \int_0^\infty \mu(\tau)\, d\tau \int_0^\infty \mu(\sigma)\, \sigma^2\, d\sigma - \int_0^\infty \mu(\tau)\, \tau\, d\tau \int_0^\infty \mu(\sigma)\, \sigma\, d\sigma \\ &= \int_0^\infty \int_0^\infty \mu(\tau)\, \mu(\sigma)\, (\sigma^2 - \tau\sigma)\, d\tau\, d\sigma \\ &= \int_0^\infty \int_0^\infty \mu(\sigma)\, \mu(\tau)\, (\tau^2 - \sigma\tau)\, d\sigma\, d\tau,\end{aligned}$$

on interchanging the variables of integration τ, σ; it follows that $\mu_0 \mu_2 - \mu_1^2$ is equal to half the sum of the expressions on the right-hand sides of the last two equations, i.e. that

$$\mu_0 \mu_2 - \mu_1^2 = \tfrac{1}{2} \int_0^\infty \int_0^\infty \mu(\tau)\, \mu(\sigma)\, (\tau - \sigma)^2\, d\tau\, d\sigma. \tag{7.24}$$

The integrand in this equation is evidently non-negative and must in fact be positive in some part of the region of integration since μ is (by hypothesis) continuous and non-zero for some range of values of its argument. Thus the required inequality (7.23) is proved.

There is one case in which μ is not continuous which is of some interest, namely that in which all network junctions (in the network theory of polymer solutions) have exactly the same age τ_0, say; we may deal with this case (non-rigorously) by using the Dirac delta function and writing

$$\mu(\tau) = \mu_0\, \delta(\tau - \tau_0); \tag{7.25}$$

on substituting this expression for μ in (7.24) and using the properties of the delta function given in Appendix 3, we obtain the result

$$\mu_0\mu_2-\mu_1^2 = \tfrac{1}{2}\mu_0^2\int_0^\infty \delta(\sigma-\tau_0)(\tau_0-\sigma)^2\,d\sigma$$

$$= \tfrac{1}{2}\mu_0^2(\tau_0-\tau_0)^2$$

$$= 0.$$

In this case, therefore, $\lambda = 1$ (by (7.16)), and there is no lateral expansion or longitudinal contraction.

If, however, there are junctions of two or more ages present, then $\lambda > 1$; for if there are two ages τ_0, τ_1 present, we may write

$$\mu(\tau) = a_0\,\delta(\tau-\tau_0)+a_1\,\delta(\tau-\tau_1),$$

and then (7.24) leads to the result

$$\mu_0\mu_2-\mu_1^2 = a_0a_1(\tau_0-\tau_1)^2 > 0, \tag{7.26}$$

which implies that $\lambda > 1$. If there are more than two ages present, the same inequality must clearly hold.

The use of discontinuous functions for μ is in conflict with the conditions of continuity assumed in the proof of the main result (7.1) concerning instantaneous recovery; inspection of the proof shows, however, that it is sufficient to have μ continuous in an interval containing the instant at which the recovery takes place. In this way, the above use of memory functions involving delta functions can be justified.

The lateral expansion and its associated longitudinal contraction are unexpected features of the recovery, if only because they imply that *the liquid "recovers" to a state which it has never previously been in.* According to the above arguments, it is seen that (on the network theory) *the lateral expansion is essentially associated with the presence in the network of junctions of different ages.* To express this without reference to the network theory, we may say that *the lateral expansion occurs when* (and, on the present theory, only when) *the current stress depends on finite strains measured from two or more distinct previous states to the current state.*

It has been pointed out in Chapter 6 that the network theory of polymer solutions can be regarded as a generalization of the two-network hypothesis for composite networks. It can be seen that the lateral expansion which occurs after shear flow in polymer solutions (according to the foregoing theory) is analogous to the strain involved in the calculation of permanent set for a composite network formed with junctions added in two states related by pure shear (cf. (4.51)).

We complete the discussion of instantaneous recovery following steady shear flow by proving the following result.

(7.27) *When the memory function can be expressed as a sum of exponentials of the form* (6.5), *the instantaneous shear recovery angle* ϵ^* *cannot exceed* 45°.

This result is rather unexpected; it implies that, as the shear rate in the steady shear flow is increased, the shear part of the instantaneous recovery is bounded, although (according to (7.16)) the lateral expansion λ is not. It should perhaps be noted here that in any case ϵ^* cannot exceed 90°; otherwise the recovery would involve a set of material lines, namely those parallel to the base vectors $\mathbf{e}_i$, changing from a right-handed to a left-handed system (this can be seen from Fig. 7.3); this would require a turning inside out of the material which must be excluded on physical grounds.

Proof of (*7.27*). We first note that $\sin\epsilon^*$, defined by (7.22), is a steadily increasing function of shear rate G; for the derivative, given by the equation

$$\frac{d}{dG}(\sin\epsilon^*) = \frac{\mu_0^2\mu_1}{(\mu_0^2+\mu_0\mu_2 G^2)^{3/2}},$$

is evidently positive.

Thus, as G increases from 0 to ∞, $\sin\epsilon^*$ increases steadily from the value 0 to the value $\mu_1(\mu_0\mu_2)^{-1/2}$. The required result (7.27) will therefore be proved if we can show that $\mu_1(\mu_0\mu_2)^{-1/2} \leqslant 2^{-1/2}$ (since $\sin 45° = 2^{-1/2}$), i.e. that

$$\mu_0\mu_2 - 2\mu_1^2 \geqslant 0. \tag{7.28}$$

When μ is given as a sum of exponentials (6.5), the quantities μ_r are given by (6.6); hence

$$\begin{aligned}\mu_0\mu_2 - 2\mu_1^2 &= \Big(\sum_r a_r\tau_r\Big)\Big(2\sum_s a_s\tau_s^3\Big) - 2\Big(\sum_r a_r\tau_r\Big)\Big(\sum_s a_s\tau_s\Big)\\ &= 2\sum_r\sum_s a_r a_s\tau_r\tau_s(\tau_s^2-\tau_r\tau_s)\\ &= 2\sum_s\sum_r a_s a_r\tau_s\tau_r(\tau_r^2-\tau_s\tau_r);\end{aligned}$$

the last step is taken by interchanging the summation suffixes r, s. Since the left-hand side of this equation must equal half the sum of the expressions on the right-hand sides of the last two lines of equations, it follows that

$$\mu_0\mu_2 - 2\mu_1^2 = \sum_r\sum_s a_r a_s\tau_r\tau_s(\tau_r-\tau_s)^2. \tag{7.29}$$

Since each term in this double sum is non-negative, the inequality (7.28), and hence also (7.27), is proved.

Moreover, the equality sign in (7.28) holds if and only if every term in (7.29) is zero; in this case, $\tau_r = \tau_s$ for all values of r, s, i.e. there is only one term in the sum of exponentials (6.5). Hence we have the further result that *the shear recovery can attain the value* $\epsilon^* = 45°$ *only if the memory function is a single exponential* of the form (6.7), and the shear rate is large compared to $(\mu_0/\mu_2)^{1/2}$.

This result has been proved subject to the restriction that μ can be expressed as a sum of exponentials; the result is not true if, for example, all network junctions have exactly the same age, for then μ is given by (7.25) and $\mu_0\mu_2 - 2\mu_1^2 = -\mu_1^2$, by the equation following (7.25), showing that the inequality (7.28) is not satisfied; it can be seen from (7.22) that in this case $\sin\epsilon^* \to 1$ as $G \to \infty$. *When all junctions have the same age,*

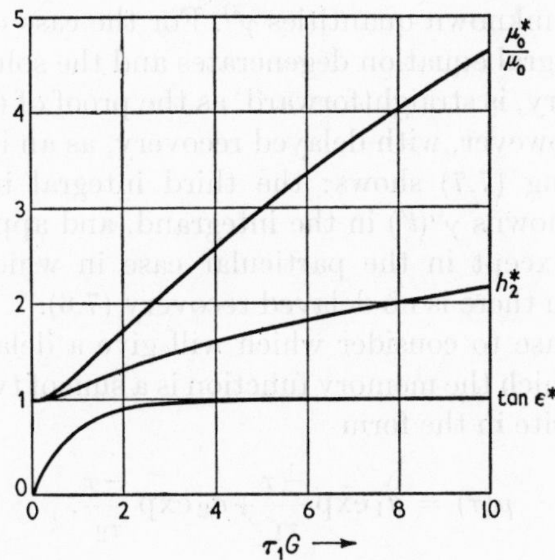

FIG. 7.4. Instantaneous free recovery following steady shear flow. Shear recovery magnitude $\tan\epsilon^*$, lateral expansion factor h_2^*, and modulus μ_0^* as functions of shear rate G for a rubberlike liquid with memory function

$$\mu(\tau) = \frac{\mu_0}{\tau_1}\exp\frac{-\tau}{\tau_1}.$$

(From equations (7.30), (7.31), and (7.32).)

therefore, *there is no lateral expansion and no limit to the magnitude,* $\tan\epsilon^*$, *of shear recovery.* These results are to be expected in view of the formal identity between the rheological equation of state (6.9) (with μ given by (7.25)) and the corresponding equation (4.12) for a rubberlike solid.

When μ is a single exponential function (6.7), it follows from (6.6), (7.15), (7.16), and (7.22) that the lateral expansion λ, the shear recovery

$\tan \epsilon^*$, and the modulus μ_0^* of the equivalent rubberlike solid are given by the following equations:

$$h_2^* = \lambda = (1+\tau_1^2 G^2)^{1/6}, \tag{7.30}$$

$$\tan \epsilon^* = \frac{\tau_1 G}{(1+\tau_1^2 G^2)^{1/2}}, \tag{7.31}$$

$$\mu_0^* = \mu_0(1+\tau_1^2 G^2)^{1/3}. \tag{7.32}$$

These functions are represented in Fig. 7.4.

Delayed Recovery after Steady Shear Flow

We have remarked that, with rheological equations of state of the present form (6.9), recovery calculations involve the solving of an integral equation for the unknown quantities γ^{ij}. For the case of instantaneous recovery, the integral equation degenerates and the solution, even for a general flow history, is straightforward, as the proof of (7.1) shows. This is not the case, however, with delayed recovery, as an inspection of the equation preceding (7.7) shows: the third integral in this equation involves the unknowns $\gamma^{ij}(t')$ in the integrand, and appears to have no simple solution except in the particular case in which μ is a single exponential, when there is no delayed recovery (7.6).

The simplest case to consider which will give a delayed recovery is perhaps that in which the memory function is a sum of two exponentials, which we shall write in the form

$$\mu(\tau) = a_1 \exp\frac{-\tau}{\tau_1} + a_2 \exp\frac{-\tau}{\tau_2}. \tag{7.33}$$

The delayed recovery in this case has been calculated by Lodge, Evans and Scully (1964) for a few values of the ratios a_1/a_2, τ_1/τ_2. The exponential form for μ enables one to express the integral equations for γ^{ij} as differential equations of second order with time as the independent variable; these equations, with the constant volume condition, constitute a non-linear system of simultaneous equations for the quantities γ^{11}, γ^{22}, γ^{33}, γ^{21}, p. A solution has been obtained using the "Mercury" electronic digital computer.

Some of the results of this solution† are represented in Fig. 7.5, in which the lateral expansion and shear recovery are plotted as functions of time; it is seen that most of the recovery is instantaneous and that the delayed shear recovery in this case does not exceed 45°. (We have already shown that the *instantaneous* shear recovery cannot exceed 45°, cf. (7.27).) The

† The delayed recovery involves a lateral expansion h_2 and a shear of angle defined in a similar way to h_2 and in instantaneous recovery (Fig. 7.3).

delayed shear recovery is in fact less than 45° in all the cases considered, namely for the values $\tau_2/\tau_1 = \frac{1}{2}$, $a_2/a_1 = \frac{1}{2}$ and 1, $\tau_1 G = 1$ and 2. In these cases, too, most of the recovery takes place instantaneously.

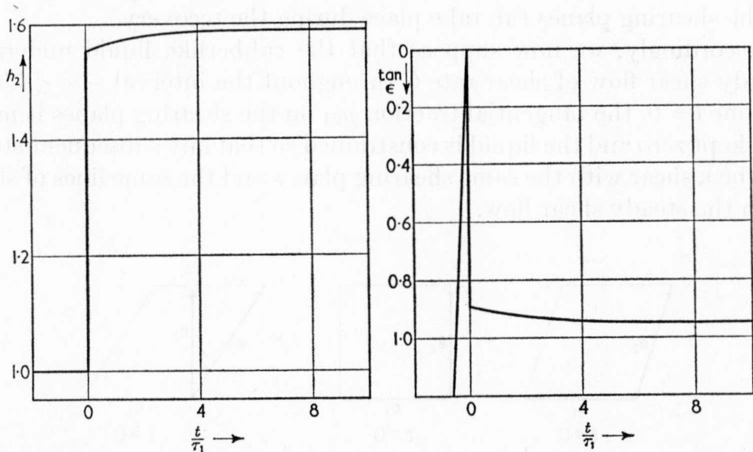

FIG. 7.5. Instantaneous and delayed free recovery following steady shear flow. Lateral expansion factor h_2 and shear recovery magnitude $\tan \epsilon$ as functions of time for a rubberlike liquid with memory function

$$\mu(\tau) = a_1 \left[\exp\frac{-\tau}{\tau_1} + \exp\frac{-\tau}{2\tau_1}\right].$$

Steady shear flow at shear rate $G = 2/\tau_1$ $(t < 0)$; zero stress $(t \geqslant 0)$. (From Lodge, Evans and Scully, 1964.)

Constrained Recovery after Steady Shear Flow

The above calculations have shown that, for a rubberlike liquid, defined by (6.9), in a state of steady shear flow, the shearing planes increase their separation after the stress has been made zero or isotropic. Measurements of recovery in liquids after shear flow have usually been made in circumstances which would not allow any change in separation of shearing surfaces to take place; in the shearing of a liquid contained in the gap between two concentric cylinders in relative rotation, for example, recovery is measured by releasing one cylinder to rotate freely: this allows a shear recovery to take place, but does not allow a change of separation of the shearing surfaces (presumed to be cylinders coaxial with the apparatus cylinders) to take place, since this would involve a change in the gap between the apparatus cylinders.

A state of flow of this type must be regarded as non-uniform, owing to the curvature of the shearing surfaces, and can be fully treated only when the present formalism is extended suitably (cf. Chapters 9 and 12).

We can, however, deal with some essential features of the matter with the present formalism by considering the problem of recovery after uniform steady shear flow and assuming that the liquid is subject to such constraints as may be necessary to ensure that no change of separation of the shearing planes can take place during the recovery.

Accordingly, we now suppose that the rubberlike liquid undergoes steady shear flow of shear rate G throughout the interval $-\infty < t' \leqslant 0$; at time $t = 0$, the tangential traction p_{21} on the shearing planes is made and kept zero and the liquid is constrained so that any subsequent strain will be a shear with the same shearing planes and the same lines of shear as in the steady shear flow.

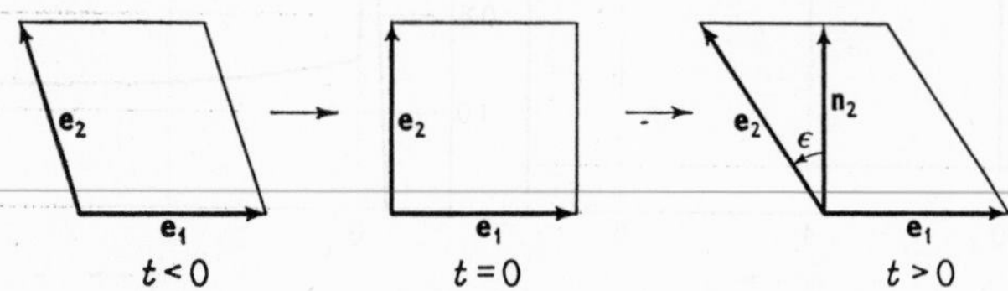

FIG. 7.6. Base vectors for constrained recovery ($t > 0$) on removal of shear stress p_{21} at $t = 0$ following steady shear flow ($t < 0$). (For proofs of equations (7.36), (7.37) and (7.38).)

We shall use a basis $\mathbf{e}_i$ which is *orthonormal in the state* $t = 0$ *immediately before the tangential traction* p_{21} *is made zero*; as usual, we take $\mathbf{e}_1$ parallel to the lines of shear and $\mathbf{e}_2$ instantaneously normal to the shearing planes, and define the angle of shear ϵ as the inclination of the vector $\mathbf{e}_2$ to the unit normal $\mathbf{n}_2$ to the shearing planes (Fig. 7.6). It is again convenient to introduce a symbol s for the magnitude of shear, so that

(7.34) $$s = \tan \epsilon.$$

Thus s decreases during the steady flow according to the equation

(7.35) $$s(t') = -Gt'; \qquad (t' < 0)$$

during recovery, it is to be expected that s will increase.

We shall prove the following results. When the tangential stress p_{21} is made zero, there is

(7.36) an instantaneous shear recovery of magnitude

$$s_0 = \frac{\mu_1 G}{\mu_0};$$

(7.37) an ultimate shear recovery of magnitude

$$s_\infty = \frac{\mu_2 G}{2\mu_1};$$

and

(7.38) an instantaneous decrease in the value of $p_{11}-p_{22}$ by an amount $G^2\mu_1^2/\mu_0$ followed by a further decrease to zero.

It is seen that the ultimate shear recovery is related to the values of the stress components in steady shear flow (given by (6.22), (6.23)) by the equation

(7.39) $$s_\infty = \frac{1}{2}\left(\frac{p_{11}-p_{22}}{p_{21}}\right)_{\text{steady flow}}.$$

If the memory function is a single exponential of the form (6.7), then

(7.40) there is an instantaneous recovery $s_0 = \tau_1 G$, no delayed recovery, and an instantaneous decrease in $p_{11}-p_{22}$ by a factor $\frac{1}{2}$ and a subsequent variation given by

(7.41) $$p_{11}-p_{22} = \mu_0 \tau_1^2 G^2 \exp\frac{-t}{\tau_1} \qquad (t > 0).$$

In this case, therefore, we have the rather interesting situation that, at times $t > 0$, the liquid is at rest, the tangential traction is zero, but $p_{11}-p_{22}$ is not zero.

If the memory function is a sum of two exponentials of the form (7.33), the delayed recovery is given by the equation

(7.42) $$s(t) = s_\infty - (s_\infty - s_0)\exp\frac{-t}{\tau_0} \qquad (t > 0),$$

where

(7.43) $$\tau_0 \equiv \frac{\mu_0}{\mu_1}\tau_1\tau_2$$

is intermediate in value between τ_1 and τ_2. The variation of $p_{11}-p_{22}$ with time is given by a sum of several exponential functions which we need not work out here.

The above values for the instantaneous and delayed recoveries and the instantaneous change in $p_{11}-p_{22}$ on removal of the tangential traction are found to be simply related to certain analogous quantities associated with the start from rest of shear flow through the instantaneous application of a constant tangential traction $p_{21} = \mu_1 G$, where G denotes the value of shear rate ultimately attained in these circumstances; the liquid is constrained to undergo shear without lateral expansion. We find, in fact, that on sudden application of a tangential traction p_{21} at a time $t = 0$ to a liquid previously at rest there is

(7.44) an instantaneous shear of magnitude

$$\frac{\mu_1 G}{\mu_0} = s_0;$$

(7.45) an instantaneous increase in the value of $p_{11} - p_{22}$ from zero to $G^2 \mu_1^2/\mu_0$ (cf. (7.38)).

(7.46) Finally, if the magnitude s of shear strain measured from the state of rest is plotted as a function of time, the curve has a linear asymptote which makes an intercept of magnitude s_∞ (given by (7.37)) with the line $t = 0$.

The above results have been given by Lodge (1958b). The proof which will now be given is straightforward, but contains two features which have not been used in proofs which we have given up to now in this book: it is convenient to use a basis which is not orthonormal or orthogonal in some of the states in which non-zero stress components have to be considered; and we use the Laplace transform to solve an integral equation to obtain the results (7.37), (7.42) and (7.46).

Proof of (7.36) and (7.38). Since any state t' is related to the state $t = 0$ (in which the basis is orthonormal) by a shear of magnitude $\tan \epsilon' = s(t') \equiv s'$, say, we have, from (2.62) and (2.65) with $t_0 = t'$ and $t = 0$, the results

$$(7.47) \qquad \gamma^{ij}(t') = \begin{pmatrix} 1+s'^2 & s' & 0 \\ s' & 1 & 0 \\ 0 & 0 & 1 \end{pmatrix}, \quad \gamma^{ij}(0) = \begin{pmatrix} 1 & 0 & 0 \\ 0 & 1 & 0 \\ 0 & 0 & 1 \end{pmatrix}.$$

For $t' \leqslant 0$, s' is given by (7.35); for $t' > 0$, s' is to be determined. For $t' > 0$, the basis is not orthogonal and so we must use the general equations (3.7), (3.17) instead of (3.14), (3.15) to determine the cartesian stress components p_{ij} defined relative to the usual orthogonal system of planes which includes the shearing planes and planes normal to the lines of shear.

For the shearing planes, the unit normal $\mathbf{n}_2$ (Fig. 7.6) has a scalar product unity with $\mathbf{e}_2$ and zero with $\mathbf{e}_1$ and $\mathbf{e}_3$, and hence $l_i = \mathbf{n}_2.\mathbf{e}_i = \delta_{2i}$. The traction $\mathbf{f}^2$ across the shearing planes is therefore given by

$$\text{(7.48)} \qquad \mathbf{f}^2 = \sum_j \pi^{2j}\mathbf{e}_j, \qquad \text{by (3.7).}$$

Resolving this traction into components normal to the shearing planes and parallel to the lines of shear (i.e. in the directions defined by unit vectors $\mathbf{n}_2$ and $\mathbf{e}_1$), we obtain the results

$$\text{(7.49)} \qquad p_{22} = \mathbf{n}_2.\mathbf{f}^2 = \pi^{22},$$

$$\text{(7.50)} \qquad p_{21} = \mathbf{e}_1.\mathbf{f}^2 = \pi^{21} - s\pi^{22},$$

since

$$\text{(7.51)} \qquad \mathbf{e}_1.\mathbf{e}_2 = -\tan\epsilon = -s, \text{ from Fig. 7.6 } (t > 0).$$

For planes normal to the lines of shear, the unit normal is $\mathbf{e}_1$, and hence $l_i = \mathbf{e}_1.\mathbf{e}_i = (1, -s, 0)$. From (3.17), it therefore follows that the normal component of traction on these planes is given by the equation

$$\text{(7.52)} \qquad p_{11} = \pi^{11} + s^2\pi^{22} - 2s\pi^{21}.$$

From (7.49), (7.50) and (7.52), it follows that

$$\text{(7.53)} \qquad p_{11} - p_{22} = \pi^{11} - (1+s^2)\pi^{22}, \quad \text{when } p_{21} = 0.$$

From the rheological equation of state (6.9), using (7.35), (7.47), and writing p_1 for p to avoid confusion with the Laplace transform variable p used later, we see that, for $t > 0$,

$$\text{(7.54)} \qquad \pi^{ij}(t) + p_1 \begin{pmatrix} 1+s^2 & s & 0 \\ s & 1 & 0 \\ 0 & 0 & 1 \end{pmatrix}$$

$$= \int_{-\infty}^{0} \mu(t-t') \begin{pmatrix} 1+G^2t'^2 & -Gt' & 0 \\ -Gt' & 1 & 0 \\ 0 & 0 & 1 \end{pmatrix} dt' + \int_{0}^{t} \mu(t-t') \begin{pmatrix} 1+s'^2 & s' & 0 \\ s' & 1 & 0 \\ 0 & 0 & 1 \end{pmatrix} dt'.$$

Using this equation and (7.50), we see that

$$p_{21}(t) = -\int_{-\infty}^{0} \mu(t-t')(Gt'+s)\,dt' + \int_{0}^{t} \mu(t-t')(s'-s)\,dt'.$$

The term in G here involves the integral I_1 already defined in (6.32); the terms in s, taken together, involve the integral μ_0 defined in (6.3); since

$p_{21}(t) = 0$ for $t > 0$, we obtain the following integral equation for the magnitude s of the recovery:

$$\mu_0 s(t) = GI_1(t) + \int_0^t \mu(t-t')\, s(t')\, dt'. \tag{7.55}$$

Since $I_1(0) = \mu_1$ (from (6.3) and (6.32)), on letting t tend to zero from positive values, equation (7.55) gives the result

$$\mu_0 s_0 = G\mu_1,$$

where

$$s_0 \equiv \lim_{\delta t \to 0} s(0+\delta t) \qquad (\delta t > 0)$$

is the instantaneous recovery. This proves (7.36). For a limit of this type, the notation $\lim\limits_{\delta t \to 0+}$ is used.

In a similar manner, using (6.3), (6.32), (7.53), and (7.54), we obtain the following equation for the difference of normal stress components at time $t > 0$:

$$p_{11} - p_{22} = G^2 I_2(t) - \mu_0 s^2 + \int_0^t \mu(t-t')\, s'^2\, dt'; \tag{7.56}$$

in this equation, the values of s and s' are to be determined from the solution of the integral equation (7.55).

Letting t tend to zero, from positive values, in (7.56), we see that

$$\lim_{t \to 0+} (p_{11} - p_{22}) = \mu_2 G^2 - \mu_0 s_0^2. \tag{7.57}$$

Since the value of $p_{11} - p_{22}$ in the steady shear flow preceding recovery is equal to $\mu_2 G^2$ (from (6.22)), it follows that, when p_{21} is made zero, $p_{11} - p_{22}$ decreases instantaneously by an amount $\mu_0 s_0^2 = \mu_1^2 G^2/\mu_0$, by (7.36). This proves (7.38).

Proof of (7.37), (7.40) and (7.42). To calculate the delayed and ultimate recovery, it is necessary to solve the integral equation (7.55); the delayed recovery will depend on the form of the memory function which occurs in the integrand, but it is possible to obtain a convenient expression for the ultimate recovery in terms of the constants μ_r.

We shall use the Laplace transform, whereby to any function $x(t)$ corresponds a function $\bar{x}(p)$ of a variable p defined by the equation

$$x(t) \to \bar{x}(p) = \int_0^\infty x(t)\, e^{-pt}\, dt, \tag{7.58}$$

provided that this integral converges. We shall make use of the following standard properties of this transformation:

(7.59) $$1 \to p^{-1}; \quad t \to p^{-2}; \quad \exp\left(\frac{-t}{\tau_s}\right) \to \left(p+\frac{1}{\tau_s}\right)^{-1};$$

$kx \to k\bar{x}$ (k constant).

(7.60) $$\int_0^t \mu(t-t')\,x(t')\,dt' \to \bar{\mu}(p)\,\bar{x}(p).$$

(7.61) $\lim_{t\to\infty} x(t) =$ coefficient of p^{-1} in the expansion in ascending powers of p of the function $\bar{x}(p)\exp(pt)$.

These results are to be found in standard textbooks on the Laplace transform; the last result is given on page 285 of Carslaw and Jaeger (1948) (cf. also Copson (1935) for the term "residue" used in the previous reference).

We first rewrite the expression for the integral I_1 in a form convenient for applying the Laplace transformation. From the definition (6.32), we have

$$I_1(t) = \left\{\int_{-\infty}^{t} - \int_0^t\right\}\mu(t-t')\,(-t')\,dt' \qquad (t \geqslant 0).$$

On writing $-t' = (t-t')-t$ in the first of these integrals, we see from (6.3) that

(7.62) $$I_1(t) = \mu_1 - \mu_0\,t + \int_0^t \mu(t-t')\,t'\,dt'.$$

Using this result together with (7.59) and (7.60), we see that the Laplace transform of the integral equation (7.55) leads to an equation which, on re-arrangement, may be written in the form

(7.63) $$\bar{s} = \frac{\mu_1 G}{p(\mu_0-\bar{\mu})} - \frac{G}{p^2}.$$

This gives the transform, $\bar{s}$, of the required solution.

We have

$$\bar{\mu}(p) = \int_0^\infty \mu(\tau)\,e^{-p\tau}\,d\tau$$

$$= \int_0^\infty \mu(\tau)\,\{1-p\tau+\tfrac{1}{2}p^2\tau^2-\ldots\}\,d\tau;$$

from (6.3), this series may be expressed in the form

(7.64) $$\bar{\mu} = \mu_0 - \mu_1 p + \tfrac{1}{2}\mu_2 p^2 - \ldots.$$

Using the binomial expansion, it then follows that

(7.65) $$\frac{1}{\mu_0 - \bar{\mu}} = \frac{1}{\mu_1 p} + \frac{\mu_2}{2\mu_1^2} + \text{higher powers of } p.$$

From (7.63) and (7.65), it follows that

(7.66) $$\bar{s} = \frac{\mu_2 G}{2\mu_1 p} + \text{higher powers of } p;$$

and hence, from (7.61), we have the result

$$s_\infty = \text{coefficient of } p^{-1} \text{ in } (1 + pt + \tfrac{1}{2}p^2 t^2 + \ldots)\, \bar{s}(p)$$

$$= \frac{\mu_2 G}{2\mu_1},$$

which proves the result (7.37) for the ultimate recovery.

If μ is a sum of exponentials of the form (6.5), it follows from (7.59) that the Laplace transform is given by the equation

(7.67) $$\bar{\mu} = \sum_s \frac{a_s \tau_s}{1 + \tau_s p},$$

and hence, from (6.6), that

(7.68) $$\mu_0 - \bar{\mu} = p \sum_s \frac{a_s \tau_s^2}{1 + \tau_s p}.$$

From this equation and (7.63), it follows that, when there is only one term (6.7) in the sum of exponentials for μ, we have the simple result

$$\bar{s} = \frac{G\tau_1}{p},$$

on using (6.6). Taking the inverse transform by means of (7.59), it follows that

(7.69) $$s(t) = G\tau_1 = s_0, \qquad (t \geqslant 0)$$

by (7.36) and (6.6). This proves the statement in (7.40) that there is no delayed recovery. It should perhaps be noted that this result cannot be deduced from the general result (7.6) concerning delayed recovery, because in the present case the stress is not made isotropic: p_{21} is made zero, but not $p_{11} - p_{22}$.

From (7.38) and (6.6), it is seen that the instantaneous decrease in $p_{11}-p_{22}$ is equal to $\mu_0 G^2\tau_1^2$, which is half the value $\mu_2 G^2 = 2\mu_0 G^2\tau_1^2$ in the steady flow; the subsequent variation of $p_{11}-p_{22}$ is readily obtained from (7.56), using (6.37), (6.7), and (7.69), and is found to be of the form (7.41), which is therefore proved.

Finally, when μ is a sum of two exponentials of the form (7.33), we find from (6.6), (7.63), and (7.68) after some straightforward reduction that

$$\frac{\bar{s}}{G} = \frac{\tau_1+\tau_2-\tau_0}{p} - \frac{\tau_1+\tau_2-\tau_0-\tau_1\tau_2/\tau_0}{\tau_0^{-1}+p},$$

where τ_0 is defined by (7.43).

From (7.59), the inverse transform of this equation is

$$\frac{s}{G} = \tau_1+\tau_2-\tau_0-\left(\tau_1+\tau_2-\tau_0-\frac{\tau_1\tau_2}{\tau_0}\right)\exp\frac{-t}{\tau_0},$$

which can be written in the stated form (7.42) by means of (6.6), (7.36), and (7.37).

To prove that τ_0 is intermediate in value between τ_1 and τ_2, we note that, from (6.6) and (7.43), we may write

$$\tau_0 = \lambda\tau_1+\mu\tau_2$$

where $\quad \lambda = a_2\tau_2^2(a_1\tau_1^2+a_2\tau_2^2)^{-1}, \quad \mu = a_1\tau_1^2(a_1\tau_1^2+a_2\tau_2^2)^{-1},$

and hence $\quad \lambda > 0, \quad \mu > 0, \quad \text{and} \quad \lambda+\mu = 1.$

Let τ_2 be the larger of τ_1, τ_2. Then since we may write $\tau_0 = \tau_2-\lambda(\tau_2-\tau_1)$, and λ and $\tau_2-\tau_1$ are positive, it follows that $\tau_0 < \tau_2$. Similarly, we may write $\tau_0 = \tau_1+\mu(\tau_2-\tau_1)$ with μ positive, and hence $\tau_0 > \tau_1$. Thus

$$\tau_1 < \tau_0 < \tau_2, \tag{7.70}$$

which proves the statement.

This completes the proof of the results stated above for constrained recovery on removal of the tangential stress following steady shear flow. The results are represented in Fig. 7.7.

The Start of Shear Flow: Constant Tangential Traction

In order to prove the remaining results (7.44), (7.45) and (7.46) stated above, we now consider the case in which the liquid is at rest throughout the interval $-\infty < t < 0$; at $t = 0$, a tangential traction p_{21} is applied and thereafter kept constant. We may write $p_{21} = \mu_1 G$, by (6.23), where G denotes the value of the shear rate attained in the steady flow after a sufficiently long time. We assume that the liquid is constrained so as to undergo shear flow of the type already described.

To calculate the variation of shear strain and $p_{11}-p_{22}$ during the initial period, it is convenient now to use a basis which is orthonormal in the state of rest ($t < 0$) but is otherwise similar to the basis used above for the recovery calculation. A comparison of the previous basis (Fig. 7.6) and the present basis (Fig. 7.8) shows that we may use the previous

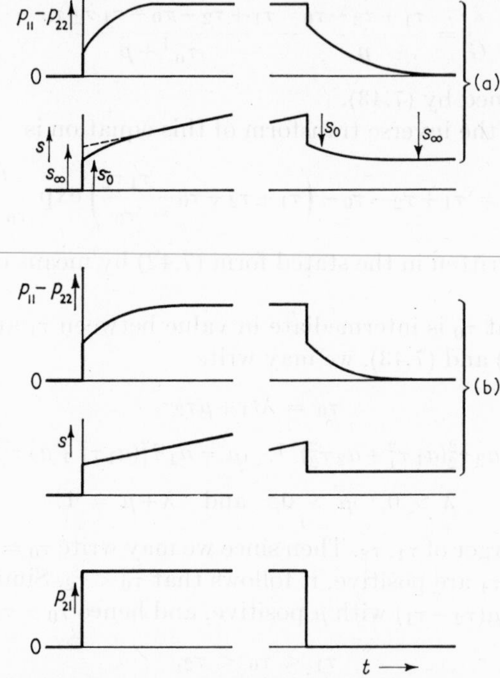

FIG. 7.7. Variation with time of normal stress difference $p_{11}-p_{22}$ and shear strain $s = \tan\epsilon$ following sudden application and following sudden removal of a shear stress p_{21}, the liquid being constrained to undergo shear flow. Rubberlike liquid with (a) general memory function $\mu(\tau)$ (showing definition of instantaneous and ultimate shear recoveries s_0, s_∞) and (b) memory function $\mu(\tau) = a_1 \exp(-\tau/\tau_1)$. (From equations (7.36), (7.37), (7.38), (7.41), (7.44), (7.45), (7.46), (7.75) and (7.76).)

formulae (7.47), (7.49), (7.50), and (7.52) if we replace ϵ by $-\epsilon$ (and therefore s by $-s$), and interpret $s(=\tan\epsilon)$ as the magnitude of shear strain measured from the state of rest, as shown in Fig. 7.8.

The instantaneous changes in s and $p_{11}-p_{22}$ when p_{21} is applied could most simply be calculated by applying the general theorem (7.1), but we shall derive them from the equations which we shall use to calculate the subsequent changes.

The rheological equations of state (6.9), on using (7.47) with s, s' replaced by $-s, -s'$, become

$$\pi^{ij}(t)+p_1\begin{pmatrix}1+s^2 & -s & 0\\ -s & 1 & 0\\ 0 & 0 & 1\end{pmatrix} \tag{7.71}$$

$$= \int_{-\infty}^{0} \mu(t-t')\begin{pmatrix}1 & 0 & 0\\ 0 & 1 & 0\\ 0 & 0 & 1\end{pmatrix} dt' + \int_{0}^{t}\mu(t-t')\begin{pmatrix}1+s'^2 & -s' & 0\\ -s' & 1 & 0\\ 0 & 0 & 1\end{pmatrix} dt'.$$

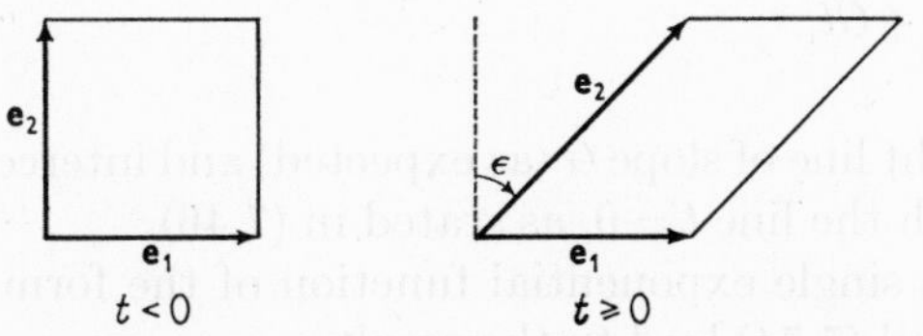

FIG. 7.8. Base vectors for the start of shear flow ($t \geqslant 0$) in a liquid previously at rest ($t < 0$). (For proofs of equations (7.44), (7.45) and (7.46).)

Hence, from (7.49), (7.50), and (7.52), with s, s' replaced by $-s, -s'$, we obtain the equations

$$p_{21} = \mu_0 s - \int_0^t \mu(t-t')\, s'\, dt', \tag{7.72}$$

$$p_{11}-p_{22} = s^2 \int_t^\infty \mu(\tau)\, d\tau + \int_0^t \mu(t-t')\,(s'-s)^2\, dt'. \tag{7.73}$$

In obtaining the first equation, (6.3) has been used; in obtaining the first integral in the second equation, the substitution $t-t' = \tau$ has been used.

From these equations, it follows that as t tends to zero from positive values, $s \to p_{21}/\mu_0 = s_0$, by (6.23) and (7.36), and hence

$$p_{11}-p_{22} \to s_0^2\,\mu_0 = G^2\,\mu_1^2/\mu_0;$$

thus (7.44) and (7.45) are proved.

The Laplace transform of (7.72) may be written in the form

$$\bar{s} = \frac{\mu_1 G}{p(\mu_0-\bar{\mu})}, \tag{7.74}$$

on writing $p_{21} = \mu_1 G$. By comparing this equation with the corresponding equations (7.63), (7.66) for recovery, it is seen that the expansion of (7.74) in ascending powers of p is of the form

$$\bar{s} = \frac{G}{p^2}+\frac{\mu_2 G}{2\mu_1 p} \quad +\text{higher powers of } p.$$

It now follows from (7.61) that, at large values of t, the asymptotic form of the function $s(t)$ is given by

$$s = \text{coefficient of } \frac{1}{p} \text{ in } (1+pt+\tfrac{1}{2}p^2t^2+\ldots)\left(\frac{G}{p^2}+\frac{\mu_2 G}{2\mu_1 p}+\ldots\right)$$

$$= \frac{\mu_2 G}{2\mu_1}+Gt.$$

This is a straight line of slope G (as expected) and intercept $\frac{1}{2}\mu_2 G/\mu_1 = s_\infty$ (by (7.37)) with the line $t = 0$, as stated in (7.46).

When μ is a single exponential function of the form (6.7), equations (7.68), (6.6), and (7.74) lead to the result

$$\bar{s} = G\left(\frac{1}{p^2}+\frac{\tau_1}{p}\right),$$

which by (7.59) is the transform of

$$s = G(\tau_1+t). \tag{7.75}$$

Using this result (which is valid for all values of $t \geqslant 0$), equation (7.73) leads, after some straightforward integration and re-arrangement, to the equation

$$p_{11}-p_{22} = \mu_2 G^2\left(1-\tfrac{1}{2}\exp\frac{-t}{\tau_1}\right), \tag{7.76}$$

by using (6.6). This shows the way in which $p_{11}-p_{22}$ approaches its value $\mu_2 G^2$ in steady flow in this particular case. The results (7.75) and (7.76) are represented in Fig. 7.7.

It is curious to note the presence of the factor $\frac{1}{2}$ in the equation (7.39), which relates the magnitude of the ultimate constrained shear recovery to the ratio of stress components in the steady shear flow preceding recovery. There is no factor $\frac{1}{2}$ in the somewhat analogous equation (4.26), which relates the magnitude of shear strain in a rubberlike solid to the same ratio of stress components. Equations analogous to (4.26) have been proposed for elastic liquids by Weissenberg (1947) and Mooney

(1951), who identify the quantity s with the "recoverable strain", which appears to mean the ultimate free recovery, in the present terminology (cf. Lodge, 1958b); the possibility that the recoverable strain might not be a simple shear does not seem to have been considered, and in this respect the theories differ from that given in the present chapter.

The main idea on which Weissenberg's theory is based, namely that the stress in a flowing elastic material is a function of finite strains in the material whether it be liquid or solid, has, however, proved most fruitful (though Eringen, 1962, p. 244, dismisses it without discussion); for example, as we have already remarked in the discussion following the proof of (7.6), the rubberlike liquid (6.9) has the property that the stress at any instant can be expressed as a function of the free instantaneously recoverable strain (7.1).

Examples 7

1. Using the rheological equations of state

$$\pi_{ij}+p\gamma_{ij} = -\int_{-\infty}^{t} \mu(t-t')\,\gamma_{ij}(t')\,dt',$$

where

$$\pi_{ij} \equiv \sum_r \sum_s \pi^{rs}\gamma_{ri}\gamma_{sj}$$

and the material is incompressible, calculate the instantaneous recovery when the stress is made zero following steady shear flow which has continued for an infinite length of time. (The minus sign is included in these equations in order to give a liquid with a positive viscosity.)

Show that this recovery involves a shear given by (7.22); a contraction by a factor λ^{-1} (where λ is given by (7.16)) of material lines parallel to $\mathbf{e}_1$; an increase in separation by a factor λ^2 of shearing planes (i.e. of material planes of normal $\mathbf{e}^2$); and a *contraction* by a factor λ^{-1} of material lines parallel to $\mathbf{e}_3$. (The base vectors $\mathbf{e}_i$ are those given in Fig. 7.3).

CHAPTER 8

Other Rheological Equations of State

The rheological equations of state derived and investigated in the earlier chapters are perhaps among the simplest equations which could describe elastic solids and liquids for which the stress is dependent on finite strains. There is reason to believe that the equations for the rubberlike solid do in fact give a reasonable representation of the properties of rubber and other polymers in the rubberlike state (cf. Chapter 10), but we are not yet in possession of sufficient reliable data to affirm or deny a similar statement with respect to the equations for the rubberlike liquid considered in Chapters 6 and 7. The equations considered have served to illustrate the great variety of rheological phenomena which can occur, and also to exemplify certain types of relation which can exist between these phenomena. It is evidently an important feature of the subject that a variety of experimental tests can be made, and that this should lead to a more stringent test of theory.

In order to be in a position to modify the theories in the light of experimental data, it is natural to consider what are the possible forms which modified or alternative theories might take. The variety of mathematically possible forms of equations is immense, and the study of some of these possibilities is a field of increasing research activity in applied mathematics; for an account of this, the mathematically-equipped reader is referred to the recent books by Prager (1961) and Eringen (1962). In the present chapter, we shall use the formalism introduced in previous chapters to indicate two of the main ways in which more general equations have been formulated, namely (i) by generalizing the form of stress–strain relation for a perfectly elastic isotropic solid, and (ii) by generalizing the form of the dependence of stress on the *history* of strain.

The content of this chapter is rather more mathematical than that of previous chapters, and could be passed over on a first reading; no new mathematical equipment is used, however, and some of the equations derived are of use in relation to the outline of experimental data given in Chapter 10.

Perfectly Elastic Isotropic Solids

We shall show that, subject to certain rather general requirements which are likely to be satisfied by any actual material which can be treated as a perfectly elastic isotropic solid, the most general possible rheological equation of state can be expressed in the form

$$\pi^{ij} = A\gamma^{ij} + B\gamma^{ij}(t_0) + C \sum_r \sum_s \gamma_{rs}\gamma^{ri}(t_0)\gamma^{sj}(t_0), \tag{8.1}$$

where the coefficients A, B, C are functions of the "strain invariants" J_1, J_2, J_3 defined by the equations

$$\begin{cases} J_1 = \sum_i \sum_j \gamma_{ij}\gamma^{ij}(t_0), \\ J_2 = \sum_r \sum_s \sum_i \sum_j \gamma_{rs}\gamma_{ij}\gamma^{ri}(t_0)\gamma^{sj}(t_0), \\ J_3 = \gamma/\gamma_0. \end{cases} \tag{8.2}$$

The strain invariants are related to the principal values of strain λ_a, λ_b, λ_c for the deformation $t_0 \to t$ by the equations

$$\begin{cases} J_1 = \lambda_a^2 + \lambda_b^2 + \lambda_c^2, \\ J_2 = \lambda_a^4 + \lambda_b^4 + \lambda_c^4, \\ J_3 = \lambda_a^2 \lambda_b^2 \lambda_c^2. \end{cases} \tag{8.3}$$

The coefficients A, B, C, which will in general depend also on the temperature, satisfy certain conditions necessary to ensure that the stress is zero in the state t_0. As usual, symbols π^{ij}, γ^{ij}, γ written without an argument refer to the current state t; $\gamma = \det \gamma_{ij}$, and $\gamma_0 = \det \gamma_{ij}(t_0)$.

It is seen that the equation (4.12) for a rubberlike solid is a particular case of (8.1) in which $A = -p$, $B = \mu_0$, and $C = 0$. The generalization (8.1) therefore amounts to addition of an extra term, bilinear in $\gamma^{ij}(t_0)$, and the replacement of constant coefficients by scalar functions of strain invariants. Both these steps are of a type which one might reasonably expect to have to take in the process of generalization; the force of the result (8.1) is that more complicated terms, involving three or more factors $\gamma^{ij}(t_0)$ for example, do not have to be considered—or, more precisely, that equations in which such terms are included can always be expressed in the comparatively simple form (8.1). This result is due to Reiner (1948). Prager (1945) has given a similar result in which strain is expressed in terms of stress. The three terms in the stress–strain relation can be chosen in other ways; the present choice is made to give easy transitions to correspondingly general equations for a purely viscous liquid and to the limiting form of equations for an elastic solid when the strain is infinitesimally small. In dealing with elastic solids in the present context, we shall raise our previous restriction of incompressibility; it is to be expected, therefore, that the term $A\gamma^{ij}$ in (8.1) (which still represents an isotropic stress) will be associated with the compressibility of the material.

Proof of (8.1). According to the definition of a perfectly elastic solid given in Chapter 4, the stress in any given state is determined by the shape of the material in that state, the temperature T being supposed constant. It is therefore reasonable to suppose that, for such a material,

(8.4) *the states of thermodynamic equilibrium may be completely described by the variables* T, γ_{ij}, in relation to any given system of embedded base vectors $\mathbf{e}_i$.

The Helmholtz free energy per unit mass must then be expressible as a function

$$F = F(T, \gamma_{ij}) \tag{8.5}$$

of these variables. For infinitesimal changes between states of thermodynamic equilibrium, the first and second laws of thermodynamics lead to the well-known relation

$$dF = dW - S\,dT \tag{8.6}$$

between the change dF in Helmholtz free energy and dW, the work done on unit mass of the material by the external surface tractions. S denotes the entropy per unit mass. When the stress is an isotropic pressure $\pi^{ij} = -p\gamma^{ij}$, $dW = -p\,dv$; for a general state of stress, the work done in an infinitesimal change of shape is given by the equation

$$\begin{aligned} dW &= \frac{1}{2\rho}\sum\sum \pi^{ij}\,d\gamma_{ij} \\ &= \frac{1}{2\rho}(\pi^{11}\,d\gamma_{11} + \pi^{22}\,d\gamma_{22} + \pi^{33}\,d\gamma_{33}) + \\ &\qquad + \frac{1}{\rho}(\pi^{23}\,d\gamma_{23} + \pi^{31}\,d\gamma_{31} + \pi^{12}\,d\gamma_{12}). \end{aligned} \tag{8.7}$$

This equation follows from the result of Examples 3, No. 4, for the rate of working dW/dt. The expression has been written without using summation signs so as to include only differentials of independent variables γ_{ij}; it will be recalled that of the nine variables γ_{ij}, only six are independent owing to the symmetry conditions $\gamma_{ij} = \gamma_{ji}$. In writing dW in this form, the symmetry relations $\pi^{ij} = \pi^{ji}$ have also been used.

In obtaining a similar expression for the differential of the free energy, we must allow for the possibility that F may be expressed as a function involving γ_{23} and γ_{32} (for example) separately, although these are equal in value; assuming that F is differentiable, we therefore have the equation

$$(8.8) \qquad dF = \frac{\partial F}{\partial T}dT + \sum_i \sum_j \frac{\partial F}{\partial \gamma_{ij}} d\gamma_{ij}$$

$$= \frac{\partial F}{\partial T}dT + \frac{\partial F}{\partial \gamma_{11}}d\gamma_{11} + \frac{\partial F}{\partial \gamma_{22}}d\gamma_{22} + \frac{\partial F}{\partial \gamma_{33}}d\gamma_{33}$$

$$+ \left(\frac{\partial F}{\partial \gamma_{23}} + \frac{\partial F}{\partial \gamma_{32}}\right) d\gamma_{23} + \left(\frac{\partial F}{\partial \gamma_{31}} + \frac{\partial F}{\partial \gamma_{13}}\right) d\gamma_{31} +$$

$$+ \left(\frac{\partial F}{\partial \gamma_{12}} + \frac{\partial F}{\partial \gamma_{21}}\right) d\gamma_{12}.$$

It now follows, from (8.6), (8.7), and (8.8), since the differentials can be given arbitrary values, that

$$(8.9) \qquad S = -\frac{\partial F}{\partial T},$$

and that

$$\pi^{11} = 2\rho \frac{\partial F}{\partial \gamma_{11}}, \quad \pi^{23} = \rho \left(\frac{\partial F}{\partial \gamma_{23}} + \frac{\partial F}{\partial \gamma_{32}}\right), \text{etc.}$$

The last equations can all be written in the concise form

$$(8.10) \qquad \pi^{ij} = \rho \left(\frac{\partial F}{\partial \gamma_{ij}} + \frac{\partial F}{\partial \gamma_{ji}}\right).$$

Thus the stress components must be derivable from a single scalar function. The simple form (8.10) for this relation has been given by Brillouin (1925), Oldroyd (1950b), and Green and Zerna (1954); it is valid for anisotropic and isotropic materials.

The most general mathematically possible stress–strain relations are not necessarily derivable from a single scalar function; it is well known in classical elasticity theory, for example, that the introduction of a "strain-energy function" reduces the number of independent elastic constants in the stress–strain relations; the restrictions on the stress–strain relations for isotropic materials in finite-strain theory have been considered by Lodge and Weissenberg (1950). Some writers have introduced the term "hyperelastic" (i.e. "less than elastic") to describe elastic materials for which the stress is derivable from a single strain-energy function; but it would appear to be rather unlikely that there should exist any actual material which is elastic (in the sense that stress is a unique function of strain) but which is not also hyperelastic; for in such a case the variables T, γ_{ij} would suffice to determine the stress but not the thermodynamic state—a rather strange possibility. If this is so, then the distinction between "elastic" and "hyperelastic" solids is of mathematical rather than of physical importance.

We now consider the simplification which results for materials which are isotropic. The essential point in this case is that the shape variables γ_{ij} (and their constant values $\gamma_{ij}(t_0)$ in the stress-free state t_0) can occur in the free energy function F only in certain combinations, represented for example by the quantities J_1, J_2, J_3 defined by (8.2), so that we may write

$$F = F(T, J_1, J_2, J_3). \tag{8.11}$$

To see that this is so, we recall the fact that an arbitrary uniform strain $t_0 \to t$ can be completely described by the lengths λ_a, λ_b, λ_c and orientations in the material of the semi-axes of a certain ellipsoid, the so-called "strain ellipsoid". By saying that a material is isotropic, we mean that all lines in the material are equivalent with respect to the physical properties with which we are concerned—in this case, the free energy, or more precisely the difference of values of free energy in stressed and stress-free states. For an isotropic elastic solid, therefore, it follows that the free energy in state t can depend on the lengths of the semi-axes of the strain ellipsoid but must be independent of their orientation *relative to the material*; hence the lengths λ_a, λ_b, λ_c can occur in F only in symmetrical combinations (such as those given in (8.3)). These requirements are evidently necessary to ensure that the same change of free energy will be obtained by two strains, $t_0 \to t$ and $t_0 \to t'$, which differ only in the orientations (relative to the material) of the principal axes.

It can be shown (and it appears in any case to be reasonable) that any symmetric algebraic combination of three variables is expressible in terms of three independent symmetric combinations. "Symmetric" here means "unchanged in value by any permutation of the variables". It is probably sufficient for all physical purposes to consider only algebraic functions, for the properties of any actual material (which can be treated as perfectly elastic) can almost certainly be treated to any desired degree of approximation by such functions. It follows, therefore, that the free energy may be expressed in the form (8.11) in terms of the strain invariants J_1, J_2, J_3.

The relations (8.2) and (8.3) between the expressions for J_1, J_2, J_3 in terms of the γ_{ij}, $\gamma^{ij}(t_0)$ and the principal values λ_a, λ_b, λ_c have been given in Examples 2, Nos. 7, 8, 9. Since the basis used for defining the quantities γ_{ij}, $\gamma^{ij}(t_0)$ is arbitrary, it will follow that the stress–strain relations which we shall derive from the scalar function (8.11) by means of (8.2) will necessarily have a form and significance which are independent of the choice of base vectors.

For an arbitrary infinitesimal change of shape $\gamma_{ij} \to \gamma_{ij} + d\gamma_{ij}$, the changes in the strain invariants are given by the following equations, obtained from the definitions (8.2):

$$\text{(8.12)} \qquad \begin{cases} dJ_1 = \sum\limits_i \sum\limits_j \gamma^{ij}(t_0)\, d\gamma_{ij}, \\ dJ_2 = 2 \sum\limits_i \sum\limits_j \sum\limits_r \sum\limits_s \gamma^{ri}(t_0)\, \gamma^{sj}(t_0)\, \gamma_{rs}\, d\gamma_{ij}, \\ dJ_3 = J_3 \sum\limits_i \sum\limits_j \gamma^{ij}\, d\gamma_{ij}. \end{cases}$$

In obtaining the second of these equations, one first has terms in $\gamma_{rs} d\gamma_{ij}$ and $\gamma_{ij} d\gamma_{rs}$, from the differential of (8.2); on interchanging the suffix pairs ij and rs in the second set of terms, it is seen that the second set is equal to the first set, because of the symmetry of γ_{ij} and γ^{ij}; this leads to the result stated. The third of equations (8.12) is obtained by using the result of Examples 1, No. 9.

According to (8.11), the differential of the free energy may be written in the form

$$\text{(8.13)} \qquad dF = \frac{\partial F}{\partial T} dT + \sum_{u=1}^{3} \frac{\partial F}{\partial J_u} dJ_u.$$

From (8.6), (8.7), (8.12), and (8.13), using the fact that the differentials $d\gamma_{ij}$ can be given arbitrary values subject to the condition $d\gamma_{ij} = d\gamma_{ji}$ and using also the symmetry relations $\gamma^{ij} = \gamma^{ji}$, $\gamma_{rs} = \gamma_{sr}$, we obtain the following equation for the stress components:

$$\text{(8.14)} \qquad \pi^{ij} = 2\rho \left\{ \frac{\partial F}{\partial J_1} \gamma^{ij}(t_0) + J_3 \frac{\partial F}{\partial J_3} \gamma^{ij} + 2 \frac{\partial F}{\partial J_2} \sum_r \sum_s \gamma^{ri}(t_0)\, \gamma^{sj}(t_0)\, \gamma_{rs} \right\};$$

we also obtain again equation (8.9). Equation (8.14) could have been obtained from (8.10) via (8.11) and (8.12), but we have preferred to go a little further back to reduce the risk of confusion arising because not all the differentials $d\gamma_{ij}$ are independent.

It can now be seen that (8.14) is of the stated form (8.1), with

$$\text{(8.15)} \qquad A = 2\rho J_3 \frac{\partial F}{\partial J_3}, \quad B = 2\rho \frac{\partial F}{\partial J_1}, \quad C = 4\rho \frac{\partial F}{\partial J_2}.$$

Finally, we note that the density can be expressed in terms of the invariant J_3 and constants:

$$\rho = \frac{m}{v} = \frac{m}{v_0} J_3^{-1/2}; \tag{8.16}$$

here, m denotes the mass of a volume v of material, and this is given in terms of J_3 by means of (1.22) and (8.2). Thus the stress components in an isotropic perfectly elastic solid are expressible in the form (8.1) where the coefficients A, B, C are functions of the strain invariants J_1, J_2, J_3, the temperature, and the density m/v_0 in the stress-free state t_0.

We can now prove that *the principal axes of stress coincide with the principal axes of strain for any isotropic perfectly elastic solid*, as stated in Chapter 4 after equation (4.13). We may choose a basis which is orthonormal in the stress-free state t_0 and which has its base vectors $\mathbf{e}_i$ parallel to the principal axes of the strain $t_0 \to t$, for any given state t. From (2.41), (2.45), and (2.46), the shape variables are then given by the equations

$$\gamma_{ij} = (e_i)^2 \delta_{ij}, \quad \gamma^{ij} = (e_i)^{-2} \delta_{ij}, \quad \gamma^{ij}(t_0) = \delta_{ij},$$

where e_i are the principal elongation ratios, these being equal to the lengths of the base vectors $\mathbf{e}_i$ in state t. Since the basis is orthogonal in state t, the cartesian stress components in state t are given by the equation

$$\begin{aligned} p_{ij} &= e_i e_j \pi^{ij}, \qquad \text{by (3.15)}, \\ &= e_i e_j \left[A(e_i)^{-2} \delta_{ij} + B\delta_{ij} + \sum_r \sum_s (e_r)^2 \delta_{rs} \delta_{ri} \delta_{sj} \right], \qquad \text{by (8.1)}, \\ &= [A + B(e_i)^2 + C(e_i)^4] \delta_{ij}. \end{aligned}$$

Thus $p_{ij} = 0$ when $i \neq j$, which shows that there is no tangential component of traction on any plane perpendicular to a base vector. Such planes are therefore principal planes of stress, according to the definition given in Examples 3, No. 1, and therefore the principal axes of stress coincide with the principal axes of strain, which completes the required proof.

Simple Shear in a Perfectly Elastic Isotropic Solid

We now calculate the stress, using (8.1), in a state t obtained by a simple shear of magnitude $\tan \epsilon = s$ from the stress-free state t_0. As usual, we take a basis $\mathbf{e}_i$ orthonormal in state t (Fig. 2.4).

From (2.62) and (2.65) we have the results

$$(8.17)\qquad \gamma^{ij}(t_0) = \begin{pmatrix} 1+s^2 & s & 0 \\ s & 1 & 0 \\ 0 & 0 & 1 \end{pmatrix}, \quad \gamma^{ij} = \gamma_{ij} = \begin{pmatrix} 1 & 0 & 0 \\ 0 & 1 & 0 \\ 0 & 0 & 1 \end{pmatrix}.$$

Thus $\gamma_{rs} = \delta_{rs}$, and hence

$$(8.18)\qquad \sum_r \sum_s \gamma_{rs}\gamma^{ri}(t_0)\gamma^{sj}(t_0) = \sum_r \gamma^{ri}(t_0)\gamma^{rj}(t_0)$$

$$= \begin{pmatrix} (1+s^2)^2+s^2 & (1+s^2)s+s & 0 \\ (1+s^2)s+s & 1+s^2 & 0 \\ 0 & 0 & 1 \end{pmatrix}.$$

Since the basis is orthonormal in the stressed state t, we have $p_{ij} = \pi^{ij}$, and hence, from (8.1), (8.17), and (8.18), we have

$$(8.19)\qquad p_{ij} = A\begin{pmatrix} 1 & 0 & 0 \\ 0 & 1 & 0 \\ 0 & 0 & 1 \end{pmatrix} + B\begin{pmatrix} 1+s^2 & s & 0 \\ s & 1 & 0 \\ 0 & 0 & 1 \end{pmatrix}$$

$$+C\begin{pmatrix} 1+3s^2+4s^4 & s(2+s^2) & 0 \\ s(2+s^2) & 1+s^2 & 0 \\ 0 & 0 & 1 \end{pmatrix}.$$

From this equation, it follows in particular that

$$(8.20)\qquad \begin{cases} p_{11}-p_{22} = s^2[B+(2+s^2)C], \\ p_{22}-p_{33} = s^2 C, \\ p_{21} = s[B+(2+s^2)C]. \end{cases}$$

Thus a non-zero value for the normal stress component difference $p_{22}-p_{33}$ implies that the coefficient C in (8.1) is non-zero. Taking the ratio of the other normal stress component difference and the tangential stress component, we obtain the interesting result

$$(8.21)\qquad \frac{p_{11}-p_{22}}{p_{21}} = s,$$

due to Reiner (1948); the value of this ratio thus depends on the magnitude s of the shear strain but does not depend on elastic constants of the material, which can occur only in the coefficients A, B, C. It also follows that the shear modulus p_{21}/s is equal to the ratio $(p_{21})^2/(p_{11}-p_{22})$.

Infinitesimal Strain in a Perfectly Elastic Isotropic Solid

It is a simple matter to derive from (8.1) the stress–strain relations of the classical theory of elasticity by considering the case in which the strain $t_0 \to t$ is small in the sense that the quantities

$$\Delta^{ij} = \gamma^{ij}(t_0) - \gamma^{ij} \tag{8.22}$$

are infinitesimals whose squares and higher powers may be neglected.

The invariants J_u do not tend to zero as Δ^{ij} tends to zero, and it is convenient to replace them by the invariants K_u, defined as follows, which do:

$$\left\{\begin{aligned} K_1 &= \sum_i \sum_j \gamma_{ij}\,\Delta^{ij}, \\ K_2 &= \sum_i \sum_j \sum_r \sum_s \gamma_{ij}\gamma_{rs}\,\Delta^{ir}\,\Delta^{js}, \\ K_3 &= \gamma \det \Delta^{ij}. \end{aligned}\right. \tag{8.23}$$

These definitions are made whether the quantities Δ^{ij} are large or small. It can be seen that K_1, K_2, and K_3 are respectively of first, second, and third order of smallness when Δ^{ij} are of first order. It can also be seen, by expressing Δ^{ij} in the form (8.22), that

$$\left\{\begin{aligned} K_1 &= J_1 - 3 = \sum (\lambda_a^2 - 1), \\ K_2 &= J_2 - 2J_1 + 3 = \sum (\lambda_a^2 - 1)^2, \\ K_3 &= (\lambda_a^2 - 1)(\lambda_b^2 - 1)(\lambda_c^2 - 1); \end{aligned}\right. \tag{8.24}$$

(cf. Examples 2, No. 9, for the last of these results); this proves that the quantities K_u are invariants (i.e. have values which are independent of the choice of base vectors used in (8.23)), as stated above.

By writing $\gamma^{ij}(t_0) = \gamma^{ij} + \Delta^{ij}$ and rearranging the terms, we may express equations (8.1) in the alternative form

$$\pi^{ij} = A'\gamma^{ij} + B'\,\Delta^{ij} + C' \sum_r \sum_s \gamma_{rs}\,\Delta^{ir}\,\Delta^{js}, \tag{8.25}$$

where the new coefficients $A' = A + B + 2C$, $B' = B + 2C$, $C' = C$, may be regarded as functions of K_1, K_2, K_3, and the temperature. This equation is exact, since no terms have as yet been neglected.

If we now make the reasonable assumption that the coefficients A', B', C' are bounded functions, i.e. that in particular they tend to finite limits as Δ^{ij} and therefore K_1, K_2, K_3 tend to zero, we see that the term in (8.25) in C' is of second order in Δ^{ij} and may therefore be neglected in the transition to the classical theory. Further, if we expand the remaining coefficients as Maclaurin series in K_1, K_2 and K_3, we need retain only the constant term in the expansion for B' and only the constant term and the term in K_1 in the expansion for A', since B' in (8.25) is multiplied by Δ^{ij}, while terms in K_2, K_3 and K_1^2, etc., are of second and higher orders in Δ^{ij} and can therefore be neglected. Furthermore, the constant term in the expansion for A' must be zero to fulfil the necessary condition that the stress must be zero when Δ^{ij} is zero. We see, therefore, that when terms of second and higher order in Δ^{ij} are negligible, the stress–strain relation (8.1) or (8.25) reduces to the form

$$\pi^{ij} = \tfrac{1}{2}\lambda K_1 \gamma^{ij} + \mu \Delta^{ij}, \tag{8.26}$$

where λ and μ are constants.

These are the equations of the classical theory, with λ and μ the so-called Lamé elastic constants. The equivalence of (8.26) and the more familiar form of equations referred to a coordinate system fixed in space, when the displacement gradients are small, will be proved in Chapter 12.

It is left as an exercise for the reader to show that Young's modulus E and Poisson's ratio σ are given in terms of the constants λ, μ of (8.26) by the following equations:

$$E = \frac{\mu(3\lambda+2\mu)}{\lambda+\mu}, \qquad \sigma = \frac{\lambda}{2(\lambda+\mu)}. \tag{8.27}$$

Isotropic Purely Viscous Liquids

In the above argument, we have shown how the equations (4.6), which relate stress and strain for a rubberlike solid, can be generalized so as to obtain a compact form (8.1) for the stress–strain relations for any isotropic perfectly elastic solid. We shall now show that the equations (5.4), which relate stress and the rate-of-strain quantities $d\gamma^{ij}/dt$ for a Newtonian liquid, can also be generalized, leading to an equation of the form

$$\pi^{ij} = a\gamma^{ij} - b\frac{d\gamma^{ij}}{dt} + c\sum_r \sum_s \gamma_{rs}\frac{d\gamma^{ri}}{dt}\frac{d\gamma^{sj}}{dt}, \tag{8.28}$$

where the coefficients a, b, c are functions of the "rate-of-strain invariants" L_1, L_2, L_3 defined by the equations

$$(8.29)\qquad \begin{cases} L_1 = \sum_i \sum_j \gamma_{ij} \dfrac{d\gamma^{ij}}{dt} \\[2ex] L_2 = \sum_i \sum_j \sum_r \sum_s \gamma_{ij}\gamma_{rs} \dfrac{d\gamma^{ir}}{dt}\dfrac{d\gamma^{js}}{dt} \\[2ex] L_3 = \gamma \det \dfrac{d\gamma^{ij}}{dt}. \end{cases}$$

If the liquid is compressible, the coefficient a will usually depend on the volume as well, or more precisely on the ratio of volumes in the stressed and stress-free states; if the liquid is incompressible, the coefficient a will not be determined by the flow alone but by the boundary conditions, and furthermore the invariant L_1 will be zero, by (5.6).

If the material represented by (8.28) is held in any constant shape, then $d\gamma^{ij}/dt = 0$, the terms in b, c vanish, and hence the stress becomes isotropic; the material is therefore a liquid (cf. Chapter 4). Since there are no time derivatives of stress or of $d\gamma^{ij}/dt$ the stress will become isotropic instantaneously; the liquid therefore satisfies the first of the two conditions (4.5) which were suggested as necessary requirements if a liquid is to be called purely viscous or inelastic. The second of these conditions is less easy to discuss, since it involves putting the stress instantaneously zero or isotropic in (8.28) and then solving the resulting differential equation for γ^{ij}: if this solution gives $\gamma^{ij} =$ constant, then the second condition (4.5) is satisfied. When the liquid is incompressible, it can be seen that $\gamma^{ij} =$ constant is in fact a solution, but the question remains as to whether it is the only possible solution. Since the differential equations for γ^{ij} are in general non-linear, it is clear that the problem may not be straightfoward, and we shall not pursue the matter further here. We shall nevertheless refer to the material represented by (8.28) as a purely viscous liquid, despite the further complication that, in the compressible case, changes of volume are in most, if not all, practical cases elastic.

Proof of (8.28). Reiner (1945) has given a rigorous proof of equations (referred to axes fixed in space) equivalent to (8.28); it is assumed that the stress can be expressed in a series of ascending powers of rate-of-strain quantities (equivalent to $d\gamma^{ij}/dt$) (cf. Weissenberg, (1935)). For isotropic materials, it can be shown, using methods of tensor analysis, that the rate-of-strain quantities can occur only in certain combinations and that in fact the most general possible series can always be reduced to the stated form (8.28).

As an alternative proof using the more elementary methods of the present book, we offer the following non-rigorous argument.

We have seen in Chapter 5 that there is a formal similarity between the rheological equations of state for a rubberlike solid and a Newtonian liquid; the equations for the liquid may, according to (5.14), be obtained from those for the solid by replacing t_0 by $t-\delta t$ and allowing δt to tend to zero; it is necessary to allow the modulus μ_0 to tend to infinity in such a way that the product $\mu_0 \delta t$ tends to a finite value η, which is equal to the viscosity. The following argument simply amounts to following a similar procedure starting with the general stress–strain relations (8.1) for an isotropic elastic solid.

For this purpose, it is more convenient to use the stress–strain relations in the form (8.25), which has been shown to be equivalent to (8.1). On writing

$$t_0 = t - \delta t, \tag{8.30}$$

we see that, from (8.22),

$$\lim_{\delta t \to 0} \frac{\Delta^{ij}}{\delta t} = -\frac{d\gamma^{ij}}{dt}. \tag{8.31}$$

Hence the stress–strain relation (8.25) leads to the equation (8.28), on taking the limit $\delta t \to 0$, if we write

$$a = A', \quad b = \lim_{\delta t \to 0} B' \,\delta t, \quad c = \lim_{\delta t \to 0} C'(\delta t)^2. \tag{8.32}$$

Moreover, a, b, and c may be regarded as functions of the quantities L_u (defined by (8.29)) which are evidently obtainable from the invariants K_u defined in (8.23) by the following limiting processes:

$$\left\{\begin{aligned} L_1 &= -\lim_{\delta t \to 0} \frac{K_1}{\delta t}, \\ L_2 &= \lim_{\delta t \to 0} \frac{K_2}{(\delta t)^2}, \\ L_3 &= -\lim_{\delta t \to 0} \frac{K_3}{(\delta t)^3}. \end{aligned}\right. \tag{8.33}$$

This completes our proof that (8.28) represents a possible form for the rheological equations of state of an isotropic material which is such that the stress can be expressed in terms of algebraic functions of the rate-of-strain quantities $d\gamma^{ij}/dt$ and an additive isotropic stress $a\gamma^{ij}$ when the material is incompressible. It will be seen that the argument lacks rigour, since the limiting processes involved in expressing the coefficients a, b, c in terms of L_u may need further consideration, and we have not proved that (8.28) represents the most general possible form of relation; this can be proved by tensor methods (Reiner, 1945).

In view of the fact that the principal axes of stress and of strain coincide for a perfectly elastic isotropic solid (described by equations (8.1)), it is natural to expect a similar result for the viscous liquid defined by equations (8.28), since these have been derived from (8.1). It is first necessary to define the principal axes of the rate-of-strain quantities $d\gamma^{ij}/dt$.

A plane of coordinates η_i is said to be a principal plane of $d\gamma^{ij}/dt$ corresponding to the principal value $\bar{\omega}$ if the equations

$$\sum_j \left(\frac{d\gamma^{ij}}{dt} - \bar{\omega}\gamma^{ij}\right)\eta_j = 0 \qquad (i = 1, 2, 3) \tag{8.34}$$

are satisfied (cf. Examples 2, No. 10). By comparing these equations with those of Examples 2, No. 11 (ii), it can be seen that the principal planes so defined coincide with the principal planes for the deformation $t-\delta t \to t$ in the limit $\delta t \to 0$, and also that $\bar{\omega} = \lim(\lambda^2-1)/\delta t$. The normals to principal planes are called principal axes.

From (8.28) we have

$$\begin{aligned}
\sum_j (\pi^{ij} - a\gamma^{ij})\eta_j &= \sum_j \left[-b\bar{\omega}\gamma^{ij} + c\sum_r\sum_s \gamma_{rs}\frac{d\gamma^{ri}}{dt}\bar{\omega}\gamma^{sj}\right]\eta_j, && \text{by (8.34)},\\
&= \sum_j \left[-b\bar{\omega}\gamma^{ij} + c\bar{\omega}\frac{d\gamma^{ji}}{dt}\right]\eta_j, && \text{by (1.21)},\\
&= (-b\bar{\omega} + c\bar{\omega}^2)\sum_j \gamma^{ij}\eta_j, && \text{by (1.19), (8.34)}.
\end{aligned}$$

This equation may be written in the form

$$\sum_j (\pi^{ij} - \sigma\gamma^{ij})\eta_j = 0$$

where $\sigma = a - b\bar{\omega} + c\bar{\omega}^2$. From Examples 3, No. 1, it follows that η_i is also a principal plane of stress, and hence that the principal axes of stress and of rate-of-strain coincide.

Steady Shear Flow in a Purely Viscous Isotropic Liquid

From (2.73), using a basis of the type usual for shear flow, orthonormal at the current time t, we have the results

$$\frac{d\gamma^{ij}}{dt} = \left(\frac{d\gamma^{ij}(t')}{dt'}\right)_{t'=t} = \begin{pmatrix} 0 & -G & 0 \\ -G & 0 & 0 \\ 0 & 0 & 0 \end{pmatrix}, \quad \gamma_{ij} = \begin{pmatrix} 1 & 0 & 0 \\ 0 & 1 & 0 \\ 0 & 0 & 1 \end{pmatrix},$$

where G denotes the shear rate. It follows that

$$\sum_r \sum_s \gamma_{rs} \frac{d\gamma^{ir}}{dt}\frac{d\gamma^{js}}{dt} = \sum_s \frac{d\gamma^{is}}{dt}\frac{d\gamma^{js}}{dt} = \begin{pmatrix} G^2 & 0 & 0 \\ 0 & G^2 & 0 \\ 0 & 0 & 0 \end{pmatrix}.$$

Hence, from (3.14) and (8.28), we see that

$$(8.35) \quad p_{ij} = \pi^{ij} = a\begin{pmatrix} 1 & 0 & 0 \\ 0 & 1 & 0 \\ 0 & 0 & 1 \end{pmatrix} + b\begin{pmatrix} 0 & G & 0 \\ G & 0 & 0 \\ 0 & 0 & 0 \end{pmatrix} + c\begin{pmatrix} G^2 & 0 & 0 \\ 0 & G^2 & 0 \\ 0 & 0 & 0 \end{pmatrix},$$

showing that the non-zero stress components satisfy the equations

$$(8.36) \quad \begin{cases} p_{11} - p_{22} = 0, \\ p_{22} - p_{33} = cG^2, \\ p_{21} = p_{12} = bG. \end{cases}$$

The invariants L_u, defined by (8.29), are seen to have the following values in shear flow:

$$(8.37) \quad L_1 = L_3 = 0; \quad L_2 = 2G^2.$$

Thus the viscosity $\eta \equiv p_{21}/G = b$ is a function of L_2 and therefore of shear rate G; and one difference of normal stress components is non-zero if the coefficient c in (8.28) is non-zero. This serves to emphasize the point that shear rate dependence of viscosity and inequality of normal stress components are two independent properties: for it is theoretically possible to have a liquid in which the coefficient c is zero and the normal stress components are equal to one another, while the coefficient b, and therefore the viscosity, depends on shear rate. We have already had an example, in the case of the rubberlike liquid, of the contrary result in which the viscosity is independent of shear rate while the normal stress components are not all equal (cf. (6.22), (6.23)).

It is important to note that the purely viscous liquid and the rubberlike liquid exhibit an essential difference in the values of normal stress differences: $p_{11}-p_{22}$ is zero for the former, while $p_{22}-p_{33}$ is zero for the latter. In this connection, it is also interesting to note that in the analogous problem of simple shear of an elastic solid, the general isotropic material (8.1) has both $p_{11}-p_{22}$ and $p_{22}-p_{33}$ different from zero (8.20); the general isotropic purely viscous liquid, on the other hand, necessarily has $p_{11}-p_{22}=0$ in shear flow.

These and other results for the purely viscous isotropic liquid have been given by Rivlin (1948).

Viscoelastic Solids and Liquids

We have shown how the stress–strain relations for a perfectly elastic solid may be generalized and expressed in a compact form (8.1) when the solid is isotropic; we now consider ways in which the dependence of stress on the *history* of strain, exemplified by the equations (6.9) for a rubberlike liquid, may be generalized in order to describe the properties of viscoelastic solids and liquids. The added complexity in these cases is such that no compact forms for the equations have been found which have a generality comparable with that of (8.1) for the perfectly elastic solid or of (8.28) for the purely viscous liquid, even when the materials considered are isotropic.

Our fundamental assumption is that the stress, or the extra stress in the case of an incompressible material, in a given material element shall be determined by the history of the shape of that element up to the instant considered. We can therefore consider any form of equations relating the stress variables π^{ij}, the shape variables γ_{ij} or γ^{ij}, and their time derivatives and time integrals, provided that the following two basic requirements are met.

(a) The equations must have a significance that is independent of any superposed rigid motion of the material relative to axes fixed in space.

(b) The equations must have a significance that is independent of the choice of base vectors used in defining π^{ij} and γ_{ij}.

For consistency, it is also necessary that the variables occur in such combinations that the symmetry relations $\pi^{ij}=\pi^{ji}$ and $\gamma_{ij}=\gamma_{ji}$ are taken care of. Further restrictions will be imposed if the material is isotropic; these are considered in Chapter 12. Finally, every term in an equation must have the same physical dimensions.

Condition (a) is automatically satisfied by any equations which involve

π^{ij}, γ_{ij}, their time derivatives and time integrals, together with material constants or material functions of time intervals. For, as we have seen in Chapters 2 and 3, if we are given π^{ij} and γ_{ij} as functions of time throughout some interval for a given stress history and a given shape history of a material, the same functions will still describe the stress and shape histories for any other motion obtained from the given motion by the superposition of any rigid motion. It follows, in particular, that the time derivatives and time integrals of π^{ij} and γ_{ij} are also unaffected by the superposition of any rigid motion.

It might be considered superfluous to mention a condition as self-evident as condition (a), when this is obviously satisfied by equations involving stress and shape variables defined in terms of a system of embedded vectors. The point needs to be made, however, in view of the widespread use of stress and strain variables which involve a reference to a system of axes fixed in space; time derivatives and time integrals of such variables in general do introduce an unwanted dependence on the motion of the material relative to axes fixed in space, and special steps have to be taken to introduce suitable additional terms in order to remove this dependence, as will be shown in Chapter 12. Perhaps the main advantage of the use of embedded vectors lies in the fact that condition (a) is automatically satisfied. The main discussion of this point is due to Oldroyd (1950a), although particular uses of embedded vectors, or convected coordinate systems, have been made earlier in rheology by Hencky (1925), Brillouin (1925), and Deuker (1941); convected coordinate systems have also been used extensively in finite-strain theories of perfectly elastic solids by Green and Zerna (1954) and Green and Adkins (1960).

It is a less straightforward matter to propose equations whose significance is independent of the choice of base vectors (condition (b)). In earlier chapters, we have ensured that this condition is satisfied by means of the technique of deriving equations from a (scalar) hypothesis which involves no reference to any system of base vectors (hypotheses (4.7), (5.2), and (6.1)); in this way, certain particular forms of equations of state have been obtained (4.9), (5.4), (6.9). It may not, however, be convenient, or even possible, to obtain more general forms of equations in such a way, and we must seek alternative ways of ensuring that condition (b) is satisfied.

In this chapter, we shall state, without proof, certain rules for combining the variables π^{ij} and γ_{ij} so as to obtain equations satisfying condition (b). The proof of these rules, which would be rather involved if we restricted ourselves to the elementary methods used hitherto, is given very readily in Chapter 12 by tensor methods; in fact, the main object of the tensor calculus is to provide a systematic method of formulating equations which have a form and therefore a significance independent of the choice of base vectors (or of coordinate system) used in the definition of the variables involved in the equations.

Admissible Combinations of the Variables π^{ij}, γ_{ij}

Equations formed from the following combinations of the variables π^{ij}, γ_{ij} and their time derivatives and time integrals have a form, and therefore a significance, which is not dependent on the choice of base vectors used in the definition of these variables. For any given shape history and stress, the *values* of these variables will depend on the choice of base vectors; but the following rules are sufficient to ensure that any change from one system of embedded base vectors to another will lead to equations in the new variables, $\bar{\pi}^{ij}$, $\bar{\gamma}_{ij}$ say, having the same *form* as the original equations in the old variables π^{ij}, γ_{ij} (cf. the illustration given in Chapter 4 in the discussion of equations (4.9) and (4.10)).

Addition and subtraction. The sum or difference of variables may be used, provided that the same letter suffix occurs in the same (upper or lower) position in each variable. Thus, for example, $\gamma^{ij}(t)-\gamma^{ij}(t_0)$ is an admissible combination, but $\gamma^{ij}(t)-\gamma_{ij}(t_0)$ is not (cf. Examples 4, No. 5).

Contraction. The sum of products of two variables having one letter suffix in common is admissible, provided that this suffix occurs in an upper position in one factor and in a lower position in the other factor and that the sum is formed by giving the values 1, 2, and 3 in turn to the repeated suffix. Thus $\sum_{r=1}^{3} \gamma_{ir}\gamma^{rj}(t_0)$ is admissible, but $\sum_{r=1}^{3} \gamma^{ir}\gamma^{rj}(t_0)$ is not.

Multiplication by scalar constant, e.g. $\mu_0\gamma^{ij}(t_0)$, where μ_0 is a material constant, can occur. If the material is isotropic, the only constants which can occur must be scalars whose value does not depend on any particular direction in the material. If the properties of the material are independent of time, then the equations must be expressible in a form in which the variable t does not occur explicitly (i.e. other than as an argument in $\pi^{ij}(t)$, $\gamma^{ij}(t)$ or in the operations $d/dt, \int^{t}\ldots dt'$).

"Reciprocal" of shape variables. The quantities γ_{ij}, defined in terms of γ^{ij} by equations (1.21) or their equivalent, (1.23), may occur.

Determinants. The ratio of determinants of two double-suffix quantities can occur; e.g. $J_3 = \gamma/\gamma_0$ (8.2) can occur.

It can be seen that the rheological equations of state (4.9), (5.4), (6.9), (8.1) and (8.28) which have been derived in the present book are all of forms consistent with the above statements; it will, in particular, be noted that the invariants J_1, J_2 (8.2) are formed using the process of "contraction". It should also be noted that the same pair of "free" letter suffixes (e.g. i, j in (8.1)) occur in the same positions (upper or lower) in every term of an equation; a "free" letter suffix is one which, in the context considered, is not subject to summation. This is a necessary consequence of the rule for addition, stated above.

It will be seen that the rheological equation of state (8.10) for a perfectly elastic solid of general type involves the process of differentiation with respect to the quantities γ_{ij}; this is also an admissible process, and the resulting quantities $\partial F/\partial \gamma_{ij}$ may in fact be treated as a double-suffix quantity with suffixes in the upper position (or in the position opposite to the position of the suffixes in the denominator), as is implied in (8.10).

From the contraction rule (applied twice), it follows that the quantities π_{ij}, defined by the equations

$$\pi_{ij} = \sum_r \sum_s \gamma_{ir} \gamma_{js} \pi^{rs}, \tag{8.38}$$

can be used in a rheological equation of state; they do, in fact, give an alternative description of stress, as can be seen from the inverse equations

$$\pi^{ij} = \sum_r \sum_s \gamma^{ir} \gamma^{js} \pi_{rs}, \tag{8.39}$$

which are obtained from (8.38) by means of (1.21); for (8.39) shows that, if π_{rs} are given, then π^{ij} and hence the state of stress are determined. It follows, in particular, that both $d\pi_{ij}/dt$ and $d\pi^{ij}/dt$ are associated with rates of change of stress; it can be shown that a definition of rate of change of stress due to Jaumann (1911) is equivalent to the particular combination

$$\frac{1}{2}\left\{\frac{d\pi_{ij}}{dt} + \sum_r \sum_s \gamma_{ir} \gamma_{js} \frac{d\pi^{rs}}{dt}\right\}; \tag{8.40}$$

(cf. Oldroyd (1958), and Chapter 12).

It will be seen that the variety of admissible forms of rheological equations of state is considerable. It is not easy to give any systematic presentation of these forms nor of those of them that have so far been considered in the literature. But we may start by considering equations formed from π^{ij}, γ^{ij} and their time derivatives, and end by considering the extra possibilities which arise from the use of time integrals.

It follows from the rheological equation of state (4.12) for a rubberlike solid that the time derivative of the extra stress Π^{ij} is zero:

$$\frac{d\Pi^{ij}}{dt} = 0, \tag{8.41}$$

$$\Pi^{ij} \equiv \pi^{ij} + p\gamma^{ij}. \tag{8.42}$$

This result does not imply that the components of *traction* on a given material plane are constant, because the values of π^{ij} and therefore of Π^{ij} depend also on the base vectors (cf. (3.8)) which are themselves time-dependent; the result in fact implies that the quantity $(\mathbf{f}.\mathbf{n}+p)/h^2$ is constant (Examples 3, No. 5).

It may be noted that the rubberlike solid is completely determined by the differential equations (8.41) and the incompressibility condition $\det\gamma^{ij} = \text{constant}$, provided that the shape in the stress-free state is given and also the value of the modulus μ_0. If, however, we use (8.41), without specifying that there is a unique stress-free state, and combine this equation with the equation (5.4) for a Newtonian liquid in some such way as the following:

$$\left(1+\tau_1\frac{d}{dt}\right)\Pi^{ij} = -\eta\frac{d\gamma^{ij}}{dt}, \tag{8.43}$$

where τ_1 is a constant, we obtain an equation which must describe a material having properties which resemble those of a Newtonian liquid under conditions in which the term in $d\Pi^{ij}/dt$ is unimportant, and resemble those of a rubberlike material (possibly a solid) when this term is dominant.

If the flow history for this material is given throughout an interval $t_0 \leqslant t' \leqslant t$, the equations (8.43) may be regarded as differential equations for the dependent variables Π^{ij}, the quantities on the right-hand side being given functions of time. The solution of these equations is straightforward (using an integrating factor $\exp(t/\tau_1)$) and leads to a result which may be expressed in the following form, if p in (8.42) is replaced by $p+\eta/\tau_1$:

$$\Pi^{ij}(t) = \Pi^{ij}(t_0)\exp\frac{t_0-t}{\tau_1} + \frac{\eta}{\tau_1}\int_{t_0}^{t}\exp\frac{t'-t}{\tau_1}\gamma^{ij}(t')\,dt'. \tag{8.44}$$

We have here carried out an integration by parts.

Thus the extra stress at time t depends on the value of the extra stress at time t_0 as well as on the flow history in the interval $t_0 \leqslant t' \leqslant t$. If we take τ_1 to be positive and suppose that $\Pi^{ij}(t_0)$ is bounded as $t_0 \to -\infty$, we see that in the limit $t_0 \to -\infty$ the term in $\Pi^{ij}(t_0)$ tends to zero and the resulting equation is identical with the equation (6.9) for the rubberlike liquid already studied, in the case in which the memory function is a single exponential (6.7). Alternatively, we can see that the equation (8.44) represents a liquid in the sense of the definition given in Chapter 4 because, if the shape variables γ^{ij} are constant from some instant t_0 on, then it can be seen that as $t \to \infty$, $\Pi^{ij}(t) \to 0$, i.e. that the stress becomes isotropic.

The differential equations (8.43) represent one of the possible generalizations, not restricted to small strains or small rates of strain, of Maxwell's equations for a material which exhibits stress relaxation (Maxwell, 1868). Another possible generalization is the following:

$$\left(1+\tau_1 \frac{d}{dt}\right) \Pi_{ij} = \eta \frac{d\gamma_{ij}}{dt}, \tag{8.45}$$

where

$$\Pi_{ij} = \pi_{ij} + p\gamma_{ij}. \tag{8.46}$$

The equations (4.12), (5.4) for the rubberlike solid and the Newtonian liquid can be "combined" in another way, without differentiation:

$$\Pi^{ij} = \mu_0\, \gamma^{ij}(t_0) - \eta \frac{d\gamma^{ij}}{dt}. \tag{8.47}$$

It is clear that this represents an elastic solid, for at any given constant shape the term $d\gamma^{ij}/dt$ is zero and the extra stress has a unique value, which is in fact the value appropriate for a rubberlike solid (4.12); moreover, this value is attained as soon as the shape is constant. When the stress is made zero or isotropic, the change of shape is determined by the equations

$$\left\{\begin{aligned} \eta \frac{d\gamma^{ij}}{dt} + p\gamma^{ij} &= \mu_0\, \gamma^{ij}(t_0), \\ \det \gamma^{ij} &= \det \gamma^{ij}(t_0), \end{aligned}\right. \tag{8.48}$$

in which p must be treated as a dependent variable; if, as seems reasonable, these non-linear equations for p, γ^{ij} have a solution such that γ^{ij} is constant at large times, then this constant value is evidently $\gamma^{ij}(t_0)$, and therefore the material has a unique shape when at rest in the absence of stress.

Equations (8.47) represent one of the possible generalizations, not restricted to small strains or small rates of strain, of equations considered by Voigt (1889, 1892) which are so restricted.

An obvious generalization of (8.43) and (8.47) is obtained if we take a sum of terms with higher order time derivatives and constant coefficients:

$$\left(1+\sum_{r=1}^{m} a_r \frac{d^r}{dt^r}\right)\Pi^{ij} = \mu_0 \gamma^{ij}(t_0) + \sum_{r=1}^{n} b_r \frac{d^r}{dt^r}\gamma^{ij}. \tag{8.49}$$

One can in fact show that an equation of this type, with μ_0 zero, is obtainable from the equations (6.9) for a rubberlike liquid, when the memory function is a sum of exponential terms, by repeated differentiation and elimination of terms containing integrals.

Again, the corresponding equation with "lower suffix" quantities is a possible form of rheological equation of state:

$$\left(1+\sum_{r} \alpha_r \frac{d^r}{dt^r}\right)\Pi^{ij} = \mu_1 \gamma_{ij}(t_0) + \sum_{r} \beta_r \frac{d^r}{dt^r}\gamma_{ij}. \tag{8.50}$$

Further, equations (8.49) and (8.50) can be combined by adding to (8.49) the equation formed by double contraction of (8.50) with $\gamma^{ik}\gamma^{jl}$ and multiplication by a new constant κ:

$$\begin{aligned}\left(1+\sum_{r} a_r \frac{d^r}{dt^r}\right)\Pi^{ij} + \kappa \sum_{k}\sum_{l} \gamma^{ik}\gamma^{jl}\left(1+\sum_{r} \alpha_r \frac{d^r}{dt^r}\right)\Pi_{kl} \\ = \mu_0 \gamma^{ij}(t_0) + \sum_{r} b_r \frac{d^r \gamma_{ij}}{dt^r} + \sum_{k}\sum_{l} \gamma^{ik}\gamma^{jl}\kappa\left(\mu_1 \gamma_{kl}(t_0) + \sum_{r} \beta_r \frac{d^r \gamma_{kl}}{dt^r}\right).\end{aligned} \tag{8.51}$$

Oldroyd (1958) has considered equations of this type in which terms in $\gamma^{ij}(t_0)$, $\gamma_{ij}(t_0)$, second and higher derivatives of stress, and third and higher derivatives of γ^{ij}, γ_{ij} are omitted, and an extra term of the form

$$\gamma^{ij} \sum_{r}\sum_{s}\sum_{k}\sum_{l} \gamma_{rk}\gamma_{sl} \frac{d\gamma^{rs}}{dt}\frac{d\gamma^{kl}}{dt}$$

is included. A similar equation, considered by Noll (1955), may be obtained from (8.51) by retaining terms up to and including the first time-derivatives, rejecting $\gamma^{ij}(t_0)$, $\gamma_{ij}(t_0)$ and higher time derivatives, and including a term of the form

$$\gamma^{ij} \sum_{r}\sum_{s}\sum_{k}\sum_{l} \gamma_{rk}\gamma_{sl}\Pi^{rs}\Pi^{kl}.$$

These and other equations quoted from the literature have, when necessary, been re-written for presentation in the present notation, using methods which are given in Chapter 12.

Combinations of the various variables other than those represented in (8.51) are admissible. Rivlin and Ericksen (1955) have considered equations which are equivalent to equations of the form

$$\Pi^{ij} = F^{ij}\left\{\gamma^{kl}(t_0), \frac{d\gamma^{kl}}{dt}, \frac{d^2\gamma^{kl}}{dt^2}, \ldots, \frac{d^n\gamma^{kl}}{dt^n}, \gamma^{kl}\right\},$$

where the function symbol F^{ij} stands for an admissible combination of the arguments, formed according to the rules laid down above. Noll (1955) has considered equations of the form

$$\frac{d\Pi^{ij}}{dt} + \sum_k \sum_l \gamma^{ik}\gamma^{jl}\frac{d\Pi_{kl}}{dt} = F^{ij}\left\{\Pi^{rs}, \frac{d\gamma^{rs}}{dt}, \gamma^{rs}\right\}. \tag{8.52}$$

Equations of this form for which the right-hand side is linear in the rate of strain terms $d\gamma^{rs}/dt$ have been considered by Truesdell (1955), who also considers the case of anisotropic materials, and has suggested the name "hypoelastic" ("more than elastic") for this class of material.

The question whether any systematic treatment or classification of the great variety of *a priori* possible equations can be found appears most likely to be answered by means of the calculus of functionals. A quantity y is said to be a *functional* of a function $x = x(t)$ if the value of y depends on and is determined by the values assumed by the function $x(t')$ throughout an interval $t_0 \leqslant t' \leqslant t$. We write this in the form

$$y = \mathscr{F}\left\{\overset{t}{\underset{t_0}{x(t')}}\right\}. \tag{8.53}$$

The most familiar example of a functional is the definite integral

$$y = \int_{t_0}^{t} x(t')\,dt'. \tag{8.54}$$

A functional can be regarded as the limit of a function $f(x_0, x_1, x_2, \ldots x_n)$, where $x_r = x(t_r)$, when the number of points t_0, t_1, t_2, ... $t_n = t$ in the interval (t_0, t) tends to infinity in a suitable manner.

A more general functional than (8.54), still linear in the function $x(t)$, may be written in the form

$$y_1 = \int_{t_0}^{t} K_1(t;t')\,x(t')\,dt', \tag{8.55}$$

where the function $K_1(t;t')$, sometimes referred to as the *kernel*, is given.

A next step in generalization may be taken by considering functionals involving a double integral which is bilinear in the function $x(t)$:

$$y_2 = \int_{t_0}^{t}\int_{t_0}^{t} K_2(t;t',t'')\,x(t')\,x(t'')\,dt'\,dt''; \tag{8.56}$$

in this case, it may be noted that no generality is lost by assuming that the kernel is symmetric in the variables of integration. This process of generalization may be continued in a similar fashion, leading to a functional involving any number n of integrations and an integrand which is homogeneous of degree n in the function $x(t)$:

$$y_n = \int_{t_0}^{t} \dots \int_{t_0}^{t} K_n(t;t',t'',\dots t^{(n)})\,x(t')\dots x(t^{(n)})\,dt' \dots dt^{(n)}. \tag{8.57}$$

There is a fundamental theorem in the calculus of functionals, due to Fréchet (1910), which states that, subject to certain continuity requirements, any functional y may be expressed as a series of integrals of the types described above, i.e. that

$$y = y_1 + y_2 + y_3 + \dots + y_n + \dots; \tag{8.58}$$

(cf. Volterra and Pérès, 1936).

The fundamental assumption on which most rheological treatments are founded is that the stress at any given time t in an element of material is determined, either uniquely for a compressible material or to within an additive isotropic stress for an incompressible material, by the history of the shape of that element. We may therefore express this in the form

$$\Pi^{ij} = \mathscr{F}^{ij}\left\{\gamma^{kl}(t')\right\}_{-\infty}^{t}, \tag{8.59}$$

where $\mathscr{F}^{ij}$ stands for a functional of the functions γ^{kl}, six of which are independent; for the values $i, j = 1, 2, 3$, we have different functionals, of which not more than six will be independent in view of the necessary condition $\Pi^{ij} = \Pi^{ji}$.

This equation represents an extension of the functionals considered above in that the single function x in the argument of the functional is replaced by six independent functions γ^{kl}. Furthermore, the range of the variable t' is extended to $-\infty$, which may give rise to complications when rigorous expansion theorems are considered.

If we suppose that, despite these complications, the expansion theorem (8.58) can be suitably extended to apply to the case (8.59), then the extra stress can be expressed in the form of a series of the type

$$\Pi^{ij} = \mathscr{F}^{ij}_{(1)} + \mathscr{F}^{ij}_{(2)} + \dots + \mathscr{F}^{ij}_{(n)} + \dots, \tag{8.60}$$

in which the first term involves a single integral and has an integrand which is linear and homogeneous in $\gamma^{ij}(t')$; the second term involves a double integral and is bilinear and homogeneous in $\gamma^{ij}(t')$; and the nth term involves an n-fold integral and is homogeneous and of degree n in $\gamma^{ij}(t')$.

The first term in this expansion must therefore be of the form

$$\text{(8.61)} \qquad \mathscr{F}^{ij}_{(1)} = \int_{-\infty}^{t} K_1(t;t')\,\gamma^{ij}(t')\,dt',$$

which is of the form considered in Chapters 6, 7 for a rubberlike liquid, if we write

$$\text{(8.62)} \qquad K_1(t;t') = \mu(t-t').$$

Functionals with a kernel depending only on the differences $t-t'$, $t-t''$, etc., are called "hereditary"; by changing the variable of integration it is easily seen that the value of a hereditary functional is not affected by any constant shift along the time axis: this is evidently a necessary property for a material whose properties are not changing with time.

The form of the second and higher terms in the expansion (8.60) is rather more complicated because the possible combinations of the functions $\gamma^{kl}(t')$, $\gamma^{ij}(t'')$, ..., are restricted by the condition that the resulting equations shall have a significance independent of the choice of basis and also possibly by the condition that the material be isotropic or, if not isotropic, possessed of some other symmetry properties. These problems have been dealt with by Rivlin and co-workers (Green and Rivlin, 1957, 1960; Green, Rivlin and Spencer, 1959; Rivlin, 1960; Pipkin and Rivlin, 1960, 1961). The complexity is understandably considerable, and we shall not give the form of the results in complete generality, even for the case of isotropic materials, to which we shall now confine our attention. Once the principles involved are grasped, the reader should have no difficulty in constructing terms of any desired degree of generality.

If we first consider the second term in the expansion (8.60), we see that we require an integrand which is bilinear in $\gamma^{ij}(t')$, $\gamma^{ij}(t'')$. According to the rules set out above, however, it is not possible to form such a set of quantities which has a significance independent of the choice of basis. If, however, we allow the inclusion of factors of the type $\gamma_{ij} = \gamma_{ij}(t)$, then the combination in the following integral is admissible:

$$\text{(8.63)} \qquad \int_{-\infty}^{t}\int_{-\infty}^{t} K_2(t;t',t'') \sum_r \sum_s \gamma_{rs}\gamma^{ri}(t')\,\gamma^{sj}(t'')\,dt'\,dt''.$$

It may be noted that the integrand here is of the form of the third term on the right-hand side of (8.1), if C is independent of the invariants and the arguments t_0, t_0 are replaced by t', t''. The third and higher order terms in (8.60) will involve more complicated expressions, which we need not consider further here.

As a somewhat simpler method of obtaining compact admissible forms of equations of type (8.59), the following tentative procedure may prove to be of some interest, although it does not cover all possibilities.

Guided by the form of (8.10), we may re-write the equations (6.9) for the rubberlike liquid in the form

$$\Pi^{ij} = \frac{1}{2}\left(\frac{\partial}{\partial \gamma_{ij}} + \frac{\partial}{\partial \gamma_{ji}}\right) \int_{-\infty}^{t} \mu(t-t') J_1(t', t)\, dt', \tag{8.64}$$

where

$$J_1(t', t) = \sum_r \sum_s \gamma_{rs} \gamma^{rs}(t') \tag{8.65}$$

in agreement with the notation of (8.2).

As a first step in generalizing equation (8.64), it is natural to consider the equation

$$\Pi^{ij} = \frac{1}{2}\left(\frac{\partial}{\partial \gamma_{ij}} + \frac{\partial}{\partial \gamma_{ji}}\right) \int_{-\infty}^{t} \mu(t-t') F[J_1(t', t), J_2(t', t)]\, dt', \tag{8.66}$$

where F denotes any function of the invariants J_1, J_2, and

$$J_2(t', t) = \sum_r \sum_s \sum_i \sum_j \gamma_{rs} \gamma_{ij} \gamma^{ri}(t') \gamma^{sj}(t'). \tag{8.67}$$

For incompressible materials, which we are considering here, it will be remembered that the third invariant, J_3 in (8.2), has the value unity, and need not therefore be included in the function F.

Equations of the form (8.66) may prove to be of interest for describing the properties of polymer solutions for which the stress–strain relation (4.9) of the kinetic theory of rubberlike elasticity does not provide a good enough starting point. An equation which can be expressed in the form (8.66) has in fact been suggested by Ward and Jenkins (1958) in connection with dynamic measurements of normal stress components in various rubbers. An equation equivalent to (8.66) has been applied to various flow problems by A. Kaye (1962).

In writing the equations in the form (8.64) and (8.66), the differentiations with respect to γ_{ij} and γ_{ji} have been taken outside the integral sign on the understanding that they apply only to the variables $\gamma_{ij} = \gamma_{ij}(t)$ and $\gamma_{ji} = \gamma_{ji}(t)$ which occur in the integrand, and do not apply to any such quantities which may arise as the result of evaluating the integral at the upper limit of integration. If this convention is acceptable, then the extra stress is evidently obtainable by applying the operation

$$\frac{1}{2}\left(\frac{\partial}{\partial \gamma_{ij}}+\frac{\partial}{\partial \gamma_{ji}}\right)$$

to a single functional in which the six functions $\gamma^{ij}(t')$ occur in only one combination, namely $F[J_1, J_2] \equiv F(t', t)$; thus we may write

$$\Pi^{ij} = \frac{1}{2}\left(\frac{\partial}{\partial \gamma_{ij}}+\frac{\partial}{\partial \gamma_{ji}}\right)\mathscr{F}\left[\overset{t}{\underset{-\infty}{F(t',t)}}\right]. \tag{8.68}$$

To this functional, we may apply the expansion theorem (8.58), again provided that any difficulties arising from the infinite range can be resolved. We then see that (8.66) arises from the first term in this expansion, and that the second term may be written in the form

$$\int_{-\infty}^{t}\int_{-\infty}^{t} K_2(t; t', t'') F(t', t) F(t'', t)\, dt'\, dt''. \tag{8.69}$$

The higher terms in the expansion can be written down at once. Thus we obtain the following series for the extra stress:

$$\begin{aligned}\Pi^{ij} = \frac{1}{2}\left(\frac{\partial}{\partial \gamma_{ij}}+\frac{\partial}{\partial \gamma_{ji}}\right)\Bigg\{&\int_{-\infty}^{t} \mu(t-t') F(t', t)\, dt' \\ &+\int_{-\infty}^{t}\int_{-\infty}^{t} K_2(t-t', t-t'') F(t', t) F(t'', t)\, dt'\, dt'' \\ &+\int_{-\infty}^{t}\int_{-\infty}^{t}\int_{-\infty}^{t} K_3(t-t', t-t'', t-t''') \times \\ &\times F(t', t) F(t'', t) F(t''', t)\, dt'\, dt''\, dt''' + \ldots\Bigg\};\end{aligned} \tag{8.70}$$

$$F(t', t) \equiv F[J_1(t', t); J_2(t', t)]. \tag{8.71}$$

We have here written the arguments in the kernels in the form appropriate to an hereditary functional.

It can be seen that this form for the rheological equation of state lacks complete generality in that, for example, the integrand of the second term in the series involves no invariants formed from $\gamma^{ij}(t')$ and $\gamma^{ij}(t'')$ together.

It is conceivable that terms involving a double integral, such as the second term in series (8.70), could be required to describe polymer solutions in order to take account of the possibility that the contribution to the extra stress at the current time t which arises from the shape which the liquid had at any given previous instant t' is influenced by the intervening flow history, i.e. by the values of $\gamma^{ij}(t'')$ for $t' \leqslant t'' \leqslant t$. It will be recalled that, in the theory for a rubberlike liquid which led to (6.9), which involves only the first term in (8.70), such an influence was excluded: contributions from chains joining the network at a given time t were assumed to be made in a manner uninfluenced by the rest of the network or by the intervening flow history. This is presumably the simplest assumption to make; it is certain to require modification to allow, for example, for the influence of flow history on the concentration of network chains of given age, and such a modification may be describable by means of a term of the form of the second in the series (8.70).

Finally, we may note that rheological equations of state which involve time derivatives of shape can be included (formally, at least) in the integral and multiple integral forms considered above if one allows the kernels to include derivatives of the Dirac delta function. In such cases, however, the conditions for the expansion theorem may not be satisfied, and it may, from the mathematical point of view, be more convenient to include time derivatives explicitly, as various writers have done.

Boltzmann (1874, 1876) was the first to consider materials for which the stress can be expressed as a time integral over the history of strain; his equations were restricted to the case of infinitesimally small strains, and were put forward in connection with experimental observations of retarded elastic recovery (the "elastic after-effect") involving the twisting and untwisting of metal wires and of rubber filaments (Kohlrausch, 1876). Boltzmann's equations, or their equivalent, are the foundation of the *linear theory of viscoelasticity* (Bland, 1960) which has been extensively applied to polymeric materials subjected to small strains (Ferry, 1961).

Because of the restriction to small strains, the linear theory is not capable of describing the Weissenberg effect and most of the effects (described in Chapter 10) with which we are concerned in this book. One particular equation not subject to such restrictions was proposed by Zaremba (1903). Weissenberg (1931, 1935) appears to have been the first to consider in some generality the possible forms which rheological equations of state might take for viscoelastic materials subjected to finite strains.

Flow Calculations with Viscoelastic Materials

Many of the published calculations using rheological equations of state for various types of viscoelastic materials have been made for the case of steady shear flow. Ericksen (1960a) has observed that many equations for isotropic materials give expressions for the stress in *steady* shear flow which are included in the comparatively simple form

$$\pi^{ij} = -p\gamma^{ij} - \beta_1 \frac{d\gamma^{ij}}{dt} + \beta_2 \sum \sum \gamma^{ir} \gamma^{js} \frac{d^2\gamma_{rs}}{dt^2} - \tfrac{1}{2}\beta_3 \frac{d^2\gamma^{ij}}{dt^2}. \tag{8.72}$$

The coefficients β_u (which are the same as in Ericksen's equation (2.17) and are not the same as in our equation (8.51)) are functions of shear rate G, and possibly also of the time interval $t-t_0$ when the material possesses a state $\gamma^{ij}(t_0)$ of permanent rheological significance. It will be recalled that time derivatives of shape of third and higher order are zero in steady shear flow (2.72).

From equation (8.72), one readily finds the following expressions for the non-zero stress components in steady shear flow of shear rate G when, as usual, $\mathbf{e}^2$ is normal to the shearing planes and $\mathbf{e}_1$ is parallel to the lines of shear:

$$\begin{cases} p_{11} - p_{22} = (\beta_3 - 2\beta_2)\, G^2, \\ p_{22} - p_{33} = 2\beta_2\, G^2, \\ p_{12} = p_{21} = \beta_1 G. \end{cases} \tag{8.73}$$

Thus, in general, both differences of normal stress components are non-zero and the viscosity β_1 depends on the value of shear rate.

Coleman and Noll (1959a) have considered the types of *non-rectilinear* shear flow which are commonly supposed to occur in laminar flow through pipes and between rigid members (cylinders, plates, or cone and plate) in relative rotation. They have shown that for a very general class of isotropic materials in *steady* shear flow the non-zero stress components are of the form (8.73) and that the differences of normal components are expressible as even functions of shear rate, while the tangential component is expressible as an odd function of shear rate. This involves an analytical derivation of results of the type (3.27), which have been given by Weissenberg (cf. Russell, 1946; Roberts, 1952) from direct arguments based on isotropy of the material and symmetry of shear flow. The author has extended the analysis so as to apply to non-steady shear flows in which the lines of shear are always represented by the same material lines (Chapter 12).

The upshot of these considerations is that, for a wide class of possible viscoelastic materials, the use of shear flow as a source of rheological information is sufficiently exemplified by rectilinear shear flow; the only reason for carrying out the detailed calculations for the various types of non-rectilinear shear flow is to see whether the assumed types of shear flow are attainable; no new information of rheological interest can be forthcoming. The values of the required stress components can be obtained from measured forces and pressures by means of general arguments given in Chapter 9.

It has in fact been found that shear flow through pipes of non-circular cross-section is not possible unless the material is such that the coefficients in (8.72) satisfy the condition

$$\frac{\beta_2}{\beta_1} = \text{constant}, \tag{8.74}$$

which implies that

$$\frac{p_{22}-p_{33}}{Gp_{21}} = \text{constant}, \tag{8.75}$$

by (8.73) (Ericksen, 1960a).

It is possible to maintain shear flows between concentric cylinders in relative rotation and between parallel plates in relative rotation, but not between cone and plate or between cone and cone in relative rotation (inertial effects being neglected in this context), unless the coefficients in (8.72) satisfy the condition

$$(2\beta_2+\beta_3)\,G^2 = \text{constant}, \tag{8.76}$$

which, by (8.73), implies that

$$p_{11}+p_{22}-2p_{33} = \text{constant}, \tag{8.77}$$

(Ericksen, 1960a; Oldroyd, 1958). This condition is not satisfied by such polymer solutions as have been investigated (it implies that the pressure distribution in the cone and plate system would be uniform (Chapter 9)), but there is reason to believe that disturbances to shear flow arising from violation of (8.77) may be unimportant for cone-and-plate systems with gap angles of a few degrees (Oldroyd, 1958).

Some calculations involving types of flow other than shear flow have been made. Green (1956) has considered simple elongation of a certain type of hypoelastic material. Leslie and Tanner (1961) have treated the motion of a rigid sphere through a viscoelastic liquid of the type considered by Oldroyd (1958) having equations included in (8.51). Rivlin (1956a) has considered stress relaxation, and Langlois and Rivlin (1959) have treated convergent flow of a slightly viscoelastic liquid through a right circular cone.

Equations Based on other Hypotheses

The hypothesis that the stress in a material element is determined by the history of shape of that element can be modified in two ways. Ericksen (1960b, c, d, e) has supposed that, in addition to variables describing shape, certain vector variables are also necessary. Truesdell (1951, 1952) and Garner, Nissan, and Wood (1950) have supposed that (in non-uniform strain) spatial gradients of shape may also influence the stress.

The theory of plasticity (Hill, 1950; Prager, 1961, Chapter VII) which has been extensively developed, is based on the idea that a material may behave like an elastic solid at low stresses and like a viscous liquid at high stresses. It is usually supposed that classical approximations are sufficient in each case, so that the infinitesimal strain equations for an elastic solid and the equations for a Newtonian liquid are used; theories differ according to the criterion used to decide whether a given state of stress is low or high. Despite the use of the term "plasticity", these theories have found more application to metals than to plastics (i.e. polymeric solids). Truesdell (1956) has shown that certain equations of the type described above for viscoelastic materials can lead to results similar to those obtained from the equations of plasticity theories (cf. Eringen, 1962, p. 322).

CHAPTER 9

The Measurement of Normal Stress Differences in Shear Flow

We have seen that, for incompressible isotropic liquids in steady shear flow, there are only three stress quantities, namely

$$p_{11}-p_{22}, \quad p_{22}-p_{33}, \quad p_{21}(=p_{12}), \tag{9.1}$$

which are of rheological interest (3.28). For the other tangential components vanish, on account of the symmetry of shear flow and the isotropy of the material, while the absolute value of any one normal component is of no interest, owing to the incompressibility. In this chapter, we shall give the principles underlying certain methods which have been and are being developed in order to measure the quantities (9.1), with particular reference to the normal stress differences $p_{11}-p_{22}$ and $p_{22}-p_{33}$.

This is a departure from the main path of the present book which we make because the comparatively recent investigations of normal stress differences are of fundamental importance in polymer rheology and are less familiar than investigations of viscosity. For Newtonian liquids, such as water and organic liquids of low molecular weight, the normal stress differences are zero and the viscosity determines the flow properties [although Reiner (1960) reports normal stress effects in toluene at very high shear rates]. For polymer solutions, however, the viscosity tells us only "one-third of the story" even for flow properties in states of steady shear flow: to complete the story, it is necessary to know also the values of $p_{11}-p_{22}$ and $p_{22}-p_{33}$. Even this information is insufficient to determine the flow properties in other states of flow; but the state of steady shear flow is, nevertheless, of particular importance because it can be realized accurately in the laboratory and because it predominates in flow processes of technological importance.

It is necessary to remove our previous restriction to uniform stress and strain in order to consider types of "curvilinear" shear flow involving shearing surfaces which are curved instead of plane and lines of shear which are curved instead of straight. The discussion should therefore more properly be given after this extension is made in Chapter 12. But Chapter 12 requires a knowledge of general tensor analysis and, in the interests of reaching a wider audience, it is possible to give a more elementary treatment of the essentials by making one or two plausible assumptions (which can be proved rigorously by more advanced methods) as we proceed.

The need for using *curvilinear* shear flow arises as a matter of principle in the following way. It will be recalled (cf. Fig. 3.5) that the stress component p_{22} represents a component of traction acting across a rigidly moving material surface; this surface could therefore be (and remain) in contact with a rigid wall of a suitable apparatus; the pressure on this wall, which would be equal to $-p_{22}$ according to our sign convention, could therefore be measured by a suitable gauge without causing any appreciable disturbance to the state of flow. But p_{22} is the only normal component which can be so measured, for the other two components, p_{11} and p_{33}, act normal to material surfaces which deform as an essential part of the flow; the use of pressure gauges in an attempt to measure p_{11} or p_{22} directly must introduce a disturbance to the state of flow which cannot be ignored. Some of the methods used by Garner, Nissan, and Wood (1950, cf. Fig. 11) must be criticized on these grounds. It is therefore necessary to seek additional pressure measurements in order to determine $p_{11}-p_{22}$ and $p_{22}-p_{33}$. According to the methods to be described in this chapter, such additional measurements are made from the spatial variation of the stress component p_{22} in suitable systems of curvilinear shear flow.

Hull (1961) suggests that, on the contrary, curvature in the stress field (such as occurs in the systems described below) complicates the interpretation of results, and uses a system involving rectilinear shear flow between a moving band and parallel plane walls; he records only a single pressure (that on the wall), however, and it is therefore difficult to see how a value for any *difference* of normal stress components could be obtained from his data. The value of a single normal component is not of rheological interest for materials which are incompressible. Moreover, in view of the smallness of the gap used by Hull (0·002 inches), it is possible that the pressures which he recorded were those which would be expected to arise when a viscous Newtonian liquid flows through a narrow gap between plane walls which are not quite parallel. It is known that apparatus developed to measure normal stress differences is peculiarly prone to the generation of unwanted pressures of this type (Roberts, 1952; Greensmith and Rivlin, 1953).

The Definition of Curvilinear Shear Flow

It will be recalled that the features of *rectilinear* shear flow are the existence of a family of parallel material planes each of which moves rigidly at constant separation from any one of its neighbours; the flow is at constant volume, and is steady if the velocity gradient across the shearing planes is independent of time and if the lines of shear are material lines, i.e. if the velocity of any one shearing plane relative to any other is always parallel to the same material line in one of the planes. These properties lend themselves to straightforward generalization so as to include all types of curvilinear shear flow which have so far been of practical interest. We accordingly introduce the following definitions.

(9.2) A state of flow will be called a *shear flow* if:

(i) there is a one-parameter family of material surfaces (called shearing surfaces) each of which moves rigidly in the sense that the separation of every pair of neighbouring particles in the surface is constant;

(ii) the volume of every material region is constant.

A shear flow will be called *uni-directional* if

(iii) there is a second one-parameter family of material surfaces orthogonal to the shearing surfaces. The lines of intersection of the two families will be called *lines of shear*; they are evidently material lines. It follows from (i) and (ii) that

(iv) the separation of any two neighbouring shearing surfaces is constant (Chapter 12, equation 12.110).

Conversely, (i) and (iv) imply (ii).

The definition (iii) is a convenient method of expressing the "constant direction" property of steady shear flow (i.e. the property that the lines of shear are fixed in the material) in a way which introduces no reference to directions fixed in space.

By a "one-parameter family of surfaces" we mean a family of surfaces described by a single equation of the form $f(x_1, x_2, x_3) = c$, where x_1, x_2, x_3 are coordinates of any point on the surface whose parameter value is c. For example, we may have a family of concentric cylinders in which case the value of the radius of a given cylinder could be taken as the parameter defining the member of the family. These are, in fact, the shearing surfaces in what is known as "Couette flow" between concentric rigid cylinders in relative rotation; in this case, the orthogonal family (iii) consists of planes at right angles to the cylinder axis, and the lines of shear are circles in these planes.

It is also necessary to extend the definition of shear rate so as to apply to shear flow which is not rectilinear. In Chapter 12, this is done by defining the shear rate G (a scalar) as a principal value (in curvilinear shear flow) of the rate-of-strain quantities $d\gamma^{ij}/dt$, whose definition is extended there to non-uniform flow. This definition of G reduces to that already given (2.69), when the shear flow is uniform. In the present chapter, we shall have to define shear rate in each case we consider, guided by the usual description of shear rate as velocity gradient.

(9.3) A state of shear flow will be called *steady* if it is uni-directional and the shear rate is independent of time.

At any particle in a material in uni-directional shear flow, we can define a "local" rectangular cartesian coordinate system with origin O at the particle, with axis Oy_1 tangential to the line of shear at O, with axis Oy_2 normal to the shearing surface through O, and with axis Oy_3 at right angles to and forming a right-handed system with Oy_1 and Oy_2. The axis Oy_1 can be chosen in either direction along the tangent to the line of shear, and there is no reason to favour either choice. Having

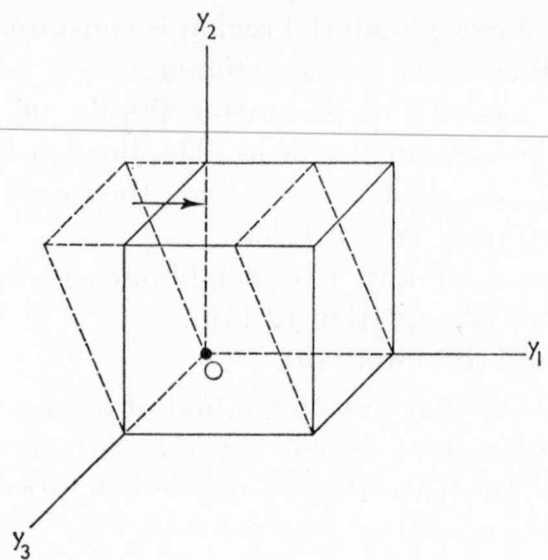

FIG. 9.1. Local rectangular cartesian coordinate system $Oy_1y_2y_3$ for shear flow.

arbitrarily made this choice, there is a difference between the two possible directions for Oy_2 (normal to the shearing surface at O); it is usual, though not essential, to choose Oy_2 so that (in steady shear flow) shearing surfaces on the positive y_2 side of O move (relative to O) in the direction of the positive y_1-axis. Oy_3 is then determined by the condition that $Oy_1y_2y_3$ is a right-handed system. This choice of axes is shown in Fig. 9.1. The local coordinate system $Oy_1y_2y_3$ is a moving and rotating system to an observer fixed in space.

In curvilinear shear flow, the stress will be non-uniform. In any sufficiently small material element, however, the state of stress can be described by cartesian stress components p_{ij} relative to the local coordinate system $Oy_1y_2y_3$, whose axes have been chosen in relation to the shearing surfaces and lines of shear so that the components p_{ij} so defined agree with those used in the discussion of rectilinear shear flow in earlier chapters.

The methods to be described make use of some or all of the following assumptions:

$$p_{23} = p_{32} = p_{13} = p_{31} = 0; \tag{9.4}$$

$$p_{11}-p_{22}, \quad p_{22}-p_{33}, \quad \text{and} \quad p_{21}(= p_{12}) \tag{9.5}$$

depend only on the local value of shear rate G.

For the type of materials considered in this book, these assumptions are valid when the shear flow is *rectilinear* and steady; for (9.4) follows from (3.27), and (9.5) follows from the basic assumption that the stress (or extra stress) is determined by the local shape history, which in turn is determined by the value of G. If the material is incompressible, the shape history will not suffice to determine the stress completely; but the arbitrariness, being an additive isotropic stress, cannot affect the values of the quantities (9.5). The assumptions are in fact also valid when the shear flow is *curvilinear* and steady, for it is shown in Chapter 12 that the shape history of any given material element in uni-directional shear flow is determined by the shear rate and is the same whether the shear flow is curvilinear or rectilinear, provided that the term "shape history" is taken to exclude *spatial* derivatives of strain. (The present methods would not apply as they stand to materials for which the extra stress is influenced by spatial derivatives of strain.)

It will be seen that (9.5) implies, in particular, that the values of $p_{11}-p_{22}$ and $p_{22}-p_{33}$ at any given particle in a shear flow are independent of the curvature of the shearing surfaces and lines of shear. It will be found, however, that the value of individual normal stress components, and in fact the value of an additive isotropic contribution to the stress, does depend on these curvatures. It is in fact the measurement of the spatial variation of such an isotropic contribution to the stress, this variation being determined by the values of $p_{11}-p_{22}$, $p_{22}-p_{33}$, and the curvatures, that is the basis of some of the following methods. The clearest illustration of this point is furnished by the cone-and-plate system: the curvature of the lines of shear and the value of pressure ($-p_{22}$) on the plate both vary with distance from the cone apex, but the shear rate and normal stress differences do not.

An elementary treatment, from first principles, of a method of determining a normal stress difference from measurements of pressure on the walls of an apparatus which subjects a liquid to a curvilinear shear flow can best be given by considering first the concentric cylinder system. We shall present the argument for this system in some detail as an aid to the understanding of the corresponding arguments for the other systems treated later in somewhat less detail.

The Concentric Cylinder System: Couette Flow

Let us consider the case in which the liquid under investigation fills the gap between two right circular rigid cylinders with a common vertical axis; the inner cylinder is fixed, and the outer cylinder rotates with a constant angular velocity Ω_0 about the common axis CC′ (Fig. 9.2).

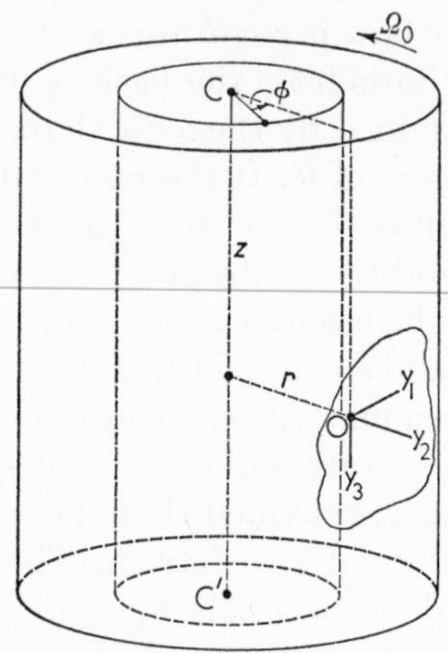

Fig. 9.2. Cylindrical polar coordinate system r, z, ϕ (origin C) and local cartesian coordinate system $Oy_1y_2y_3$ for Couette flow between cylinders in relative rotation.

Relative to a cylindrical polar coordinate system, fixed in space, with its axis along the cylinder axis, let a typical particle O of the liquid have coordinates r, z, ϕ.

Let us suppose that a state of flow, known as *Couette flow*, can be set up such that each infinitesimally thin liquid cylinder coaxial with the rigid cylinders rotates rigidly about the common axis with an angular velocity $\Omega = \Omega(r)$ which increases steadily with r from the value zero at the inner cylinder to the value Ω_0 at the outer cylinder. The angular velocity Ω of the particle O is then related to the variation of the ϕ-coordinate of O by the equation

$$\Omega = \frac{d\phi}{dt}. \tag{9.6}$$

Couette flow is evidently a uni-directional shear flow in the sense of the definition (9.2); for the cylinders r = constant form a one-parameter family of rigidly-moving material surfaces, which are therefore shearing surfaces (9.2)(i); the separation of any two shearing surfaces is constant (iv), and therefore the flow is at constant volume (ii), and is a shear flow. The horizontal material planes $z = $ constant are always orthogonal to the shearing surfaces $r = $ constant (iii); the shear flow is therefore unidirectional, and the lines of shear, being the intersection of the vertical cylinders and horizontal planes, are circles. It now follows that the loca cartesian coordinate system $Oy_1y_2y_3$, whose axes are related to the characteristic directions of the shear flow at the particle O as shown in Fig. 9.1, are oriented relative to the cylinders as shown in Fig. 9.2, the axes being in the following directions:

$$\begin{cases} Oy_1 : \phi\text{-increasing}, \\ Oy_2 : r\text{-increasing}, \\ Oy_3 : z\text{-increasing}. \end{cases} \tag{9.7}$$

The speed of a particle at a distance r from the cylinder axis is $r\Omega$, and the relative speed of two particles on the same radius vector at distances r, $r+\delta r$ from the axis is $\delta(r\Omega) = r\,\delta\Omega + \Omega\,\delta r$; we cannot in this case take the shear rate as being equal to the gradient of speed, $d(r\Omega)/dr$, because this is non-zero even when the liquid mass rotates as a rigid whole and Ω is constant. It is reasonable, therefore, to subtract the term $\Omega\,\delta r$ which represents the difference of speed in a rigid rotation and hence to define the shear rate G as the gradient formed with the resulting difference, namely

$$G = r\frac{d\Omega}{dr}, \qquad \Omega = \Omega(r). \tag{9.8}$$

This in fact agrees with the definition of shear rate as a principal value of the rate-of-strain quantities $d\gamma^{ij}/dt$ (Chapter 12, equation (12.138)). It follows from (9.8) that G, and therefore (by (9.5)) p_{21}, are independent of ϕ. From the symmetry of the system as a whole with respect to rotations about the cylinder axis, it is reasonable to assume that all stress components are independent of ϕ; we shall, in particular, need to assume that

$$\frac{\partial p_{11}}{\partial \phi} = 0. \tag{9.9}$$

We now consider the forces acting at time t on an infinitesimally small volume element bounded by cylinders of radii r, $r+\delta r$; by horizontal planes of coordinates z, $z+\delta z$; and by vertical planes, passing through the cylinder axis, of coordinates ϕ, $\phi+\delta\phi$. The non-zero tractions acting on the faces of this element are shown in Fig. 9.3, to an order of approximation sufficient for the arguments developed below; (9.4) and (9.9) have been used.

There will also be an inertial body force, acting radially outwards, due to the radial acceleration, of magnitude $\rho r^2 \Omega \delta v$, where ρ is the density and $\delta v = r\,\delta\phi\,\delta r\,\delta z$ is the volume of the element. We shall neglect forces due to inertia. It is, in practice, necessary to work at speeds which are small enough for inertial forces to be either negligible or so small that their effects can be allowed for by a fairly simple type of approximate

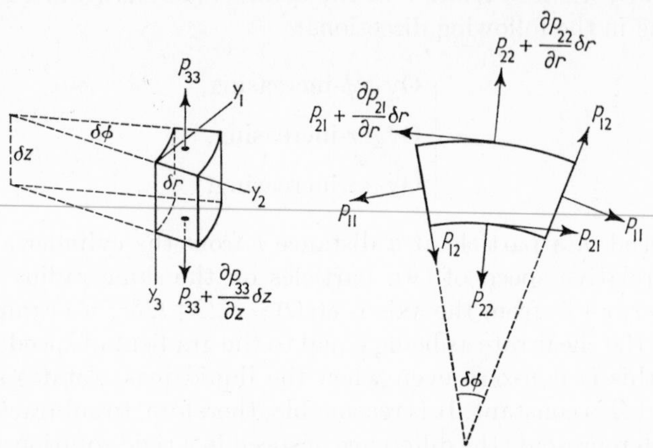

FIG. 9.3. Vertical and horizontal components of tractions acting on a volume element in Couette flow.

theory (cf. Greensmith and Rivlin, 1953; Roberts, 1952); for otherwise the inertial forces are likely to introduce disturbances to the required state of shear flow in this and in other rotational systems. The effects of inertial forces in a rotational system can usually be directly assessed by control measurements made with Newtonian liquids (having equal normal stress components in shear flow).

We first resolve the forces acting on the volume element in the direction normal to the shearing surfaces. Allowing for the difference in area of the faces in the shearing surfaces, and the fact that p_{21} is independent of ϕ (so the contributions from p_{21} cancel), we obtain the equation

$$\left(p_{22}+\frac{\partial p_{22}}{\partial r}\,\delta r\right)(r+\delta r)\,\delta\phi\,\delta z - p_{22}\,r\,\delta\phi\,\delta z \;=\; p_{11}\,\delta r\,\delta z\sin\delta\phi$$

which, in the limit $\delta r,\ \delta\phi \to 0$, leads to the equation

$$\left(r\frac{\partial p_{22}}{\partial r}\right)_{\mathrm{cc}} = p_{11}-p_{22}, \tag{9.10}$$

where the label cc is introduced to remind us that the pressure gradient refers here to the concentric cylinder system.

Equation (9.10), and analogous equations derived below for other systems, are the fundamental equations of the methods for determining differences of normal stress components. We may note the valid analogy between (9.10) and the equation $R = T/r$ for the normal reaction per unit length, R, exerted by a thin string in tension T wound round a cylinder of radius r. We shall see that with other systems there are similar equations relating the gradients of pressure normal to shearing surfaces with the relevant radii of curvature and the differences of normal stress components.

In practice, one can measure the pressures $(-p_{22})$ on the two cylinder walls and thus obtain values for

$$\Delta p_{22} \equiv p_{22}(r_0) - p_{22}(r_1), \tag{9.11}$$

where r_0 and r_1 are the radii of the outer and inner cylinders. As a first approximation, which one can expect to be valid when the ratio $\Delta r/r_0$ is small, we can take

$$\frac{\partial p_{22}}{\partial r} \doteqdot \frac{\Delta p_{22}}{\Delta r}, \qquad \Delta r \equiv r_0 - r_1, \tag{9.12}$$

and hence obtain values for $p_{11} - p_{22}$, by (9.10). An improvement on this approximation has been made by Markovitz (1957) for the case in which Δr is comparable to r_0.

To the same order of approximation as that involved in (9.12), it would be reasonable to evaluate the shear rate by means of the equation

$$G \doteqdot r_0 \frac{\Delta \Omega}{\Delta r} = \frac{r_0 \Omega_0}{r_0 - r_1}. \tag{9.13}$$

Equation (9.10) was obtained by resolving in the radial direction the forces acting on a volume element. It is necessary also to consider the equations obtained by resolving the forces in the other two directions, Oy_3 and Oy_1, in order to see whether they are compatible, i.e. to see whether the assumed state of flow is a possible one. The last requirement also means that we must consider the boundary conditions, especially at the upper and lower liquid boundaries.

By resolving the forces in the Oy_3 direction and using the fact that $p_{13} = p_{23} = 0$ (9.4), it is found that

$$\frac{\partial p_{33}}{\partial z} = \rho g, \tag{9.14}$$

where ρ is the density of the liquid and g is the acceleration due to gravity.

By resolving the forces in the Oy_1 direction, using (9.9) and the fact that $p_{31} = 0$ (9.4), it is found that

$$\{p_{11}\cos\delta\phi - p_{11} + p_{12}\sin\delta\phi\}\,\delta r\,\delta z + \left(p_{21} + \frac{\partial p_{21}}{\partial r}\delta r\right)(r+\delta r)\,\delta\phi\,\delta z$$
$$= p_{21}\,r\,\delta\phi\,\delta z,$$

which is equivalent to the equation

$$r\frac{\partial p_{21}}{\partial r} + 2p_{21} = 0, \tag{9.15}$$

when terms of order higher than $\delta\phi\,\delta r\,\delta z$ are neglected. Equations which would be obtained by taking moments of the forces acting on the volume element are satisfied by virtue of the symmetry conditions (3.3) and the fact that there are no external couples proportional to the volume.

Equations (9.14) and (9.15) are satisfied by solutions of the form

$$\begin{aligned} p_{33} &= \rho g z + \alpha(r), \\ r^2 p_{21} &= \beta(z), \end{aligned} \tag{9.16}$$

where α and β are functions of the arguments indicated; a possible dependence of these functions on the variable ϕ is omitted in view of the symmetry of the whole system with respect to arbitrary rotations about the cylinder axis.

Since p_{21} is a function of G alone, and G is independent of z ((9.5), (9.8)), it follows that β must be independent of z. It can be seen that β is proportional to the torque M exerted on unit height of either cylinder, and that we have the equation

$$r^2 p_{21} = r^2\eta G = \frac{M}{2\pi}. \tag{9.17}$$

This equation can be used in determining the viscosity η.

To investigate the boundary conditions at the upper and lower liquid surfaces in the gap, we note that the traction acting across any plane liquid surface $z = \text{constant}$ must have zero tangential component, by (9.4), and a normal component p_{33} whose dependence on r is represented by the as yet unknown function α in (9.16). This function is in fact determined by the assumed flow conditions and the properties of the liquid, for by differentiating the identity

$$p_{33} = p_{22} - (p_{22} - p_{33})$$

we can obtain the equation

$$\left(r\frac{dp_{33}}{dr}\right)_{cc} = p_{11} - p_{22} + \nu G\frac{d}{dG}(p_{22} - p_{33}), \tag{9.18}$$

where

$$\nu \equiv 2\frac{d\log G}{d\log p_{21}}. \tag{9.19}$$

On the right-hand side of (9.18), the first term comes from (9.10); the second term is obtained by using (9.15), which may be written in the form

$$r\frac{dG}{dr}\frac{dp_{21}}{dG}+2p_{21} = 0$$

or

$$\frac{r}{G}\frac{dG}{dr} = -\frac{2p_{21}}{G}\frac{dG}{dp_{21}} = -\nu. \tag{9.20}$$

For a given liquid (in steady shear flow), the tangential stress component p_{21} by (9.5) is a definite function of shear rate G, and we may suppose that this function has been determined; it follows that ν, defined by (9.19), is also a known function of G, and hence G is determined, to within a constant of integration, as a function of r by (9.20).

The right-hand side of (9.18) is therefore a definite function of r, since $p_{11}-p_{22}$ and $p_{22}-p_{33}$ are functions of G, and therefore the dependence of p_{33} on r is determined to within a constant of integration by (9.18); this determines the function α in (9.16). If, in particular, we consider the case (6.22), in which

$$p_{11}-p_{22} > 0, \quad p_{22}-p_{33} = 0,$$

then it follows from (9.18) that

$$\frac{d}{dr}(-p_{33}) < 0,$$

which means that the pressure on a horizontal liquid surface is greater near the inner cylinder.

If the upper liquid surface is left free, the pressure will be uniform over this surface as long as it remains horizontal, and the above condition will not be satisfied. It is therefore to be expected that the liquid will tend to climb up the inner cylinder in order to produce, on lower horizontal liquid planes, a pressure distribution which approximates to that required in shear flow; any such climbing would be expected in practice to interfere with the state of shear flow required in the gap, but nevertheless the occurrence of a climbing effect can, according to (9.18), be taken as evidence that one or both of the normal stress differences in shear flow are different from zero. Many liquids, such as polymer solutions and solutions of aluminium soaps in hydrocarbon liquids, in fact tend to climb up a rotating rod; the implications of such effects (which must have often been observed) in relation to the state of stress in shear flow of *liquids* were first pointed out by Weissenberg (cf. Russell, 1946, p. 58; Weissenberg, 1946, 1947), who also developed other methods for determining normal stress differences to be described below. A brief reference to rod-climbing effects has also been made by Garner and Nissan (1946).

It may also be remarked that at the lower liquid surface, which will in practice be in contact with a rigid wall, it is to be expected that some disturbance to the state of shear flow required in the gap will occur owing to the impossibility of satisfying the condition that the tangential stress components p_{31}, p_{32} should be zero.

It is possible, however, that by making measurements of pressure on the cylinder walls at points sufficiently far from the top and bottom of the gap, the state of flow will approximate sufficiently well to shear flow and hence the values of one difference, $p_{11}-p_{22}$, of normal stress components can be obtained.

In order to obtain values for the other difference, $p_{22}-p_{33}$, it is natural to seek methods which involve shear flow having curvatures of the shearing surfaces and lines of shear which differ from those leading to the basic equation (9.10) for the concentric cylinder system.

The Parallel Plate System: Torsional Flow

In this system, we suppose that the liquid fills the gap between two horizontal circular plates in relative rotation; let us suppose that the upper plate rotates with angular velocity Ω_0 about a vertical axis through its centre, the rotation in this case being anti-clockwise when viewed from above. We take a cylindrical polar coordinate system r, ϕ, z with origin C at the centre of the lower disc and axis CC′ vertically upwards (Fig. 9.4).

We consider a state of *torsional flow* in which each liquid plane $z = \text{constant}$ rotates rigidly about CC′ with an angular velocity Ω which depends on z and increases steadily from the value zero at the lower plate to the value Ω_0 at the upper plate. It is clear that this is a state of unidirectional shear flow in which the shearing surfaces are horizontal planes $z = \text{constant}$ and the orthogonal family are cylinders $r = \text{constant}$ (the roles of these two families are thus the reverse of their roles in the concentric cylinder system); the lines of shear are again horizontal circles. For the rate of shear, we may in this case take the velocity gradient, namely

$$G = r\frac{d\Omega}{dz}, \qquad (\Omega = \Omega(z)) \tag{9.21}$$

since this is zero when the system rotates as a rigid whole; this agrees with the expression obtained from the definition of G as a principal value of the rate-of-strain quantities (12.139).

At a typical particle in the liquid, it is seen that the local rectangular cartesian coordinate system $Oy_1y_2y_3$ now has axes in the following directions:

$$\begin{cases} Oy_1: \phi\text{-increasing}, \\ Oy_2: z\text{-increasing}, \\ Oy_3: r\text{-increasing}. \end{cases} \tag{9.22}$$

By analogy with (9.10), we would expect to have an equation

$$\left(r\frac{\partial p_{33}}{\partial r}\right)_{\text{pp}} = p_{11} - p_{33}, \tag{9.23}$$

for the pressure gradient in the parallel plate (pp) system, since, in going from (9.7) to (9.22), Oy_2 and Oy_3 are interchanged. It can in fact be

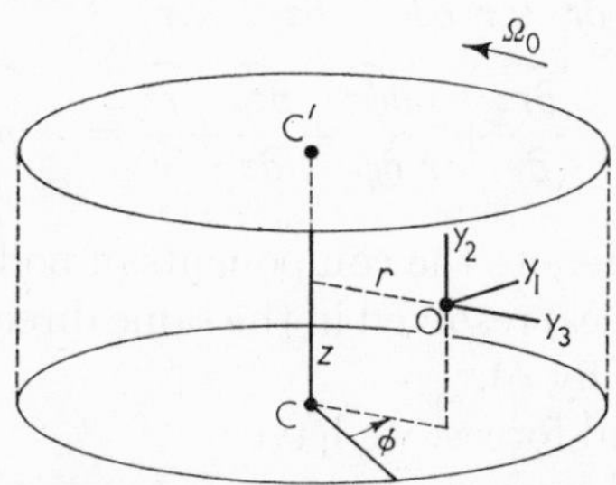

FIG. 9.4. Cylindrical polar coordinate system r, z, ϕ (origin C) and local cartesian coordinate system $Oy_1y_2y_3$ for torsional flow between parallel plates in relative rotation.

readily verified that (9.23) is correct by resolving in the radial direction the forces acting on a suitably chosen volume element and using the results $p_{13} = p_{23} = 0$ (9.4); but having used this elementary form of argument in the concentric cylinder case in order to make clear how the equations arise, it is now preferable to make use of certain known general equations of this type which are satisfied by the local cartesian stress components and their derivatives with respect to the coordinates in any given orthogonal coordinate system.

In the present case, we take the orthogonal coordinate system to be the cylindrical polar system r, ϕ, z. The usual notation for local cartesian stress components at a typical point r, ϕ, z is to write $\widehat{rr}$, $\widehat{r\phi}$, $\widehat{rz}$ for the components of traction across a plane which touches the coordinate surface r = constant at the point r, ϕ, z; the first symbol (r) denotes the surface across which the traction acts, and the second symbol denotes the direction (r-, ϕ-, z-increasing) in which the traction is resolved. Thus in our case we have, by (9.22), the following relations between the two notations:

$$\begin{pmatrix} p_{11} & p_{12} & p_{13} \\ p_{21} & p_{22} & p_{23} \\ p_{31} & p_{32} & p_{33} \end{pmatrix} = \begin{pmatrix} \widehat{\phi\phi} & \widehat{\phi z} & \widehat{\phi r} \\ \widehat{z\phi} & \widehat{zz} & \widehat{zr} \\ \widehat{r\phi} & \widehat{rz} & \widehat{rr} \end{pmatrix} \quad \text{(parallel plates).} \tag{9.24}$$

The equations obtained by resolving the forces acting on a volume element along directions r-, ϕ-, and z-increasing—the so-called "stress equations of motion"—are as follows:

$$\left\{\begin{aligned} \frac{\partial \widehat{rr}}{\partial r} + \frac{1}{r}\frac{\partial \widehat{r\phi}}{\partial \phi} + \frac{\partial \widehat{rz}}{\partial z} + \frac{\widehat{rr} - \widehat{\phi\phi}}{r} &= -\rho F_r, \\ \frac{\partial \widehat{r\phi}}{\partial r} + \frac{1}{r}\frac{\partial \widehat{\phi\phi}}{\partial \phi} + \frac{\partial \widehat{\phi z}}{\partial z} + 2\frac{\widehat{r\phi}}{r} &= -\rho F_\phi, \\ \frac{\partial \widehat{rz}}{\partial r} + \frac{1}{r}\frac{\partial \widehat{\phi z}}{\partial \phi} + \frac{\partial \widehat{zz}}{\partial z} + \frac{\widehat{rz}}{r} &= -\rho F_z, \end{aligned}\right. \tag{9.25}$$

where F_r, F_ϕ, and F_z denote the components of body force per unit mass (including inertial forces) resolved in the same directions (cf. Love, 1944, p. 90, with θ replaced by ϕ).

If we neglect inertial forces, we have

$$F_r = F_\phi = 0, \quad F_z = -g,$$

and, using (9.4) and (9.24), the stress equations of motion (9.25) reduce to (9.23) and

$$\frac{\partial p_{21}}{\partial z} = 0, \tag{9.26}$$

$$\frac{\partial p_{22}}{\partial z} = \rho g, \tag{9.27}$$

provided that we take

$$\frac{\partial p_{11}}{\partial \phi} = \frac{\partial p_{21}}{\partial \phi} = 0 \tag{9.28}$$

which is reasonable on account of the symmetry of the state of flow with respect to arbitrary rotations about CC′.

Since p_{21} is a function of G alone (9.5), it follows from (9.26) that

$$\frac{dG}{dz} = 0, \tag{9.29}$$

and hence, from (9.21), that

$$\frac{d^2\Omega}{dz^2} = 0, \qquad \Omega = \Omega_0 z, \tag{9.30}$$

since $\Omega = 0$ when $z = 0$.

Thus, in the parallel plate system, the angular velocity of the shearing surfaces has to vary linearly with z, whatever the relation between tangential stress p_{21} and shear rate may be; this contrasts with the concentric cylinder system, in which the angular velocity of the shearing surfaces varies with r in a manner which depends on the relation between p_{21} and G.

The shear rate at any point in the liquid is, from (9.30), given in terms of the angular velocity of the upper plate, Ω_0, and the distance, z_0, between the plates by the exact equation

$$G = \frac{\Omega_0}{z_0} r. \tag{9.31}$$

From this equation, it follows that stress components which depend on G may be regarded as depending on r, and that

$$\frac{\partial}{\partial G} = \frac{z_0}{\Omega_0}\frac{\partial}{\partial r}, \qquad G\frac{\partial}{\partial G} = r\frac{\partial}{\partial r}. \tag{9.32}$$

Equation (9.27) is satisfied by a solution of the form

$$p_{22} = \rho g z + f(r) \tag{9.33}$$

where f denotes any function of r; the possible dependence on ϕ may be ignored owing to the symmetry of the state of flow. The function f, and the dependence of p_{22} on r, are determined by the properties of the liquid; for on differentiating the identity

$$p_{22} = p_{33} + (p_{22} - p_{33})$$

and using (9.23) and (9.32), we obtain the equation

$$\left(r\frac{\partial p_{22}}{\partial r}\right)_{\text{pp}} = p_{11} - p_{33} + G\frac{d}{dG}(p_{22} - p_{33}). \tag{9.34}$$

Here, the right-hand side, for a given liquid, is a definite function of G, or of r, and hence the variation of p_{22} with r is determined to within a constant of integration. The suffix pp denotes "parallel plate".

The stress equations of motion (9.23), (9.26), and (9.27) are in fact compatible, and the assumed state of shear flow is therefore a possible state of flow when inertial forces are negligible, provided that the boundary conditions can be satisfied.

At the surfaces of the plates, the boundary conditions simply require that p_{22} and p_{21} vary with r in ways which depend on the properties of the liquid; any such conditions will be automatically satisfied by the thrust and torque exerted by the plates. At the free liquid boundary, however, the condition that there should be zero tangential component of traction is satisfied if, and only if, the free boundary has the form of a cylinder $r =$ constant, for in this case the tangential components of traction are equal to p_{31} and p_{32}, which are both zero, by (9.4). While in practice it is usually possible, with sufficiently viscous liquids and sufficiently narrow gaps, to keep the liquid in the gap with a free liquid boundary at the rim of the plates, it is not, of course, possible to keep this boundary in a cylindrical form, owing to the effects of gravity, surface tension, and angle of contact. It follows, therefore, that in such a situation, the required boundary conditions will not be accurately realized at the free boundary; this will presumably mean that there will be some disturbance to the state of shear flow near the free boundary, but it is not yet known how important the effects of such a disturbance might be.

The basic equation for the parallel plate system is (9.34), which relates the distribution of pressure $(-p_{22})$ on either plate (the right-hand side is independent of z because G is independent of z, by (9.29)) to both differences of normal stress components. It is seen that, for the particular case

$$p_{11}-p_{22} > 0, \quad p_{22}-p_{33} = 0, \qquad \text{cf. (6.22)}$$

the pressure increases towards the axis of rotation. Such an effect, first demonstrated by Garner, Nissan and Wood (1950) using capillary tubes erected on one plate, has been investigated in a variety of polymer solutions (Greensmith and Rivlin, 1953; Kotaka *et al.*, 1959).

It will be seen, however, from (9.34), that the information obtainable from the pressure gradient $r\,\partial p_{22}/\partial r$ in the parallel plate system by itself relates to a rather complicated function of the normal stress differences involving the derivative of one of them with respect to shear rate. It is natural, therefore, to attempt to use this information in conjunction with that obtained from some other system, either the concentric cylinder system (9.10) or the cone-and-plate system, which yields a different combination of normal stress differences.

The Cone-and-plate System

We consider a right circular wide-angled cone (i.e. whose semi-vertical angle is slightly less than 90°) rotating about its axis, which is vertical, with its apex C in contact with the centre of a fixed horizontal circular plate. Let the angular velocity of the cone be Ω_0, the rotation being anti-clockwise when viewed from above.

We introduce a system of spherical polar coordinates r, θ, ϕ in which the origin is C and the axis $\theta = 0$ is vertically downwards, coinciding with the axis of rotation. The surface of the plate is thus given by

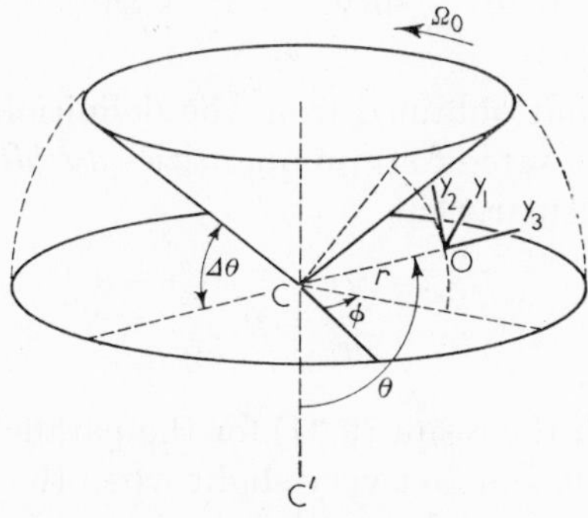

FIG. 9.5. Spherical polar coordinate system r, θ, ϕ (origin C) and local cartesian coordinate system $Oy_1y_2y_3$ for shear flow between a cone and plate in relative rotation.

$\theta = \frac{1}{2}\pi$, and the surface of the cone by $\theta = \frac{1}{2}\pi + \Delta\theta$, where $\Delta\theta$ is the gap angle (Fig. 9.5).

We consider a state of flow for a liquid filling the gap between cone and plate which is such that each liquid cone $\theta =$ constant rotates rigidly about the cone axis $\theta = 0$ with an angular velocity $\Omega = \Omega(\theta)$ which depends only on θ and varies from the value zero at the plate to the value Ω_0 at the rigid cone $\theta = \frac{1}{2}\pi + \Delta\theta$. This state of flow is evidently a uni-directional shear flow in which the shearing surfaces are the cones $\theta =$ constant and the orthogonal family of material surfaces are the spheres (or parts of spheres) $r =$ constant. The intersections of these surfaces, the lines of shear, are circles ($r =$ constant, $\theta =$ constant) in horizontal planes.

To obtain an expression for the shear rate, we consider two particles, $O = (r, \theta, \phi)$ and $O' = (r, \theta + \delta\theta, \phi)$, on neighbouring shearing surfaces.

Each has a velocity in the direction Oy_1; the magnitude of the velocity of O is $r\Omega \sin\theta$, and therefore the velocity of O′ relative to O is of magnitude

$$\delta\theta \frac{\partial}{\partial\theta}(r\Omega \sin\theta) = r\,\delta\theta\left\{\frac{d\Omega}{d\theta}\sin\theta + \Omega\cos\theta\right\}.$$

The particles O, O′, however, are at different distances from the axis of rotation, and therefore have a non-zero relative velocity, represented by the second of the above terms on the right-hand side, when the liquid mass rotates as a rigid whole. In defining the shear rate, therefore, it is reasonable to subtract this term, and then to divide by the separation $OO' = r\,\delta\theta$; we thus obtain the expression

$$G = \frac{d\Omega}{d\theta}\sin\theta, \qquad \Omega = \Omega(\theta), \tag{9.35}$$

which agrees with that obtained from the definition of shear rate as a principal value of the rate-of-strain quantities $d\gamma^{ij}/dt$ (12.149).

It follows, in particular, that

$$\frac{\partial G}{\partial r} = 0, \tag{9.36}$$

which contrasts with the result (9.31) for the parallel plate system. The dependence of G on θ is in fact very slight when the gap angle does not exceed a few degrees, and hence the shear rate is virtually constant throughout the gap in the cone-and-plate system.

The local rectangular cartesian coordinate system $Oy_1y_2y_3$ with origin at the particle $O = (r, \theta, \phi)$ evidently has its axes in the following directions:

$$\begin{cases} Oy_1 : \phi\text{-increasing}, \\ Oy_2 : \theta\text{-increasing}, \\ Oy_3 : r\text{-increasing}. \end{cases} \tag{9.37}$$

The cartesian stress components in the notations p_{ij} and $\widehat{rr}$, $\widehat{r\theta}$, $\widehat{\phi\theta}$, etc. (appropriate to the (orthogonal) spherical polar coordinate system r, θ, ϕ) are therefore related as follows:

$$\begin{pmatrix} p_{11} & p_{12} & p_{13} \\ p_{21} & p_{22} & p_{23} \\ p_{31} & p_{32} & p_{33} \end{pmatrix} = \begin{pmatrix} \widehat{\phi\phi} & \widehat{\phi\theta} & \widehat{\phi r} \\ \widehat{\theta\phi} & \widehat{\theta\theta} & \widehat{\theta r} \\ \widehat{r\phi} & \widehat{r\theta} & \widehat{rr} \end{pmatrix}. \tag{9.38}$$

Hence (9.4) imply that

$$\widehat{r\phi} = \widehat{r\theta} = \widehat{\phi r} = \widehat{\theta r} = 0. \tag{9.39}$$

The stress equations of motion in a spherical polar coordinate system (obtainable by resolving, in the directions r-, θ-, and ϕ-increasing, the forces acting on a suitably-shaped volume element) have the following form (Love, 1944, p. 91):

$$\left\{\begin{aligned} &\frac{\partial \widehat{rr}}{\partial r}+\frac{1}{r}\frac{\partial \widehat{r\theta}}{\partial \theta}+\frac{1}{r\sin\theta}\frac{\partial \widehat{r\phi}}{\partial \phi}+\frac{1}{r}(2\widehat{rr}-\widehat{\theta\theta}-\widehat{\phi\phi}+\widehat{r\phi}\cot\theta) = -\rho F_r, \\ &\frac{\partial \widehat{r\theta}}{\partial r}+\frac{1}{r}\frac{\partial \widehat{\theta\theta}}{\partial \theta}+\frac{1}{r\sin\theta}\frac{\partial \widehat{\theta\phi}}{\partial \phi}+\frac{1}{r}[(\widehat{\theta\theta}-\widehat{\phi\phi})\cot\theta+3\widehat{r\theta}] = -\rho F_\theta, \\ &\frac{\partial \widehat{r\phi}}{\partial r}+\frac{1}{r}\frac{\partial \widehat{\phi\theta}}{\partial \theta}+\frac{1}{r\sin\theta}\frac{\partial \widehat{\phi\phi}}{\partial \phi}+\frac{1}{r}[3\widehat{r\phi}+2\widehat{\theta\phi}\cot\theta] = -\rho F_\phi, \end{aligned}\right. \tag{9.40}$$

where F_r, F_θ, F_ϕ denote the components per unit mass of the body forces (including inertia) in the directions r-, θ-, and ϕ-increasing.

Neglecting inertial forces, the only body force is that due to gravity, and this has components

$$F_r = g\cos\theta, \quad F_\theta = -g\sin\theta, \quad F_\phi = 0. \tag{9.41}$$

Using (9.39), (9.41), and the first two of the equations

$$\frac{\partial \widehat{\phi\theta}}{\partial \phi} = \frac{\partial \widehat{\phi\phi}}{\partial \phi} = \frac{\partial \widehat{\theta\theta}}{\partial \phi} = 0, \tag{9.42}$$

which we may accept because of the symmetry of the state of flow with respect to arbitrary rotations about the cone axis, the stress equations of motion (9.40) reduce to the following equations:

$$\frac{\partial p_{33}}{\partial r}+\frac{1}{r}(2p_{33}-p_{22}-p_{11}) = -\rho g\cos\theta, \tag{9.43}$$

$$\frac{1}{r}\frac{\partial p_{22}}{\partial \theta}+\frac{1}{r}(p_{22}-p_{11})\cot\theta = \rho g\sin\theta, \tag{9.44}$$

$$\frac{1}{r}\frac{\partial p_{21}}{\partial \theta}+\frac{2}{r}p_{21}\cot\theta = 0. \tag{9.45}$$

The last of these equations can be written in the form

$$\sin^2\theta\frac{\partial}{\partial \theta}(p_{21}\sin^2\theta) = 0,$$

which, on integration, gives

$$p_{21}(\theta)\sin^2\theta = \text{constant},$$

since $\sin\theta \neq 0$ for points in the gap; the constant here must be independent of r and ϕ, as well as θ, because p_{21} is a function of G alone, and G is a function of θ alone. Since the total torque M exerted by the liquid on the plate $\theta = \pi/2$ is given by the equation

$$M = \int_0^R r\,p_{21}\left(\frac{\pi}{2}\right) d(\pi r^2) = \frac{\pi}{3} R^3 p_{21}\left(\frac{\pi}{2}\right),$$

where R is the radius of the plate, supposed just filled with liquid in the assumed state of flow, we may express the constant in terms of M, thus obtaining the equation

$$p_{21}(\theta)\sin^2\theta = p_{21}\left(\frac{\pi}{2}\right) = \frac{3M}{\pi R^3}. \tag{9.46}$$

Since $p_{21} = \eta G$, the viscosity η is given in terms of the torque M by the equation

$$\eta = \frac{3M}{\pi R^3 G} \tag{9.47}$$

where G denotes the value of shear rate at the plate. With the gap angles of a few degrees usually used in practice, it is sufficient to evaluate the shear rate by the equation

$$G \doteqdot \frac{\Omega_0}{\Delta\theta}, \tag{9.48}$$

which evidently represents a first approximation to (9.35); for a liquid for which η is independent of G, the error involved in this approximation can be shown to be 0·02%, 0·18%, 0·50%, and 2·0% for values 1, 3, 5, and 10 degrees for the gap angle (Adams and Lodge, 1964).

The use of a cone-and-plate system for measuring viscosity was considered by Mooney and Ewart (1934); various commercial instruments built on this principle are now available (McKennell, 1954; Jobling and Roberts, 1959; Képès, 1956; cf. also Markovitz *et al.*, 1955, and Mell, 1956). This system, which operates at virtually constant shear rate, is of particular value for use with polymer solutions for which the viscosity usually depends on shear rate; absolute values for the viscosity are usually obtainable with an accuracy of the order of 1%.

For later use, we note that, provided p_{21} is an increasing function of G (a condition which is usually satisfied), this functional relation may be inverted and we may regard G as a function of p_{21}. Then we have

$$\frac{dG}{d\theta} = \frac{dG}{dp_{21}} \frac{\partial p_{21}}{\partial \theta},$$

and therefore, by (9.19), (9.45), we have

$$\frac{1}{G}\frac{dG}{d\theta} = -\nu \cot\theta. \tag{9.49}$$

From the definition of ν in (9.19), since $p_{21} = \eta G$, we see that

$$\frac{2}{\nu} = \frac{d \log p_{21}}{d \log G} = 1 + \frac{d \log \eta}{d \log G}.$$

For many (but not all) polymer solutions, the viscosity η is a non-increasing function of shear rate G, and hence

$$\frac{d \log \eta}{d \log G} = \frac{G}{\eta}\frac{d\eta}{dG} \leqslant 0,$$

which implies that $2/\nu \leqslant 1$, i.e. that

$$\nu \geqslant 2 \quad \text{when} \quad \frac{d\eta}{dG} \leqslant 0. \tag{9.50}$$

Returning to the stress equations of motion, we have shown that (9.45) can be satisfied. The first two equations, (9.43) and (9.44), however, are in general incompatible, as the following argument shows.

From (9.43) we can obtain an expression for $\partial^2 p_{33}/\partial r\, \partial\theta$, and from (9.44) (multiplied by r) an expression for $\partial^2 p_{22}/\partial r\, \partial \theta$. These two quantities must be equal, because $p_{22} - p_{33}$ is a function of G alone (9.5) and G is independent of r, by (9.36); thus $\partial(p_{22} - p_{33})/\partial r = 0$, and hence, using the similar result $\partial(p_{11} - p_{22})/\partial r = 0$, equations (9.43) and (9.44) lead to the equation

$$\frac{\partial}{\partial \theta}(2p_{33} - p_{22} - p_{11}) = 0,$$

which, since $2p_{33} - p_{22} - p_{11} = (p_{33} - p_{22}) + (p_{33} - p_{11})$ and is therefore a function of G alone by (9.5), is equivalent to the equation

$$G\nu \cot\theta \frac{d}{dG}(2p_{33} - p_{22} - p_{11}) = 0, \tag{9.51}$$

by (9.49).

This equation is satisfied for points on the plate ($\theta = \pi/2$, $\cot\theta = 0$) but not for points in the gap unless the properties of the liquid are such that

$$\frac{d}{dG}(2p_{33}-p_{22}-p_{11}) = 0. \tag{9.52}$$

This condition is satisfied for Newtonian liquids (5.9), and for a certain visco-elastic liquid considered by Zaremba (1937), Fromm (1948), and DeWitt (1955), but is not satisfied by the rubberlike liquid considered in Chapter 6 (6.22) nor by most visco-elastic liquids described by equations of the types considered in Chapter 8. It is unlikely that (9.52) would be satisfied unless

$$2p_{33}-p_{11}-p_{22} = 0; \tag{9.53}$$

for any combination of normal stress differences, if not equal to zero, will presumably have a value which depends on the shear rate. We shall see that a liquid for which (9.53) is satisfied would give a uniform distribution of pressure on the plate of a cone-and-plate system (in which the state of flow is one of shear flow of the type assumed).

In practice, therefore, (9.51) will not be satisfied in the cases of present interest; and there will presumably as a consequence be some disturbance to the state of shear flow assumed above. This point has been made by Oldroyd (1958) and Ericksen (1960a). However, since the factor $\cot\theta$ is small for points near the plate, it is reasonable to expect that (9.51) will be approximately satisfied when the gap is small and that the associated disturbance to the state of shear flow will also be small; this expectation has been confirmed by the author by means of certain approximate calculations which involve applying to a fictitious Newtonian liquid of viscosity equal to that of the liquid under test a distribution of body force of a type which, when applied to the liquid under test, would enable the compatibility condition (9.51) to be satisfied. These results are in course of publication. It should, perhaps, be emphasized that the condition (9.51) is not connected with inertial forces (which have been neglected, and which can also give rise to disturbances in the state of shear flow) and has no analogue in the shear flows between concentric cylinders and between parallel plates.

Let us suppose, therefore, that (9.51) is satisfied to a sufficient approximation: it is reasonable to regard this approximation as being equivalent to the neglect of the quantity $\cot\theta$ or $\cos\theta$ ($\theta \doteqdot \frac{1}{2}\pi$).

To this approximation, the second stress equation of motion (9.44) becomes

$$\frac{\partial p_{22}}{\partial\theta} = +\rho g r \sin\theta$$

which, on integration, gives

$$p_{22} = -\rho g r \cos\theta + f(r), \tag{9.54}$$

where f is a function (independent of ϕ by the last of equations (9.42)) to be determined. This function plays a central role in the present method of determining normal stress differences; we note that when $\theta = \pi/2$, $-f(r) = -p_{22}$ which equals the pressure on the plate at a distance r from the cone apex.

The third stress equation of motion, (9.43), may be written in the form

$$\left(r\frac{\partial p_{33}}{\partial r}\right)_{\mathrm{cp}} = p_{11} + p_{22} - 2p_{33}, \tag{9.55}$$

for points on the plate ($\cos\theta = 0$), or when the term $r\rho g\cos\theta$ is neglected. We may note that this equation is of the form which would be expected on the basis of an argument similar to that outlined in connection with the corresponding equation (9.10) for the concentric cylinder system: for (9.55) gives the pressure gradient normal to a spherical surface ($r = \text{constant}$) which has two principal radii of curvature (each equal to r) with which will be associated the following terms:

$$\frac{p_{11} - p_{33}}{r} + \frac{p_{22} - p_{33}}{r}.$$

Now $-p_{33}$ (whose derivative appears on the left-hand side of (9.55)) is the pressure normal to a surface $r = \text{constant}$, which is part of a sphere whose centre is at the cone apex. If the free liquid boundary lies in the gap and is of this spherical shape, then the condition of equilibrium at the free boundary, neglecting effects of surface tension, requires that

$$-p_{33}(R) = p_a, \tag{9.56}$$

where p_a denotes the atmospheric pressure. Thus $p_{33}(R)$ can be determined.

Weissenberg and Roberts (cf. Roberts, 1952) use this fact to obtain values of p_{33} for different values of R by repeating the experiment with different amounts of test liquid in the gap; in some cases, the liquid removed is replaced by an immiscible Newtonian liquid to facilitate the measurement of p_{33}. At the same time, values of the pressure ($-p_{22}$) on the plate at different values of r are obtained. (The pressures were in fact measured at points on the surface of the cone, using capillary gauges, but these pressures should equal those on the plate, to a sufficient approximation, when the gap is small.) By extrapolation, the value of $p_{22}(R)$ in each case was obtained. From the data, the values of the derivative

$\partial p_{33}/\partial r$ were obtained, and hence values of the third normal stress component p_{11} could be calculated by using (9.55).

Thus this method in principle is capable of giving all three normal components of stress in steady shear flow; from these, of course, the differences may be derived. Moreover, as Roberts (1952) has pointed out, the method has an advantage over other methods in that the basic equation (9.55) can be derived from the first stress equation of motion (9.40) without using the assumption (9.5): it is only necessary to use (9.4), and this can be substantiated for isotropic liquids by appeal to the symmetry of the state of flow between cone and plate with respect to a

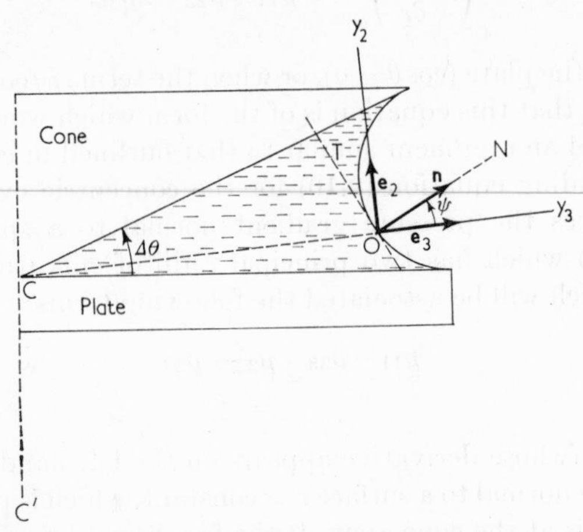

FIG. 9.6. Local cartesian coordinate system $Oy_1y_2y_3$ at a point O on a free liquid boundary in shear flow between cone and plate; axis Oy_1 (not shown) is normal to the plane of the paper. The diagram is a vertical section through the cone axis CC′. ON is normal and OT is tangential to the free liquid boundary at O.

rotation through 180° about the radius vector. This symmetry holds when the radius vector lies in the plate and can therefore be presumed to hold to a sufficient approximation for other radius vectors when the gap is narrow. Furthermore, it is not necessary to assume that the stress, or extra stress, is dependent only on the flow history and not on spatial gradients of the flow history. Thus information to test this point, and also to test (9.5), should be obtainable from this method (see below), which is therefore of fundamental importance.

In practice, however, the free boundary of the test liquid will not usually be of spherical shape, owing to the effects of gravity and angle of contact with the rigid members, and there will therefore be some disturbance to the state of shear flow near the boundary because, as the following argument shows, the conditions for equilibrium at the boundary when surface tension is neglected can be satisfied if, and only if, the boundary is of spherical shape. If surface tension cannot be neglected, then its presence will in any case influence the measurement of pressure; for moderately concentrated polymer solutions, the pressures associated with normal stress differences are often comparable with pressures associated with surface tension.

At a free liquid boundary, the traction exerted by the liquid on a surface element must be equal and opposite to the traction exerted by the atmosphere, which can have no component tangential to the surface. To see what this implies in terms of the local stress components p_{ij}, we consider an arbitrary point O on the free liquid boundary and introduce the local coordinate system $Oy_1y_2y_3$ with its axes in the usual directions relative to the shearing surface and lines of shear, supposing for the present that the assumed state of shear flow persists up to the free boundary (Fig. 9.6). Let us also introduce an orthonormal system of base vectors $\mathbf{e}_i = \mathbf{e}^i$ which lie along the axes Oy_i.

We must allow the liquid boundary to have any shape in a section by a vertical plane through the cone axis; we shall suppose that the boundary is a surface of rotation about the cone axis. Then Oy_1 is a horizontal tangent to the boundary at O; the tangent OT in the vertical plane through O is represented by the unit vector

$$\cos\psi\mathbf{e}_2 - \sin\psi\mathbf{e}_3,$$

where ψ is the angle between the surface normal ON and the axis Oy_3; and the normal ON is represented by the unit vector

$$\mathbf{n} = \sin\psi\mathbf{e}_2 + \cos\psi\mathbf{e}_3$$

so that the direction cosines of the normal are

$$l_i = \mathbf{n}\cdot\mathbf{e}_i = (0, \sin\psi, \cos\psi). \tag{9.57}$$

From (3.7) and (3.14), it follows that the traction $\mathbf{f}$ exerted by the liquid across a surface element of unit normal $\mathbf{n}$ is

$$\mathbf{f} = \sum_i \sum_j \pi^{ij} l_i \mathbf{e}_j = \sum_j (p_{2j}\sin\psi + p_{3j}\cos\psi)\,\mathbf{e}_j$$

by (9.57), and hence

$$\mathbf{f} = p_{21}\sin\psi\mathbf{e}_1 + p_{22}\sin\psi\mathbf{e}_2 + p_{33}\cos\psi\mathbf{e}_3, \tag{9.58}$$

by (9.4). Resolving this traction in turn along the normal and along the tangents Oy_1 and OT (i.e., taking the scalar products of $\mathbf{f}$ with unit vectors along these directions), we obtain the following set of boundary conditions:

$$p_{22}\sin^2\psi + p_{33}\cos^2\psi = -p_a, \tag{9.59}$$

$$p_{21}\sin\psi = 0, \tag{9.60}$$

$$(p_{22}-p_{33})\sin 2\psi = 0, \tag{9.61}$$

where p_a denotes the atmospheric pressure. In obtaining these equations, the relations $\mathbf{e}_i.\mathbf{e}_j = \delta_{ij}$ for an orthonormal basis have been used.

When the free boundary is part of a sphere whose centre is at the cone apex, the axis Oy_3 coincides with the normal ON and hence $\psi = 0$; the condition (9.59) then reduces to (9.56) and the other two conditions (9.60) and (9.61) are satisfied. When the free boundary is not sphercial, then $\psi \neq 0$, $\sin\psi \neq 0$ and $\sin 2\psi \neq 0$, if we reject the possibilities $\psi = \frac{1}{2}\pi, \pi$, which evidently cannot apply all over the boundary; then the conditions (9.60), (9.61) are not satisfied.

It follows that, when the free liquid boundary is not part of a sphere whose centre is at the cone apex, the hypothesis that the assumed state of shear flow persists up to and at all points of the free boundary is untenable.

Even for a Newtonian liquid, or indeed for any liquid for which $p_{22}-p_{33} = 0$ and (9.61) is satisfied, the condition (9.60) is not satisfied, so there must be some disturbance to the state of shear flow near the free boundary.

If the outside of the free boundary of the test liquid is filled with a Newtonian liquid, as in Roberts's experiments, then it is clear that the last two boundary conditions at the interface will be of the form

$$p_{21}\sin\psi = p'_{21}\sin\psi,$$

$$(p_{22}-p_{33})\sin 2\psi = (p'_{22}-p'_{33})\sin 2\psi = 0,$$

where p'_{ij} denote stress components in the Newtonian liquid. The first of these conditions can be satisfied if $p_{21} = p'_{21}$, i.e. if both liquids have the same viscosity, but the second condition is not satisfied except for liquids for which $p_{22}-p_{33} = 0$.

It is, therefore, desirable to seek methods of determining normal stress differences which do not depend on the state of flow near a free liquid boundary or near an interfacial boundary between two liquids.

For this purpose, we may use measurements of pressure $(-p_{22}(r))$ at various points on the plate, and use the following argument, which makes use of (9.5).

By (9.5), $p_{22}-p_{33}$ is a function of G alone and is therefore, by (9.36), independent of r; thus

$$\frac{\partial p_{22}}{\partial r} = \frac{\partial p_{33}}{\partial r} \tag{9.62}$$

and hence, from (9.55), it follows that

$$\left(r\frac{\partial p_{22}}{\partial r}\right)_{\text{cp}} = p_{11}+p_{22}-2p_{33}. \tag{9.63}$$

The pressure gradient on the left-hand side of this equation can be determined from measurements of pressure on the plate, and therefore the particular combination of normal stress differences on the right-hand side can be evaluated. The shear rate is given by (9.48).

For the rubberlike liquid (6.22), or for any liquid for which $p_{11}-p_{22} > 0$ and $p_{22}-p_{33} = 0$, it is seen from (9.63) that the pressure $(-p_{22})$ increases towards the axis of rotation, as in the case of the parallel plate system (9.34). In contrast to the case with the parallel plate system, however, *the form of the pressure distribution in the cone-and-plate system is the same for all liquids* (which satisfy (9.4) and (9.5)), because the shear rate is independent of r. To show this, we note that the right-hand side of (9.63), being a function of G alone, is independent of r, and therefore the equation can be integrated to give the result

$$p_{22}(r) = p_{22}(R)+(p_{11}+p_{22}-2p_{33})\log\frac{r}{R}; \tag{9.64}$$

the integration constant, which we have written as $p_{22}(R)$, is independent of θ by virtue of (9.54) and the fact that $\theta = \frac{1}{2}\pi$ on the plate. We have thus determined the function $f(r)$ in (9.54).

The pressure thus varies logarithmically with r. A determination of the slope of the line obtained by plotting pressure against $\log r$ would appear to furnish one of the more promising methods of obtaining values for a combination of normal stress differences.

We may note that a significant departure from the logarithmic relation (9.64) would suggest that the assumptions (9.4), (9.5) were untenable for the liquid concerned, provided, of course, that the state of shear flow were sufficiently well attained; this, in turn, might be evidence for reconsidering the possibility that the extra stress could depend explicitly on spatial gradients of flow history, for in such a case the quantity $p_{11}+p_{22}-2p_{33}$ could depend on the curvature of the shearing surfaces, for example, and hence on r. The author has verified this expectation in unpublished calculations for one particular hypothetical liquid.

We may obtain an expression for the total thrust F on the plate due to the normal stress effect by an integration using (9.64); since $-p_{22}$, the pressure exerted by the liquid, includes the contribution due to atmospheric pressure transmitted from the free liquid boundary, it is necessary to subtract a term $p_a \pi R^2$ representing the upthrust due to atmospheric pressure on the underside of the plate. We therefore obtain the equation

$$F = -\int_{r=0}^{R} p_{22}(r)\, d(\pi r^2) - p_a \pi R^2$$

$$= -[p_{22}(R)+p_a]\pi R^2 + \tfrac{1}{2}\pi R^2(p_{11}+p_{22}-2p_{33}).$$

The value of the last bracket on the right-hand side is independent of r, by (9.5) and (9.36), and its terms may therefore be evaluated at $r = R$, where R is the radius of the free liquid boundary. The equation may then be rearranged and expressed in the form

$$F = \tfrac{1}{2}\pi R^2(p_{11}-p_{22}) - \pi R^2[p_{33}(R)+p_a]. \tag{9.65}$$

If the free boundary is part of a sphere of radius R, then the boundary condition (9.56) is satisfied and the last term in this equation is zero; thus

$$p_{11}-p_{22} = \frac{2F}{\pi R^2}. \tag{9.66}$$

A measurement of the total thrust therefore leads to the evaluation of $p_{11}-p_{22}$, which is a different combination of normal stress differences than that which is obtained from measurements of pressure distribution (9.63). The derivation of (9.66) depends, however, on the assumption that the state of shear flow persists up to the free liquid boundary, and the use of the total thrust to determine $p_{11}-p_{22}$ may therefore involve error when the free boundary is not part of a sphere whose centre is at the cone apex. It is not yet known, however, whether such errors are important.

A commercially available instrument, the Weissenberg Rheogoniometer, enables thrust and torque to be measured under conditions of steady shear flow, oscillatory shear flow, and a combination of the two; pressure distributions can be measured in steady shear flow by means of capillary gauges (Jobling and Roberts, 1959). Pollett (1955) uses a cone-and-plate system in which the plate is in two parts: a central circular part surrounded by a part in the form of a circular annulus; from measurements of the thrusts on each part, values for both differences of normal stress components can be obtained, again provided that the shear flow persists up to the free boundary.

The measurement of pressure gradient in the cone-and-plate system enables one to evaluate, using (9.63), one combination of normal stress differences by a method which does not depend on the state of flow near the free boundary; for a change in the state of flow near the free boundary could affect the values of stress components in that neighbourhood, and could affect the value of $p_{22}(R)$ in (9.64), where R may be taken to denote the radius of a region within which the state of flow is one of shear flow; according to (9.64), however, the variation of $p_{22}(r)$ with r, and hence the value of $\partial p_{22}/\partial r$, for $r \leqslant R$ is independent of the value of $p_{22}(R)$ and hence of flow conditions for $r > R$.

A second combination of normal stress differences may be obtained from measurements of pressures on the walls of a concentric cylinder system (9.10), but it is natural to try to use the parallel plate system in conjunction with the cone-and-plate system, since by changing the rotating member from cone to plate the same pressure-measuring devices on the plate may be used for both systems.

Assuming that (9.5) is valid, this can be done. For, by (9.5), the differences $p_{11}-p_{22}$ and $p_{22}-p_{33}$, being independent of curvature of the various surfaces involved, can be treated as functions of G which are to be determined by solving the simultaneous equations (9.34), (9.63). In these equations, $(r\,\partial p_{22}/\partial r)_{\text{pp}}$ and $(r\,\partial p_{22}/\partial r)_{\text{cp}}$ may be regarded as given functions (determined by measurement) of the independent variable G.

On subtracting (9.63) from (9.34), we eliminate one difference, $p_{11}-p_{22}$, and obtain the following differential equation for the other:

$$\left(G\frac{d}{dG}-1\right)(p_{22}-p_{33}) = \left(r\frac{\partial p_{22}}{\partial r}\right)_{\text{pp}} - \left(r\frac{\partial p_{22}}{\partial r}\right)_{\text{cp}}. \tag{9.67}$$

The solution of this equation ($1/G^2$ is an integrating factor) may be written in the form

$$p_{22}-p_{33} = G\int\limits_{G'=0}^{G}\left[\left(r\frac{\partial p_{22}}{\partial r}\right)_{\text{pp}} - \left(r\frac{\partial p_{22}}{\partial r}\right)_{\text{cp}}\right]_{(G')}\frac{dG'}{G'^2}, \tag{9.68}$$

where the constant of integration is determined by assuming that the values of $p_{22}-p_{33}$ and the pressure gradients are unchanged when G is replaced by $-G$. For isotropic materials, it is to be expected that $p_{11}-p_{22}$ and $p_{22}-p_{33}$ will be unchanged in value when G is replaced by $-G$, for this corresponds to reversal of the direction of shear relative to the material; this would be expected to change the sign of the tangential stress component p_{21}, but not of the normal stress components. The assumption that pressure gradients are independent of the sign of G can in principle be verified simply by reversing the direction of rotation (and hence, by (9.63), the same property can be verified for $p_{11}+p_{22}-2p_{33}$); in practice, however, it is usually convenient to use the reversal of rotation direction and the average of the corresponding pressure distributions to minimize experimental errors.

Coleman and Noll (1959a) have verified that, for a wide class of rheological equations of state for isotropic materials, $p_{11}-p_{22}$ and $p_{22}-p_{33}$ are even functions of G, and p_{21} is an odd function of G.

We see, therefore, that both normal stress differences can be calculated, using (9.63) and (9.68), at a given value of shear rate G from measurements of pressure gradients on the plate in cone-and-plate and parallel plate systems for shear rates G' in the range $0 \leqslant G' \leqslant G$. This method has been used by Lodge (1960a, 1961a), Adams (1960), Markovitz (1962), and Adams and Lodge (1964).

As Markovitz (1957) has remarked, the sensitivity of this method for determining $p_{22}-p_{33}$ may be low for certain types of liquid; if, for example, in some range of shear rate, we have

$$p_{22}-p_{33} = A|G|^n, \tag{9.69}$$

where A, n are constants, then (9.67) becomes

$$(n-1)(p_{22}-p_{33}) = \left(r\frac{\partial p_{22}}{\partial r}\right)_{\text{pp}} - \left(r\frac{\partial p_{22}}{\partial r}\right)_{\text{cp}}.$$

If $n \fallingdotseq 1$, the left-hand side, and therefore also the right-hand side, will be small, and thus $p_{22}-p_{33}$ must be determined from the ratio of two small quantities and may therefore be liable to appreciable error. In general, even if $n-1$ is not small or if (9.69) is not valid, it can be seen that the presence of the factor G'^{-2} in the integrand of (9.68) gives great weight to the values of pressure gradients determined at the lower values of shear rate, where errors are liable to be larger, and that in consequence the extrapolation to zero shear rate which will be required to evaluate the integral in practice may be unreliable.

It can be seen that this drawback is associated with the particular form of the differential equation (9.67); it is therefore natural to consider whether the use of a rotating member having a profile different from that of the cone or plate would lead to another equation of more convenient form. Unfortunately, however, this hope appears to be ill-founded; in the case of a sphere-and-plate system, the author has obtained an equation for the pressure gradient in which the normal stress differences occur in combinations which can be expressed as linear combinations (with constant coefficients) of those occurring in (9.34) and (9.63); thus a differential equation of the same form as (9.67) is obtained, and so no advantage is gained. These calculations are to be published.

Rod-climbing Effects and Pressure Gradients in Parallel Plate and Cone-and-plate Systems

In the few measurements of pressure gradients in parallel plate and cone-and-plate systems which have been made (Lodge, 1961a; Markovitz, 1962), it is found that

$$\left(r\frac{\partial p_{22}}{\partial r}\right)_{\text{pp}} - \left(r\frac{\partial p_{22}}{\partial r}\right)_{\text{cp}} > 0, \tag{9.70}$$

which implies, by (9.68), that

$$p_{22}-p_{33} > 0. \tag{9.71}$$

The discrepancy between this result and Roberts's result (1957) that $p_{22}-p_{33} = 0$ has yet to be resolved.

According to the concentric cylinder equation (9.18), the value of $r\,\partial p_{33}/\partial r$, where $-p_{33}$ denotes the pressure on a horizontal plane, and hence presumably the rod-climbing tendency depend on the values of both normal stress differences $p_{11}-p_{22}$ and $p_{22}-p_{33}$. In the case of one solution (3% polymethyl methacrylate in dimethyl phthalate), the author finds that $p_{11}-p_{22}$ at first increases with increase of G, and then decreases, reaching negative values (Adams and Lodge, 1964); in qualitative experiments, the same solution gave a (positive) rod-climbing effect. Although the results for $p_{11}-p_{22}$, obtained from parallel plate and cone-and-plate data, are open to question, the question arises whether the value of $p_{22}-p_{33}$ was large enough to outweigh, in (9.19), the term in $p_{11}-p_{22}$. (If $p_{22}-p_{33} = 0$ and $p_{11}-p_{22} < 0$, then according to (9.18) the liquid would tend to *descend* the inner cylinder.)

It is therefore natural to enquire whether there is any simple criterion based directly on the pressure gradients measured in parallel plate and cone-and-plate systems which would enable one to predict that a given liquid would climb a rotating cylinder.

We shall now show that, for a liquid satisfying the general conditions (9.4) and (9.5),

$$\text{if} \quad \frac{d\eta}{dG} \leqslant 0 \quad \text{and} \quad \left(r\frac{dp_{22}}{dr}\right)_{\text{pp}} > \left(r\frac{dp_{22}}{dr}\right)_{\text{cp}} > 0, \tag{9.72}$$

then

$$(9.73)\qquad \left(r\frac{\partial p_{33}}{\partial r}\right)_{cc} > 0,$$

so that a positive rod-climbing effect should occur.

The conditions (9.72) are sufficient, but not necessary, to give (9.73). The results on the solution referred to above are consistent with this statement.

It should perhaps be recalled that the suffixes pp, cp, and cc in these equations refer to the parallel plate, cone-and-plate, and concentric cylinder systems; η is the viscosity, and G denotes the magnitude of shear rate, supposed positive.

Proof of (9.73). Since (9.5) is valid by hypothesis, we may regard equations (9.18), (9.34), and (9.63) as simultaneous equations between which the unknown quantities $p_{11}-p_{22}$, $p_{22}-p_{33}$ may be eliminated, provided that in each case these quantities are evaluated at the same value of shear rate G. This should lead to a relation between the pressure gradients in the three systems.

If we first eliminate the term $Gd(p_{22}-p_{33})/dG$ (which is of unknown sign) between (9.18) and (9.34), and then in the resulting equation substitute for p_{11} the expression obtainable from (9.63), we finally obtain an equation which can be re-arranged in the form

(9.74)

$$\left(r\frac{\partial p_{33}}{\partial r}\right)_{cc} = \left(r\frac{\partial p_{22}}{\partial r}\right)_{cp} + \nu\left\{\left(r\frac{\partial p_{22}}{\partial r}\right)_{pp} - \left(r\frac{\partial p_{22}}{\partial r}\right)_{cp}\right\} + (\nu-2)(p_{22}-p_{33}).$$

This is as far as the elimination needs to be taken. For, by (9.68) and (9.50), the given conditions (9.72) imply that $p_{22}-p_{33} > 0$ and that $\nu \geqslant 2$, and thus that the last term on the right-hand side of (9.74) is positive or zero. The other two terms on the right-hand side of (9.74) are evidently positive, by (9.72), and therefore the left-hand side is positive. This proves that, as stated, the conditions (9.72) are sufficient to ensure that (9.73) is satisfied.

That the conditions (9.72) are not necessary for (9.73) to be satisfied can be seen simply by considering any particular case in which $p_{11}-p_{22} > 0$ and $p_{22} = p_{33}$ (e.g. (6.22)). In this case, (9.18) shows that (9.73) is satisfied, but the centre inequality in (9.72) is not satisfied, as one can see from (9.67).

Shear Flow through a Tube of Circular Cross-section

Finally, we consider a state of flow through a straight tube of circular cross-section such that each infinitesimally thin liquid cylinder, of radius r say, coaxial with the tube moves rigidly parallel to the tube axis with a speed $v = v(r)$ which depends only on the radius r and varies from zero at the tube wall to a maximum at the tube axis.

We may refer to such a state of flow as *telescopic flow*, for brevity; telescopic flow is called *Poiseuille flow* when v depends linearly on r^2, and is called *plug flow* when v is independent of r over some range of values of r, usually including $r = 0$.

The dependence of speed on radius is determined by the relation between viscosity and shear rate and is quadratic for a Newtonian

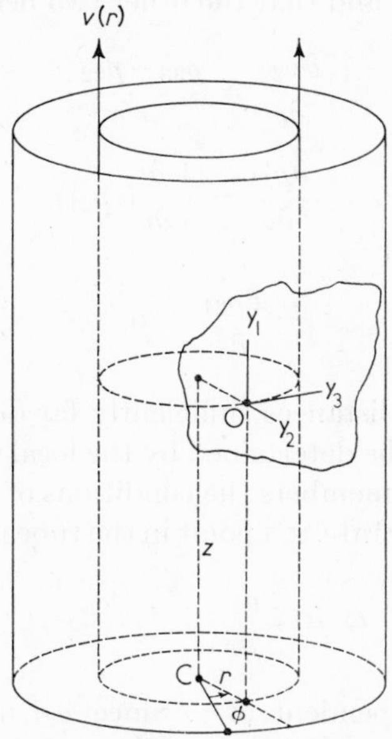

FIG. 9.7. Cylindrical polar coordinate system r, z, ϕ (origin C) and local cartesian coordinate system $Oy_1y_2y_3$ for telescopic flow through a tube of circular cross-section.

liquid, or for any liquid for which the viscosity is independent of shear rate. The flow is evidently a uni-directional shear flow, with the cylinders $r =$ constant as shearing surfaces and with planes passing through the tube axis as the orthogonal family of material surfaces; the lines of shear are straight lines parallel to the tube axis.

For this state of flow, the usual local cartesian coordinate system $Oy_1y_2y_3$ at a typical particle O has the axis Oy_1 parallel to the tube axis and the axis Oy_2 perpendicular to the tube surface (Fig. 9.7). Compared with the orientations of axes in Couette flow (Fig. 9.2), the axes Oy_1 and Oy_3 are interchanged in position relative to the tube or cylinder. The same cylindrical polar coordinate system is used.

We therefore see that in this case

$$\begin{pmatrix} p_{11} & p_{12} & p_{13} \\ p_{21} & p_{22} & p_{23} \\ p_{31} & p_{32} & p_{33} \end{pmatrix} = \begin{pmatrix} \widehat{zz} & \widehat{zr} & \widehat{z\phi} \\ \widehat{rz} & \widehat{rr} & \widehat{r\phi} \\ \widehat{\phi z} & \widehat{\phi r} & \widehat{\phi\phi} \end{pmatrix}. \tag{9.75}$$

Using (9.4) and the fact that $\partial\widehat{\phi\phi}/\partial\phi = 0$, because of the symmetry of the system with respect to arbitrary rotations about the tube axis, we find that the second of the equations of motion (9.25) (with zero body forces) is satisfied identically, and that the other two become

$$\frac{\partial p_{22}}{\partial r} = \frac{p_{33}-p_{22}}{r}, \tag{9.76}$$

$$-\frac{\partial p_{11}}{\partial z} = \frac{1}{r}\frac{\partial}{\partial r}(rp_{21}), \tag{9.77}$$

provided that

$$\frac{\partial p_{21}}{\partial z} = 0. \tag{9.78}$$

This is satisfied at distances sufficiently far downstream in the tube for the extra stress to be determined by the local shear rate alone, where the liquid no longer remembers the conditions of flow at the entrance to the tube. For the shear rate at a point in the tube is given by the equation

$$G = -\frac{dv}{dr}, \qquad v = v(r), \tag{9.79}$$

and is therefore independent of z. Since p_{21}, and also $p_{11}-p_{22}$ and $p_{22}-p_{33}$ are functions of G alone, it follows that (9.78) and

$$\frac{\partial}{\partial z}(p_{11}-p_{22}) = \frac{\partial}{\partial z}(p_{22}-p_{33}) = 0 \tag{9.80}$$

are satisfied.

It should be noted that there is an important practical difference between telescopic flow and flow in any of the rotational systems considered above; for the same liquid remains in the latter, and the condition that flow should continue at constant shear rate in any given liquid element long enough for p_{21} etc. to become dependent on shear rate alone can be realized simply by continuing the rotation of the apparatus for a sufficient length of time. In flow through a tube, on the other hand, fresh liquid is continually being used, and the required condition can be met only by using a sufficiently long tube. A check can be made by repeating the necessary measurements with tubes of different lengths, and also by checking that the pressure $(-p_{22})$ on the wall of the tube varies linearly with position z along the tube, a result which follows at once from (9.80), (9.77), and (9.78).

Further, we have

$$\frac{\partial^2 p_{11}}{\partial r\,\partial z} = \frac{\partial^2 p_{22}}{\partial r\,\partial z} \qquad \text{from (9.80)}$$

(9.81)

$$= \frac{\partial}{\partial z}\frac{p_{33}-p_{22}}{r} = 0, \qquad \text{from (9.76), (9.80).}$$

Thus the pressure gradient $\partial p_{11}/\partial z$ is independent of r, and hence, on integrating (9.77) with respect to r, we have

$$-\frac{r^2}{2}\frac{\partial p_{11}}{\partial z} = rp_{21}+a$$

where a is a constant. Putting $r = 0$, it follows that $a = 0$, and therefore that *the shear stress is proportional to the distance from the tube axis*:

$$\text{(9.82)} \qquad p_{21} = -\frac{r}{2}\frac{\partial p_{11}}{\partial z} = -\frac{r}{2}\frac{\partial p_{22}}{\partial z} \qquad \text{by (9.80).}$$

It is convenient to use the notation

$$p_{21}(r) \equiv \tau, \quad p_{21}(R) \equiv \tau_R,$$

where R is the tube radius; it then follows from (9.82) that

$$\text{(9.83)} \qquad \frac{\tau}{\tau_R} = \frac{r}{R}.$$

Thus, from (9.82) with $r = R$, it follows that the shear stress at the wall can be determined from the distribution of pressure on the wall, and this can be measured without disturbing the state of flow.

The shear rate at the wall can be determined from the volume Q of liquid flowing through the tube in unit time; for evidently

$$Q = \int_{r=0}^{R} v\,d(\pi r^2) = [v\pi r^2]_0^R - \int_0^R \pi r^2 \frac{dv}{dr}\,dr$$

$$= 0+\pi\frac{R^3}{\tau_R^3}\int_{\tau=0}^{\tau_R} \psi(\tau)\,\tau^2\,d\tau.$$

The first term is zero because the velocity at the wall is zero. In the integral, we have used (9.79) and have written

$$G = \psi(\tau), \tag{9.84}$$

thus expressing the shear rate in terms of the shear stress, where ψ is a function which depends on the material; ψ/τ is a constant (equal to the reciprocal of the viscosity) for a Newtonian liquid. We have also changed the variable of integration, using (9.83). From the equation, we see that

$$\psi(\tau_R) = \frac{1}{\tau_R^2}\frac{\partial}{\partial \tau_R}\left(\frac{\tau_R^3 Q}{\pi R^3}\right), \tag{9.85}$$

which is the desired result. It shows that, whether the liquid is Newtonian or not, the shear rate at the wall can be determined from the volume of liquid flowing through the tube and from the pressure distribution along the tube wall, which determines the shear stress at the wall; hence the viscosity can be determined as a function of shear rate.

This method of determining viscosity for non-Newtonian liquids, due to Weissenberg, was first used by Rabinowitsch (1929), who used tubes of various lengths and diameters to check the consistency of the results. In most cases, the pressure gradient is determined in practice not from the distribution of pressure on the tube wall but from the total pressure drop (Δp_{11}) along the whole length of the tube. Since this necessarily involves the flow conditions at the entrance and at the exit, it would seem to be liable to error, especially for polymer solutions which have a memory comparable with the time of transit through the tube, or which exhibit appreciable thixotropy (defined in Chapter 10).

The method is an extension of the well-known method, attributed to Poiseuille, for determining the viscosity of a Newtonian liquid; the velocity varies as r^2 for a Newtonian liquid, but not for a non-Newtonian liquid whose viscosity varies with shear rate. On the other hand, as noted above, the spatial variation of stress components, represented by (9.78) and (9.82), is the same whether the liquid is or is not Newtonian.

If the above measurements of output Q and pressure distribution on the wall are supplemented by a measurement of total thrust T exerted by the liquid on the tube in a direction parallel to the tube axis, then *the value of the combination* $2p_{11}-p_{22}-p_{33}$ *of normal stress differences* appropriate to the value of shear rate at the wall *can be determined*, as the following argument shows.

We consider the quantity

$$T \equiv \int_{r=0}^{R} p_{11}\, d(\pi r^2), \tag{9.86}$$

where the integration is taken over the plane cross-section of liquid at the exit of the tube. Since p_{11} is the component of traction normal to this cross-section, it follows from the equilibrium of the tube that this integral is equal to the force acting on the tube minus the net momentum flow in the direction of the tube axis. (This can be proved rigorously most conveniently by means of a general theorem concerning the integral of momentum flux over an arbitrary closed surface in a moving liquid.) If the input to the tube is at right angles to the tube axis in the region under consideration, there is no contribution to the momentum flux (parallel to the axis) from the incoming liquid, and hence the required momentum flux is just ρQ, where ρ is the density (supposed uniform). Thus T is a measurable quantity.

Evaluating the integral (9.86) by parts, we have

$$\frac{T}{\pi} = [p_{11} r^2]_0^R - \int_0^R r^2 \frac{\partial p_{11}}{\partial r} dr$$

$$= R^2 p_{11}(R) - \int_0^R (p_{33} - p_{22})\, r\, dr - \int_0^R r^2\, d(p_{11} - p_{22}),$$

since
$$\frac{\partial p_{11}}{\partial r} = \frac{\partial p_{22}}{\partial r} + \frac{\partial}{\partial r}(p_{11} - p_{22})$$

$$= \frac{p_{33} - p_{22}}{r} + \frac{\partial}{\partial r}(p_{11} - p_{22}), \qquad \text{by (9.76).}$$

Evaluating the last integral by parts, we have

$$\int_0^R r^2\, d(p_{11} - p_{22}) = [r^2(p_{11} - p_{22})]_0^R - \int_0^R (p_{11} - p_{22})\, 2r\, dr,$$

and hence, on taking the two integrals together, we find that the terms in $p_{11}(R)$ outside the integrals cancel, and that we are left with the result

$$T - \pi R^2 p_{22}(R) = \pi \int_0^R (2p_{11} - p_{22} - p_{33})\, r\, dr. \tag{9.87}$$

To extract an expression for the integrand from this equation, we proceed as before by changing the variable of integration from r to τ, using (9.83). On dividing throughout by τ_R^2 and then differentiating with respect to τ_R, we finally obtain the result

$$(2p_{11} - p_{22} - p_{33})_{\tau_R} = \frac{1}{\tau_R} \frac{\partial}{\partial \tau_R} \left\{ \frac{T - \pi R^2 p_{22}(R)}{\pi R^2 \tau_R^2} \right\}. \tag{9.88}$$

Since $p_{22}(R)$ here is the pressure on the tube wall at the exit, the right-hand side consists of measurable quantities, and hence the left-hand side can be determined, as stated.

Sakiadis (1962) has performed complete sets of measurements of this type for a 14% solution of polyvinyl alcohol in water; in interpreting his results, however, he uses an assumption (not made in the above analysis) that the pressure $-p_{11}$ at the centre of the tube exit is atmospheric, and then obtains expressions for both differences of normal stress components. This assumption requires justification.

Rivlin (1956b) and Coleman and Noll (1959b) have considered a further type of flow, which may be regarded as a combination of Couette flow and telescopic flow. As in Couette flow, the liquid is sheared between concentric cylinders in relative rotation, but a pressure is applied to the liquid at one end of the annulus causing a telescopic flow of liquid through the annulus; further liquid is supplied so that the flow continues. The advantage of this *helical flow* is that, in principle, from measured values of pressure difference on the cylinders for different values of the ratio of the Couette and telescopic contributions to the flow, both differences of normal stress components can be calculated.

Normal Stress Differences in Elastic Solids

We have seen that elastic solids give rise to unequal normal stress components in rectilinear shear; in particular, for the rubberlike solid, $p_{11}-p_{22}=\mu_0 s^2$ and $p_{22}-p_{33}=0$ (4.24), where $s=\tan\epsilon$ is the magnitude of shear; for a general type of isotropic perfectly elastic solid, both $p_{11}-p_{22}$ and $p_{22}-p_{33}$ can have non-zero values (8.20). Measurement of the values of the normal stress differences in shear strain will therefore give information about the form of the free energy function (8.11).

Normal stress differences arising from the shear of an elastic solid can in principle be determined by methods similar to those described above for the shear flow of liquids, because these methods depend essentially on the analysis of stress using the stress equations of motion (or equilibrium) (9.25) and (9.40), the assumptions (9.4) and (9.5), and the geometric properties of curvilinear shear flow. The stress equations are valid for solids and liquids; assumptions (9.4) and (9.5) can be taken over for solids, if the shear rate G is replaced by the magnitude s of curvilinear shear strain, suitably defined. Curvilinear shear strain may be defined as a strain $t_0 \to t$ where t_0 and t denote any two states related as in a curvilinear shear flow, defined in (9.2); the magnitude s may be defined in terms of a principal value of strain variables $\gamma^{ij}(t_0)-\gamma^{ij}(t)$, generalized in Chapter 12 so as to apply to non-uniform as well as to uniform strain.

The possibility that a finite shear in an elastic solid could give rise to unequal normal stress components appears to have first been considered by Poynting (1909, 1912), who measured the elongation of a cylindrical sample in torsion. This is the type of strain analogous to the shear flow between parallel plates in relative rotation considered above; to maintain a state of torsion (i.e. without change of separation of the plates), a distribution of pressure over the plates must be applied, in addition to a torque, if the normal stress components are unequal. If the torque is applied without the pressure distribution, it is to be expected that a change of separation of the plates would occur. Poynting measured such changes of separation in metal wires and in rubber filaments (1913). Rivlin (1947) has measured the distribution of pressure, and Rivlin and Saunders (1951) the total thrust and torque, in a rubber sample in torsion between parallel plates. A useful account of these experiments is given by Treloar (1958, Chapter 8).

CHAPTER 10

Rheological Properties of Concentrated Polymer Solutions

The main application of the theories and mathematical techniques described in previous chapters is to materials containing very long molecules, or *polymers*, as they are called. It is the great length of the constituent molecules which is largely responsible for the useful mechanical properties of polymeric solids such as plastics and textile fibres and for certain flow properties of polymer-containing liquids such as "viscostatic" lubricating oils, thixotropic paints, and various body fluids of physiological interest. Rheological studies of polymeric materials are thus of widespread practical importance; they are also of considerable intrinsic interest because of the variety of properties, some of which are most striking, which can be exhibited in suitable circumstances.

In this chapter, we outline the main properties of polymers in concentrated solution and in the rubberlike state, with particular reference to deformations which involve large changes of shape. Concentrated solutions exhibit a greater variety of properties than dilute solutions, which have received more attention in the textbook literature, and are of more direct technological interest; not only are concentrated solutions used in the manufacture of certain textile filaments, but many manufacturing processes in the plastics industry involve the flow of molten polymers, or polymer melts, as they are called, and these possess many of the rheological properties exhibited by polymers in concentrated solution. The importance of the rubberlike state, as distinct from the harder glassy or crystalline states, lies in the fact that it furnishes a sound foundation on which to build an understanding of the relation between macroscopic properties and molecular structure using the kinetic theory of rubberlike elasticity outlined in Chapter 4. Properties in the rubberlike state, which have been fully treated by Treloar (1958), will be dealt with briefly at the end of this chapter.

The rheological properties of concentrated polymer solutions will be discussed under the following headings.

1. Viscosity
2. Elongational viscosity and spinnability
3. Weissenberg effects
4. Elastic recovery

5. Die swell
6. Stress relaxation
7. Thixotropy
8. Miscellaneous properties (melt fracture, jets, Kaye effect).

Important properties not discussed here include swelling and flow birefringence; the description of these properties requires extensions of theory which have been omitted from the present treatment in the interests of brevity. Swelling and birefringence of rubberlike solids have been described by Treloar (1958), and flow birefringence in polymer solutions by Peterlin (1956). We make only a very brief reference to properties involving very small strains; such properties have been very extensively investigated for polymers in all states and are well described in the literature (Ferry, 1961).

In describing the properties of concentrated solutions, we shall be content to mention a few particular solutions which exhibit the properties under discussion, and shall not attempt to give a complete account of published data; our main objective is to illustrate the variety of rheological properties which are to be found. It should, however, be emphasized that the properties are not at all specific to any one polymer or group of polymers; on the contrary, most if not all the properties can be exhibited to a greater or less extent by any polymer of sufficiently great molecular length when dissolved in a suitable solvent.

Partly in the interests of readability, and partly because data for several different properties are available, we shall in particular consider the following three liquids:

A: a solution containing 2·44 g polymethyl methacrylate ($M_n \sim 10^6$) in 100 ml dimethyl phthalate;

B: a solution containing 5·76 g polyisobutylene ($M_n \sim 10^6$) in 100 ml decalin;

C: a "silicone fluid" (MS 200/1000 cs) (polydimethylsiloxane, $M_w(?) \sim 2 \times 10^4$).

A and B are thus solutions containing approximately $2\frac{1}{2}\%$ and 6% of different polymers of roughly the same high molecular weight in organic solvents. C is a pure polymer, of considerably lower molecular weight, which is a liquid at room temperatures. C is included as a "control" liquid which has a viscosity comparable to the viscosities of A and B but which does not exhibit the other rheological properties exhibited by A or B; A exhibits most of the properties listed above, while B exhibits somewhat fewer.

The chemical structure of these and a few other polymers is shown in Table 10.1. The term *polymer* (*macromolecule*, or *long chain molecule*) is applied to a molecule of high molecular weight (say 10^3 to 10^8) and great length, formed by covalent bonding together of a number n (the DP, or *degree of polymerization*) of identical *monomer* groups separated by broken

TABLE 10.1

Structural formulae of polymers, showing repeating ("monomer") units enclosed by dotted lines.

Polyethylene (Polythene)	$—CH_2—CH_2—¦—CH_2—¦—CH_2—$
Polyisobutylene	$—CH_2—¦—C(CH_3)_2—CH_2—¦—C(CH_3)_2—CH_2—$
Polyisoprene (natural rubber, gutta percha)	$—¦—CH_2—C(CH_3){=}CH—CH_2—¦—CH_2—$
Polystyrene	$—CH_2—¦—CH(C_6H_5)—CH_2—¦—CH(C_6H_5)—CH_2—$
Polymethylmethacrylate (Perspex, Plexiglas)	$—CH_2—CH(CH_3)(COOCH_3)—CH_2—¦—CH(CH_3)(COOCH_3)—CH_2—¦—$
Polyvinyl chloride (PVC)	$—CH_2—¦—CH(Cl)—CH_2—¦—CH(Cl)—CH_2—$
Polydimethylsiloxane (silicone rubber and fluids, "bouncing putty")	$—Si(CH_3)_2—O—¦—Si(CH_3)_2—O—¦—$

lines in Table 10.1), which in some cases have a molecular weight of about 15–100. There are usually other groups at the ends of a chain molecule; and a chain molecule may be *linear* (when there are two and only two ends) or *branched* (when there are more than two ends; side groups, such as the benzene ring in polystyrene, not being regarded as ends).

A given sample or solution of a polymer will usually contain polymer molecules of different degrees of polymerization; the composition of such a mixture may be characterized by a distribution function

$$\nu_i = \frac{\text{number of molecules of DP } n_i}{\text{total number of molecules}},$$

or by a distribution function

$$w_i = \frac{\text{weight of molecules of DP } n_i}{\text{total weight of molecules}}.$$

From these, we define the *number-average molecular weight*

$$M_n \equiv \sum_i \nu_i M_i,$$

where M_i is the molecular weight when the DP is n_i, and the *weight-average molecular weight*

$$M_w \equiv \sum_i w_i M_i = \frac{\sum_i \nu_i M_i^2}{\sum_i \nu_i M_i}.$$

Using very dilute solutions (so that the polymer molecules are substantially separated from one another), values for M_n and M_w may be obtained from osmotic pressure and from light-scattering measurements, respectively; other types of average molecular weight may be obtained from viscosity measurements and from measurements of concentration gradients in the ultracentrifuge (cf. Flory, 1953).

The structural formulae of Table 10.1 give no indication of the actual shape of a given polymer molecule, which, in solution for example, will change rapidly through a sequence of configurations most of which will be highly kinked (Fig. 10.1). In the first instance, the polyethylene chain can be regarded as made up of rigid C—C links so joined that any one link is free to rotate on the surface of a cone whose axis is the next link along the chain and whose semi-vertical angle is determined by the C—C—C valence angle. For a free chain with, say, one end fixed, there will therefore be a large number (or a large number density) of equally probable configurations when the number of links is large. Figure 10.1 represents a model of a 1000-link polyethylene chain in which successive orientations of links were chosen (out of six equally spaced orientations on the cones of correct valence angle) by the throw of a die (Treloar, 1958, p. 47).

Similar considerations apply to other polymer molecules, although there may be differences of detail due, for example, to possible restrictions to otherwise free rotation about neighbouring bonds; these are in fact a matter of current investigation.

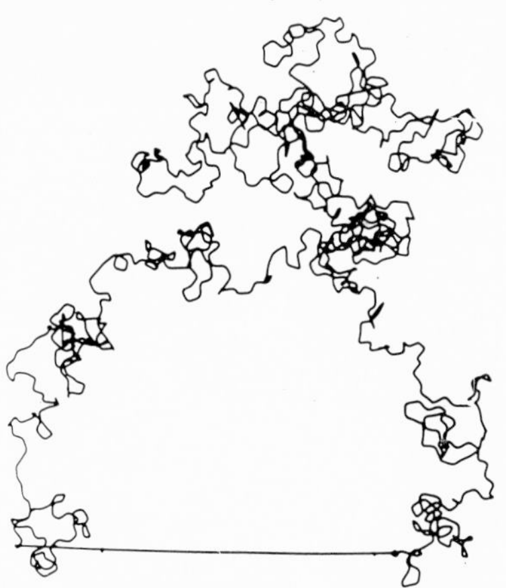

FIG. 10.1. Model of a 1000-link polyethylene molecule. The ends are joined by a horizontal straight wire (Treloar, 1958).

Viscosity

Magnitude of viscosity. The viscosity of solution A (Fig. 10.2) is about 300 times greater than the viscosity of the solvent (dimethyl phthalate), although the concentration of polymer is only about $2\frac{1}{2}\%$. Although this may be an extreme example, it is in fact a striking and characteristic feature of polymers of sufficiently high molecular weight that they give solutions of high viscosity even at comparatively low concentrations. It should be noted, however, that for a given polymer at given concentration a change of solvent can have a profound effect on the solution viscosity; for example, a change of solvent from toluene to n-butyl acetate gives an increase of viscosity by a factor of over 20 for 3% solutions of polymethylmethacrylate ($M_n \sim 4 \times 10^5$) (Toms and Strawbridge, 1953). On the other hand, solutions of polyisobutylene in decalin, xylene, and cyclohexanol have similar viscosities (Ferry, 1961, p. 379).

It is convenient to call a solution *dilute* if the solute molecules are, on the average, so far apart that they have negligible influence on one another; the viscosity of such a solution would be expected to vary *linearly* with solute concentration. When the solute is a polymer of high molecular weight, it is in many cases necessary to go to concentrations as low as 0·01% before the linear region is reached. As the concentration is increased, the viscosity increases very rapidly and can in some cases increase as the 10th power of concentration. It must be concluded that in concentrated solutions the *interactions* between polymer molecules play a predominant role in determining the viscosity and therefore presumably also other rheological properties of the solutions. Comparatively little attention has been paid to concentrated solutions in the literature; most attention has been paid to dilute solutions in order to develop methods of determining the size and shape of individual polymer molecules. An account of viscosity data for concentrated solutions has been given by Fox, Gratch, and Loshaek (1956).

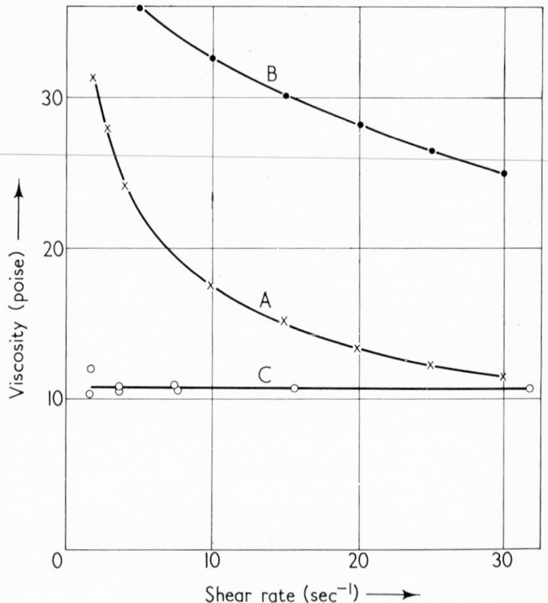

FIG. 10.2. Viscosity as a function of shear rate for liquids A, B, and C (from data of Kaye).

Dependence on shear rate. The viscosities of the three liquids A, B, C are given at different shear rates in a limited range in Fig. 10.2; the data were obtained with a concentric cylinder viscometer (Kaye, unpublished). It will be seen that the viscosity of C is independent of shear rate and that the viscosities of A and B decrease with increase of shear rate. Such a decrease is the most common feature of polymer solutions, although a few cases are known in which the viscosity increases with increase of shear rate, e.g. a 1·25% solution of polymethyl methacrylate in amyl alcohol (Jha, 1955).

For a given solution, there is usually a range of low values of shear rate where the viscosity is substantially constant; for example, the viscosity of a 4% solution of polymethyl methacrylate ($M_n = 4 \times 10^5$) in pyridine at 25° C has a viscosity of 4 poise which varies less than 3% for a four-fold increase in shear rate (0·05–0·20 sec^{-1}) (from concentric cylinder viscometer data of Toms and Strawbridge, 1954 and private communication). There is also a similar range at high shear rates where the viscosity is constant. The shear rate and concentration dependence of the viscosity of polyisobutene/decalin solutions has been studied by DeWitt, Markovitz, Padden, and Zapas (1955).

Dependence on molecular weight. It is seen from Fig. 10.2 that the viscosity of liquid C, a pure polymer, is less than the viscosities of solutions A and B although these contain only a few per cent of polymer; the great difference of concentration is presumably offset by the fact that the average molecular weights are some 50 times greater for A and B than for C. More extensive measurements using a given polymer/solvent combination with polymer samples of different average molecular weights have shown in some cases that above a certain average molecular weight the viscosity varies as the 3·4th power of the weight average molecular weight (Fox, Gratch, and Loshaek, 1956), a relation which has been explained by F. Bueche (1956) in terms of entanglements of polymer molecules with one another.

Elongational Viscosity and Spinnability

While viscosity is perhaps the most often measured property of polymer solutions, elongational viscosity (5.13) is one of the least often measured, no doubt because of the experimental difficulty of producing a state of elongational flow and measuring the tension in liquids of moderate viscosity. Trouton's measurements (1906) of elongational viscosity were made on materials (wax and pitch) of very high viscosities in the region of 10^6 and 10^{10} poise, and gave values for the elongational viscosity equal to about 3 times the viscosity, in agreement with the expected result for a Newtonian incompressible liquid (equation (5.12)); it is interesting to note that Trouton observed elastic effects with these materials in that the elongation was faster when the load was first applied than during the subsequent steady elongation, and that there was a partial recovery when the load was removed.

Aeschlimann (1952) measured the tension and rate of elongation in the continuous flow of a liquid stream of viscosity in the region of 10^3–10^4 poise; solutions containing 30–57% polyvinyl alcohol in diacetone alcohol were used at room temperature. It was found that the elongational viscosity *increased* with increase of elongation rate although the viscosity decreased with increase of shear rate. There is some doubt, however, as to whether these measurements did in fact give values for the elongational viscosity, defined as the ratio of tensile stress and rate of elongation under conditions of *steady* flow when both these quantities attain constant values; in one case at least, the tensile stress was still increasing in a region where the elongation rate had reached a constant value (Lodge, 1964). There is no doubt, however, that the behaviour in elongational flow was very different from that in shear flow, for the increase of the elongational viscosity with increase of elongation rate was so pronounced that, in comparison, the viscosity in some cases appeared to be almost independent of shear rate.

In this respect, the results bear some resemblance to the results obtained in Chapter 6 for the rubberlike liquid (Fig. 6.3), and are in any case of fundamental interest as an instance of the possibility that the behaviour of a material in one type of flow may be qualitatively different from its behaviour in another type of flow.

The results are also of technological importance in relation to the *spinnability*, or ability to be drawn out into long thin threads, which many polymer solutions and polymer melts exhibit, and which is an essential feature in the process of producing man-made textile fibres. Solution A above can very readily be drawn out into liquid threads over a foot long and a fraction of a millimetre in width; liquid C does not have this property. Solution A must presumably possess some rheological property which, in simple elongation, furnishes stability with respect to the small local changes in diameter which must occur in an elongating liquid filament. A Newtonian liquid would not be expected to possess such a property; for the tension may to a first approximation be assumed uniform along the length of an elongating filament, and a local decrease in diameter would result in an increase in tensile stress and an increase of elongation rate, with the consequence that the diameter would in that region decrease more rapidly than in other regions where the diameter is larger; in this sense, simple elongation is an unstable process for a filament of a Newtonian liquid. For stability of elongation, it would seem necessary that an increase of tensile stress should lead to a decrease in the rate at which the filament diameter decreases, but sufficient conditions for stability have yet to be determined. While a sufficiently rapid increase of elongational viscosity with increase of elongation rate may ensure stability of elongation (Lodge, 1961b), it would seem more likely that in practice the spinnability of polymeric liquids will depend also on what we may call the *dynamic elongational viscosity*, defined under conditions in which the stress is changing with time. Spinnability has been investigated by Jochims (1932), Erbring (1934), Kast (1954), and Nitschmann and Schrade (1948).

Weissenberg Effects

When liquid C is sheared between concentric cylinders in relative rotation (with a common vertical axis), there is a slight rise in level of the free horizontal liquid surface towards the outer cylinder, as one would expect due to the effect of centrifugal forces; when solution A is sheared in similar circumstances, there is a much more pronounced rise towards the inner cylinder, and an even greater rise occurs when the polymer concentration (A') is increased from 2·5–4% (Fig. 10.3).

While similar effects must have occurred and may have been noticed long ago, e.g. when polymer solutions were stirred in the course of preparation, Weissenberg (1947) appears to have been the first to suggest that this and allied effects could arise from a state of stress in shear flow radically different from that which occurs in a Newtonian liquid, and hence that the investigation of the effect could lead (for the first time) to the development of methods for determining completely (or to within an unimportant additive hydrostatic pressure) the state of stress in a liquid in a known state of flow. The theory of such methods has been given in Chapter 9.

If the concentric cylinder system is to be utilized in this way to determine the values of differences of normal stress components in shear flow, then it is clear that one must make measurements (e.g. of the difference of pressures exerted on the cylinders) at points sufficiently far away from the upper (and lower) liquid surfaces for disturbances to the required state of shear flow caused by the rod-climbing (or by the presence of a horizontal rigid plate closing the bottom of the gap between the cylinders) to be negligible. Alternatively, it is perhaps helpful to visualize a hypothetical experiment in which the upper liquid surface is constrained by a horizontal frictionless rigid plate which enables the required state of shear flow to be maintained by preventing the liquid from climbing the inner cylinder. The combination of unequal normal stress components and curvature of shearing surfaces, which is the cause of the rod-climbing effect when the horizontal plate is absent, will give rise to a non-uniform distribution of pressure on the horizontal plate, the pressure being greater near the inner cylinder. The relation between the pressure gradient and the normal stress component differences is given by (9.18).

Alternatively, one can replace the concentric cylinders by horizontal parallel plates in relative rotation, with the liquid sheared in the gap

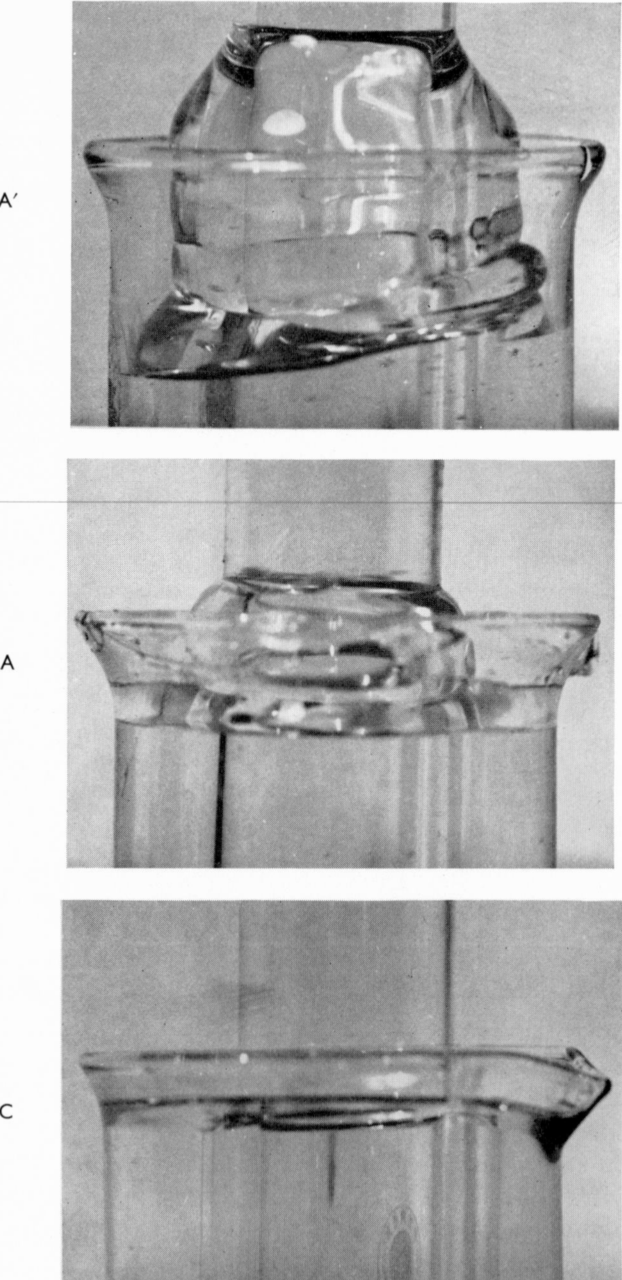

Fig. 10.3. The Weissenberg effect. A $2\frac{1}{2}\%$ solution (A) and a 4% solution (A′) of polymethylmethacrylate in dimethyl phthalate climb the inner cylinder, which is rotated; the outer cylinder is fixed. A silicone fluid (C), of viscosity similar to that of A, does not show the effect.

between the plates, and measure the radial distribution of pressure on either plate. It is true that the state of flow is thereby changed; for the shearing surfaces are vertical cylinders in the concentric cylinder system and horizontal planes in the parallel plate system, while the orthogonal material surfaces are respectively horizontal planes and vertical cylinders. However, as the analysis of Chapter 9, equation (9.34), has shown, the curvature of the orthogonal surfaces (which contain the lines of shear) gives rise to a non-uniform distribution of pressure over the plates of a parallel-plate system when the normal components of stress

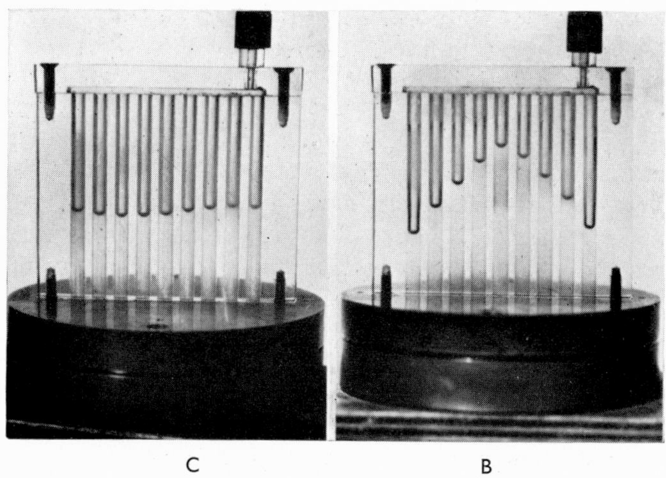

Fig. 10.4. Pressure distributions generated by the shear flow of liquids B and C between a fixed upper plate (with capillary tubes) and a parallel rotating lower plate (not visible). The reference level of pressure is arbitrary (owing to a uniform reduction of air pressure made to raise the liquid levels into view).

are unequal; in general, this distribution would differ from that obtained on a horizontal frictionless plate restraining the top surface of the liquid in a concentric cylinder system.

Pressure distributions on the plate of a parallel plate system are shown in Fig. 10.4 for solution B and liquid C. Apart from a slight asymmetry (possibly due to lack of flatness or parallelism in the apparatus), the distribution for liquid C is of the form expected for centrifugal forces in the absence of any contribution from unequal normal stress components. The very different distribution for solution B must mean that the normal stress components are not all equal, according to equation (9.34). Similar distributions have been obtained in other polyisobutylene solutions by Greensmith and Rivlin (1953) and Padden and DeWitt (1954); and in polystyrene, methyl cellulose, and sodium carboxymethylcellulose solutions by Kotaka *et al.* (1959). Garner, Nissan and Wood (1950) reported a similar pressure distribution in a rather crude parallel plate system, but in view of the fact that their similar experiments using a cone-and-plate system gave a uniform pressure distribution, there is reason to doubt whether their state of flow was sufficiently close to an unperturbed shear flow; it is in fact very easy to get unwanted pressure distributions from other sources in apparatus of this type, unless very careful precautions are taken with the alignment of the rotating and stationary members.

If a cone-and-plate system is used instead of a parallel plate system, then (provided that the appropriate state of shear flow is set up, as described in Chapter 9) the shear rate becomes independent of distance from the axis of rotation, and the orthogonal family of material surfaces become parts of spheres (instead of cylinders). The pressure on the plate must then vary as the logarithm of distance from the axis of rotation (9.64), for all materials satisfying our general assumption that the extra stress can be expressed in terms of strain history without reference to spatial gradients of strain. While the slope of a graph of pressure versus logarithm of distance depends on the material (and on the shear rate), the form of this graph does not, in contrast to the case of the parallel plate system.

Pressure distributions of the expected form have been observed by Russell (1946), Roberts (1952, 1954, 1957), and Markovitz and Williamson (1957); various solutions of polymers, including rubber and polyisobutylene, have been investigated, as well as solutions of a non-polymer, aluminium laurate, in hydrocarbon solvents. (It has been suggested that such hydrocarbon/soap systems may possess a temporary network structure formed by association of the soap molecules into linear aggregates.) Pressure distributions obtained with solution B in a cone-and-plate system and in a parallel plate system are shown in Fig. 10.5 (Adams and Lodge, 1964); the difference in the form of the distributions is clearly visible.

As shown in Chapter 9, the slope of the graph of pressure versus logarithm of distance in the cone-and-plate system gives one combination, $p_{11}+p_{22}-2p_{33}$, of the two required normal stress differences, and (under suitable conditions) the intercept of this graph at the rim of the rotating member gives another, $p_{22}-p_{33}$. There is disagreement over the value obtained for the intercept at the rim, or rim pressure, as we may call it; Roberts (1957) found the value zero for various solutions, which included a polyisobutylene solution for which a negative value had been found by Greensmith and Rivlin (1953). These measurements were made with different flow conditions at the rim; however, Adams and Lodge (1964) have found negative values for the rim pressure, using solutions A and B, under conditions at the rim (free liquid boundary in the gap between cone and plate) comparable with those in Roberts's measurements.

An independent determination of $p_{22}-p_{33}$, from values of pressure gradient in the cone-and-plate and parallel plate systems at points

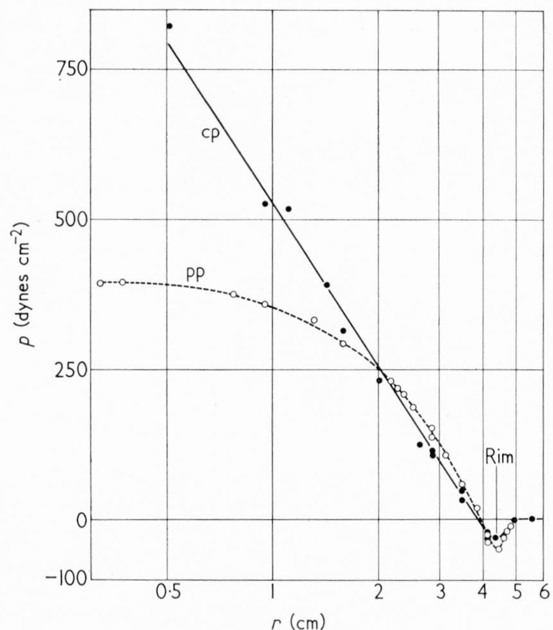

Fig. 10.5. Pressure p, as a function of the logarithm of distance r from the axis of rotation, generated by the shear flow of liquid B between cone-and-plate (cp) and between parallel plates (pp) in relative rotation. Shear rate 23 sec^{-1} in cp system, and in pp system at $r = 3$ cm. Gap at rim $= 0{\cdot}25$ cm in both systems. The liquid extends beyond the rim of the rotating member. (Adams and Lodge, 1964.)

within the gap away from the rim, has recently yielded negative values for $p_{22}-p_{33}$ for solutions A and B (Adams, 1960; Lodge, 1961a; Adams and Lodge, 1964) and for a solution of polyisobutylene in cetane (Markovitz, 1962). In the case of solutions A and B, the values obtained in this way are several times greater in absolute magnitude than those obtained from rim pressures. The matter evidently calls for further investigation.

Sakiadis (1962) also finds non-zero values for $p_{22}-p_{33}$ for an aqueous solution of polyvinyl alcohol flowing through a tube of circular cross-section; the total axial thrust on the tube and the radial thrust on the tube wall are measured. The method involves an assumption (that the pressure at the centre of the tube exit is atmospheric), however, which is open to question.

According to equation (9.66), the total thrust on the plate in a cone-and-plate system is proportional to $p_{11}-p_{22}$, subject to suitable conditions at the rim. Following the early measurements of total thrust in a simple cone-and-plate apparatus (Russell, 1946), Weissenberg and Roberts have developed an instrument, the "Weissenberg Rheogoniometer", which is commercially available (Farol, Ltd., Bognor Regis, Sussex), and has been used by various workers (Jobling and Roberts, 1959; Philippoff, 1956, 1960; Brodnyan, Gaskins and Philippoff, 1957; Pilpel, 1954). Benbow and Howells (1961) have used a similar apparatus, and Pollett (1955) has used a cone-and-plate apparatus in which two thrusts can be measured, one on a central part of the plate and the other on an outer annular ring part of the plate: values of both normal stress differences deduced from these thrusts gave the result that $|p_{22}-p_{33}|$ was less than about 3% of $p_{11}-p_{22}$ for polyethylene at high temperatures (128° C).

It will be recalled that $p_{11}-p_{22} > 0$ and $p_{22}-p_{33} = 0$ for the rubber-like liquid considered in Chapters 6 and 7 (6.22); the result $p_{11}-p_{22} > 0$ is in qualitative agreement with the above data (since the thrust in the cone-and-plate system is always positive), but the result $p_{22}-p_{33}$ conflicts with the data of Adams and Lodge. Non-zero values for $p_{22}-p_{33}$ are obtained with a different form of rheological equation of state (e.g. Examples 6, No. 4) for an elastic liquid, and for a non-Newtonian purely viscous liquid (8.36).

Elastic Recovery

Qualitative demonstrations of elastic recovery (involving appreciable changes of shape at constant volume) in liquids can readily be given. If a bottle of solution A is rotated and then suddenly brought to rest, the recoil of any suspended air bubbles is readily visible; solution B and liquid C give no visible recoil. "Bouncing putty", a very viscous elastic liquid composed of a silicone (similar to C) of high molecular weight, flows slowly under its own weight but bounces with about 70% resilience (depending on composition) when dropped from a height of a few feet on to a rigid table; samples are obtainable which may be said to have a "memory" of a few seconds in the sense that if a sample is first rapidly elongated and then held at constant length for a few seconds, no recovery occurs on release; whereas, on immediate release following the initial elongation, appreciable recovery (i.e. decrease in length, in this case) occurs. Cooper (1955) has reported a "bouncing putty" not made from a silicone.

The aluminium soap systems already referred to are capable of exhibiting very well-marked recovery, as shown in Fig. 10.6; if such a liquid is poured from a bottle, and the pouring is suddenly arrested while the liquid stream is cut about 2 or 3 in. below the mouth of the bottle, the top part of the stream snaps back into the bottle. The third of the photographs in Fig. 10.6 shows an increase in width of the liquid stream in the lower container; this is presumably a consequence of the decrease in length of the stream on recovery. When large quantities of liquid are used, this demonstration can be very striking. Suitable liquids can be prepared by the following procedure (which I owe to J. E. Roberts). To 1 l. decalin at about 40° C, add 40 g aluminium dilaurate (vacuum-dried for 2 or 3 days at about 60° C) followed by 15 ml *m*-cresol; the decalin should be well stirred mechanically before, during, and for 10–20 min after addition of the last two ingredients. The system will set to a gel, but will return to a liquid in a few days' time, when it is ready for use.

Quantitative measurements of recovery in liquids have been made, using the recoil in a concentric cylinder system when one cylinder is set free to rotate following a period of imposed relative rotation, by Schwedoff (1889) for solutions of gelatine in water; by Philippoff, Gaskins and Brodnyan (1957) for polyisobutylene and for nitrocellulose in n-butyl acetate; by Carver and van Wazer (1947) and Trapeznikov and Shalopalkina (1956) for aluminium soap solutions; by Ferry (1942) for solutions of polystyrene in xylene; and by Trapeznikov and Assonova (1958) for solutions of rubber in decalin. In most cases, the shear recoveries observed are not very large, being of the order of one shear unit, but in some cases extremely large recoveries have been observed; in the last reference, recoveries of the order of 50 shear units are reported for a solution containing 2% pale crêpe rubber in decalin, "vulcanized with 0·2% S_2Cl_2".

Similar recovery measurements have been made using other types of rotational apparatus; Pollett (1954) and Benbow and Howells (1961) have used the cone-and-plate system, and Watkins (1956) and Boyd (1958) have used a cone-and-cone system. Benbow and Howells' recovery data for a high molecular weight silicone fluid of viscosity 3×10^5 poise are given in Fig. 10.7, which also includes values of the ratio $\frac{1}{2}(p_{11}-p_{22})/p_{21}$ obtained from stress measurements in steady shear flow; the fair agreement between the two sets of points is consistent with equation (7.39), but is definitely inconsistent with the equation obtained by omitting the factor $\frac{1}{2}$ from (7.39) (cf. the discussion at the end of Chapter 7).

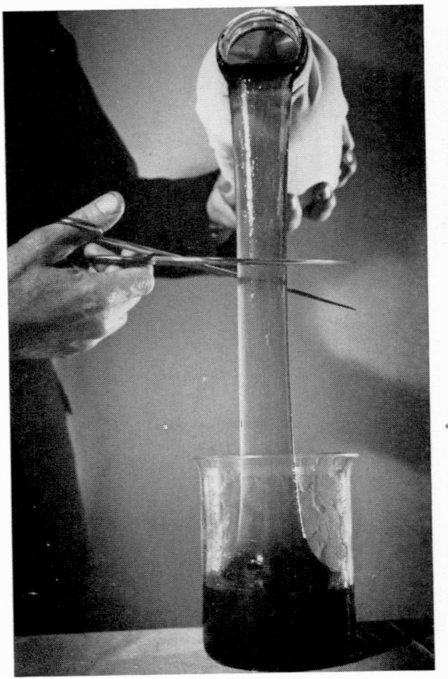

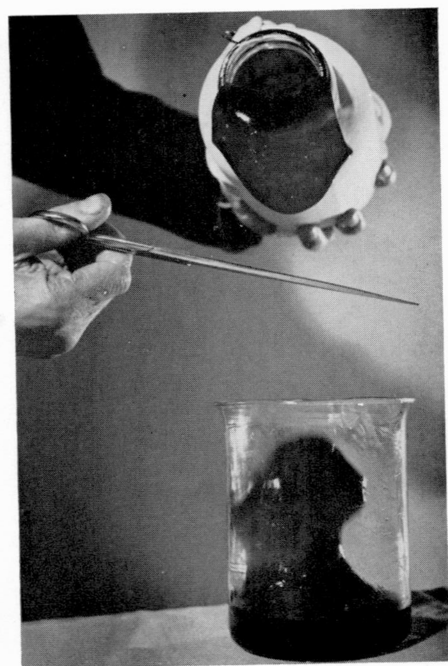

Fig. 10.6. Elastic recovery in a liquid. A solution of aluminium dilaurate in a hydrocarbon oil is poured from a bottle (left); the pouring is stopped, and the stream cut (centre); the upper stream retracts quickly towards the mouth of the bottle, and the lower stream decreases in length and increases in width (right). (Photos by R. A. Barker.)

Qualitative recovery measurements have been made by observing the recoil of a liquid meniscus in a capillary tube on removal of an applied pressure (Jensen and Koefoed, 1954; Weber and Bauer, 1956); since this method can be used with very small samples of liquid, it has been applied to liquids of physiological interest (Scott-Blair and Burnett, 1957).

According to the terminology introduced at the beginning of Chapter 7, the above measurements all refer to *constrained* shear recovery, since the material is constrained by the presence of the apparatus walls to undergo

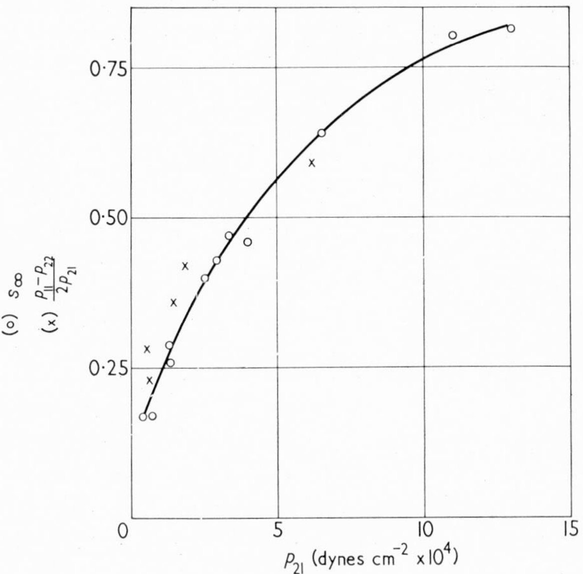

FIG. 10.7. Magnitude of shear recovery s_∞ and value of the ratio $(p_{11}-p_{22})/(2p_{21})$ as functions of the value of shear stress p_{21} in the preceding shear flow of a silicone liquid (viscosity 3×10^5 poise at low shear rates). (From data of Benbow and Howells, 1961, Table 1.)

shear (without lateral expansion) during the recovery process. The measurement of *free* recovery following shear flow would necessitate removal of the apparatus walls during recovery; this seems impracticable when a rotational apparatus (cone and plate, or concentric cylinder) is used, but the appropriate conditions may occur when a liquid emerges from a tube; this case is discussed below under the heading Die Swell.

Conditions intended to simulate free recovery following shear flow in a cone-and-plate apparatus have been utilized by Pollett (1958), in order to investigate the unexpected lateral expansion predicted by the theory for the rubberlike liquid (equation (7.19), Figs. 7.4 and 7.5). A very concentrated polymer solution (polyvinyl chloride in diethyl hexyl phthalate) was used, which was solid at room temperature and liquid at high temperatures (175° C to 195° C). The liquid was sheared in a cone-and-plate apparatus at a high temperature, the shearing suddenly stopped, and the whole system rapidly cooled until the material solidified. A small sample was then cut out of the sheared material, and its dimensions measured; on heating again for a brief period at the high temperature, it was found that a change of shape occurred; this was measured, and regarded as a measure of the free recovery which would occur if the sample could be removed after the shear flow and allowed to deform at zero stress without cooling and re-heating. The cooling and re-heating evidently complicates any detailed comparison of the results with the predictions of the theory for the free recovery experiment treated in Chapter 7, but such complications were minimized by the use of "blank tests" in which similar experiments were made without the shear flow. The main point of the method is that a sample can be cut which is sufficiently small for the recovery to be substantially uniform and unconstrained.

Pollett's results are given in Table 10.2 in terms of the shear recovery angle ϵ and the lateral expansion factors h_2 and e_3 whose corresponding values for the case of instantaneous recovery are defined in Fig. 7.3; h_2 denotes the separation after recovery of a pair of material planes which were shearing planes at unit separation during the shear flow preceding recovery, and e_3 is the corresponding separation ratio for material planes which were orthogonal to the shearing planes during the shear flow. In relation to these data, the predictions of the theory for the rubberlike liquid may be summarized as follows:

$$h_2^* > 1, \quad h_2^* = e_3^*, \quad 0 < \epsilon^* \leqslant 45°.$$

These results for instantaneous free recovery (the asterisk is used to signify instantaneous) are given in (i), (ii) and (iii) (following (7.22)) and (7.27); the data of Pollett presumably refer to ultimate rather than instantaneous recovery, but the few calculations so far made give similar results for ultimate recovery (Fig. 7.5).

It is seen that Pollett's data are consistent with the prediction $h_2 > 1$ and (with two exceptions) with the prediction $\epsilon \leqslant 45°$, but are not consistent with the prediction $h_2 = e_3$. In view of the control measurements made on samples subject to the same heating and cooling cycles but not subjected to the shear flow (as described in Pollett's paper), the results may be regarded as establishing the reality of the lateral expansion phenomenon.

In relation to Pollett's result $h_2 > e_3$, it is interesting to note that another form of rheological equation of state for an elastic liquid does lead to a result $h_2^* > e_3^*$ (Examples 7, No. 1), so that a sum of the two equations (with use of appropriate factors $\gamma^{ij}(t)$ to obtain equations

TABLE 10.2

Measured shear recovery and lateral expansions in a solution of polyvinyl chloride in diethyl hexyl phthalate following shear flow, cooling, cutting, and re-heating (from data of Pollett (1958, and private communication)). Shear rate 1·0 sec^{-1}.

Series	Applied shear in shear units	Shear recovery angle ϵ in degrees	Lateral expansion factors e_3	h_2
A	0	0	0·98	1·02
	50	22	1·25	1·86
	100	20	1·21	1·74
	300	18	1·12	1·33
	600	10	1·08	1·23
	1200	2	0·97	1·08
	3000	4	0·97	1·07
B	0	0	0·97	1·04
	1·6	40	1·00	1·12
	5·0	50	1·17	1·31
	10	46	1·40	1·83
	15	24	1·35	1·84
	50	9	1·30	1·71
	180	6	1·20	1·34
	720	2	1·05	1·09

Shear flow at 175°C, recovery 3 min. at 185°C (series A).
Shear flow at 190°C, recovery 1 min. at 195°C (series B).

having a significance independent of the choice of base vectors) might be one simple way of obtaining equations which can be made to fit all Pollett's observations. Equations of this type have in fact been used by Ward and Jenkins (1958) in another context; they are of a form which bears some similarity to equations which Mooney (1940) proposed for rubber. There are, however, many other ways of modifying the equations for a rubberlike liquid, and it is premature to do more than indicate these possibilities until more experimental data are available. A further point which should be realized is that Pollett's data were not taken following a shear flow which had continued for an "infinite" length of time (i.e. in practice, for a time sufficiently long for the stress components on the plate to reach constant values), whereas this is the case considered in the theory of Chapter 7.

Die Swell

When a solution of a polymer of sufficiently high molecular weight, or a polymer melt, flows out of a tube, the diameter of the emerging liquid stream increases, in some cases to as much as three or four times the diameter of the tube. For a purely viscous incompressible Newtonian liquid, on the other hand, a consideration of momentum conservation

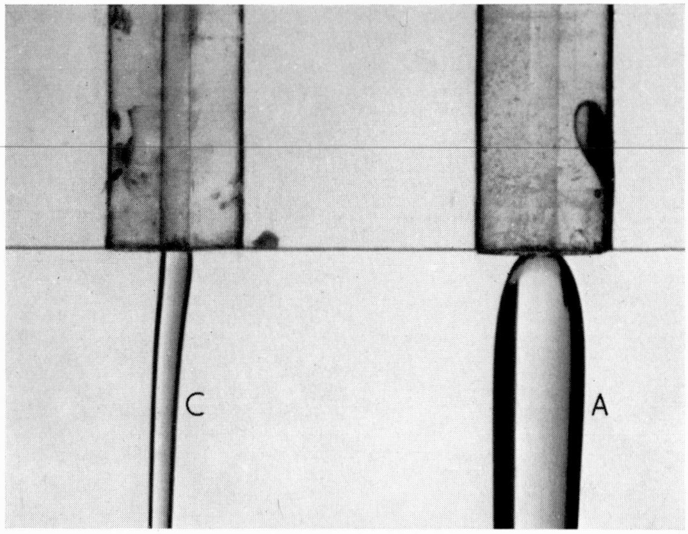

FIG. 10.8 Die swell. On flowing (downwards) out of a capillary tube, a stream of liquid A increases in diameter by 200%. Liquid C (of viscosity similar to that of A) does not show the effect.

leads to the conclusion that the diameter should *decrease* by about 13%. The effect is clearly shown in Fig. 10.8, where solution A shows a diameter increase of over 200%; liquid C, on the other hand, shows little or no significant change in diameter. Since these two liquids have comparable viscosities (Fig. 10.2) and are given identical flow histories prior to emergence from the tubes, it is clear that the effect, in this case at least, is not attributable to the fact that the viscosity is appreciable.

Changes in shape of a material on emerging from a tube appear to have been first commented on by Barus (1893), an American biologist who used a very viscous material called marine glue. The diameter increase, or *die swell*, is a common feature of extrusion processes in the man-made fibre and plastics industries; diameter increases of the order of 10% occur in rayon spinning (Kast, 1954; Klare and Gröbe, 1955), and larger increases occur in the extrusion of molten plastics through dies. Similar effects occur for other shapes of die; in the formation of plastic sheet, for example, by extrusion through a die whose cross-section has the form of a long thin slit, the emerging plastic sheet is thicker than the slit. Die swell is now being increasingly studied in the laboratory (Merrington, 1943; Spencer and Dillon, 1948; Clegg, 1958).

The effect is so large that it cannot be explained in terms of a change of volume; enormous pressures would be required to change the volume of a liquid element by a factor of two or three, and the compressibility of solution A would have to be much higher than that of liquid C. Furthermore, if the effect was entirely due to a volume change, the average speed of the liquid would not change as the liquid left the tube; in the experiment shown in Fig. 10.8, however, there is a marked reduction in speed which is easily visible from the motion of small air bubbles in the liquid.

The effect could be due to a combination of elasticity in the liquid and converging flow at the entry to the tube (Clegg, 1958). If the liquid flows into and through the tube in such a way that liquid particles move parallel to the tube axis and those off the axis have a component of velocity towards the axis in the region of converging flow at the entry to the tube, then it follows that a liquid cylinder coaxial with the tube axis must increase in length and decrease in diameter as it moves into the tube. If the liquid is sufficiently elastic so that by the time it reaches the tube exit it still has some memory of its flow history at the tube entrance, then it is reasonable to expect that on leaving the tube a change of shape in some sense opposite to the previous changes of shape will occur, i.e. that a liquid cylinder will decrease in length and increase in diameter. In this case, the effect would be lessened if the tube length were increased, and this in fact occurs (Clegg, 1958); in the few published measurements, however, the effect does not seem to tend to zero as the tube length is increased. The "residual diameter increase" observed with long tubes must (if real) require a different explanation.

The reality of this residual diameter increase may be established by allowing the elastic liquid to remain at rest in the tube for a time longer than its effective memory before forcing it out of the tube (Howells, discussion on Lodge, 1961c). This experiment is shown in Fig. 10.9; a silicone "bouncing putty" is used, which has a memory of the order of a few seconds as judged by the elongation and retraction procedure mentioned above, and is left for up to an hour after filling before it is forced out of the tube by a rod; the increase in diameter and decrease in length are clearly visible. As a control experiment, plasticine is subjected to similar treatment, and shows no such change in diameter.

A possible explanation of the residual diameter increase is furnished by the nature of the free recovery following shear flow in a rubberlike liquid (Lodge, 1958a); the increase in separation of the shearing surfaces and decrease in length of material lines coinciding with the lines of shear

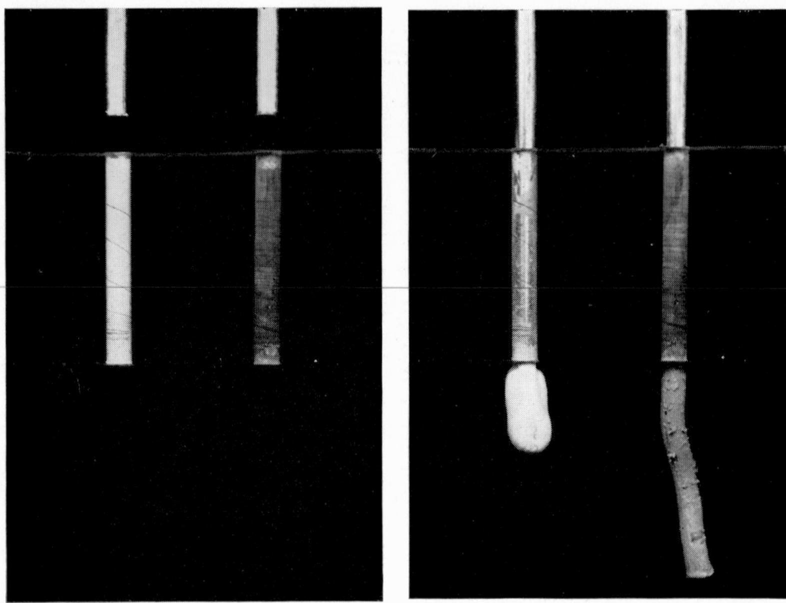

Fig. 10.9. Die swell not attributable to previous convergent flow. Equal holes in a transparent block are filled with an elastic liquid ("bouncing putty") and an inelastic material (plasticine), and are left for a period longer than the "memory" of the elastic liquid (left). On being forced out of the holes by rods moving downwards, the elastic liquid decreases in length by 60% and increases in diameter, while the inelastic material does not change in length or diameter. (From a suggestion of E. R. Howells; photos by D. G. Backhouse.)

in the previous shear flow (as given by (ii), (iii), following (7.22), for the case of rectilinear shear flow) are just such as would lead one to expect an increase of diameter following curvilinear shear flow through a tube. This calculation is for *steady* shear flow, i.e. for a shear flow which has continued for an infinite length of time, and thus, as a possible cause of die swell, is quite distinct from the cause due to convergent flow at the die entry; both causes, however, depend on the liquid having a finite memory. Rigbi (1953) has also discussed the cause of die swell, but in terms which I have not been able to understand.

Stress Relaxation

When a polymer solution is subjected to a flow history and then held at constant shape, the stress usually takes a measurable time to decrease to zero (or to become isotropic). Schwedoff (1889) found that, following shear flow of a $\frac{1}{2}$% solution of gelatine in water in a concentric cylinder apparatus, the torque (and therefore the shear component of stress) decreased with time according to an exponential relation with an exponent of about 4 sec. With water, and low molecular weight liquids generally, stress relaxation is usually too rapid to measure; theoretical estimates for water, based on Maxwell's idea of regarding a liquid as a relaxing elastic solid, give a relaxation period of the order of 10^{-13} sec (Frenkel, 1955).

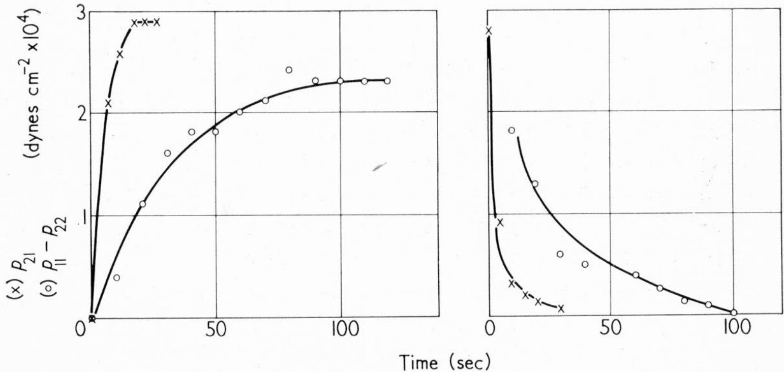

FIG. 10.10. Variation with time of shear stress p_{21} and normal stress difference $p_{11}-p_{22}$ at start of and at cessation of steady shear flow in the silicone liquid of Fig. 10.7. $p_{11}-p_{22}$ relaxes more slowly than p_{21}. (From torque and total thrust in a cone-and-plate apparatus; Benbow and Howells, 1961, and private communication.)

Very many investigations of stress relaxation in polymer solutions and solids have been reported in the literature (Tobolsky, 1958; Ferry, 1961); distributions of relaxation times extending over 10 decades of relaxation time have been obtained, from a variety of experimental methods, and have been compared with the predictions of a number of molecular theories. In most cases, the strains involved in these investigations are very small, and when the strain is a shear strain it is the relaxation of the shear component of stress which is determined. In relation to the theory for a rubberlike liquid, such information determines the function I_1, given in (6.31) and (6.32), and from this (by differentiating twice with respect to t), the memory function μ can in principle be determined.

Comparatively few measurements of relaxation of normal stress components (following cessation of shear flow) have been published (Weissenberg and Freeman, 1948; Jobling and Roberts, 1958; Benbow and Howells, 1961). In each case, the normal stress component difference $p_{11}-p_{22}$ is found to relax more slowly than the shear stress component p_{21}; this can be seen from Fig. 10.10, which represents Benbow and Howell's data for the silicone fluid whose recovery data are given in Fig. 10.7. This result is in qualitative agreement with the prediction (6.33) of the theory for a rubberlike liquid when the memory function is a sum of two or more exponential functions.

Thixotropy

The data of Figs. 10.2 and 10.5 relate to values of shear stress and normal stress components obtained under conditions which were steady in the sense that a constant shear rate had been applied long enough for these stress components to attain constant values. With some polymer solutions, changes in the values of the stress components are observed after the constant shear rate is first imposed on a solution which has been at rest for a sufficiently long period. Figure 10.11 shows the variation of pressure with time under these conditions for solutions A and B; it is seen that, despite the fact that these solutions exhibit similar behaviour with respect to steady values of stress components (cf. Figs. 10.2 and 10.5; liquid A gives pressure distributions similar to those of B in Fig. 10.5), the transient behaviour is very different: solution B attains a steady value of pressure immediately, whereas solution A gives a pressure which passes through two pronounced maxima before reaching a more-or-less steady value.

These results were obtained from measurements of pressure at one point on the plate of a cone-and-plate apparatus using a diaphragm-capacitance gauge to measure the pressure (Lodge, 1960b); this gauge had a response time of less than a second, whereas capillary gauges used in other investigations of normal stress effects have response times of the order of an hour, and would not therefore respond to changes of the type shown in Fig. 10.11.

Quick-response transducers have been used for measurements of total thrust and torque in the Weissenberg rheogoniometer and in other cone-and-plate systems (Pollett, 1954, 1955; Ward and Lord, 1957; Benbow and Howells, 1961; Trapeznikov, Morozov and Petrzhik, 1960). Pollett found a single pronounced broad maximum in the variation of total thrust with time in a polyvinyl chloride system; Trapeznikov *et al.* found two maxima in an aluminium naphthenate system, for shear stress as well as normal stress difference. The occurrence of maxima in shear stress has been known for some time (cf. e.g. Carver and van Wazer, 1947), and is usually referred to as a *thixotropic* effect; the ratio of shear stress to shear rate is greatest at the shear stress maximum, and decreases with prolonged shearing.

Thixotropic effects are found with various materials, which become easier to stir after prolonged stirring, and find a practical application in the recently-developed "one-coat" paints. The effects are usually attributed to some (often unspecified) change of structure brought about by prolonged flow. This view is reasonable in the case of solution A, for

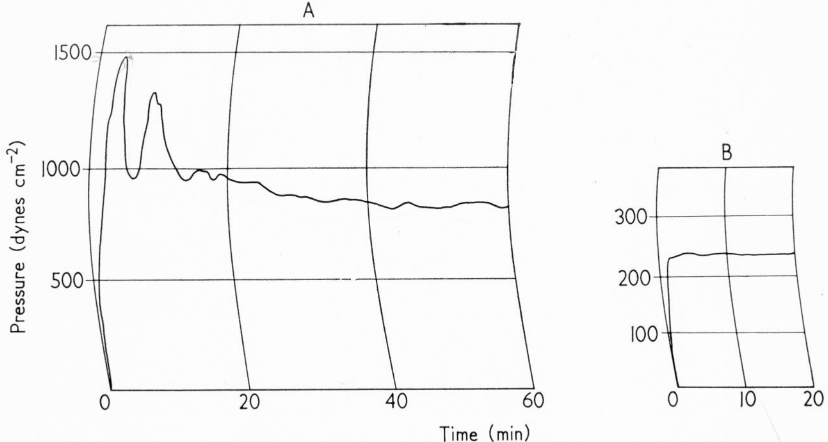

Fig. 10.11. Variation with time, after start of steady shear flow, of pressure at a point on the plate of a cone-and-plate apparatus. Liquid A at a shear rate of 23 sec^{-1}; liquid B at 42 sec^{-1}. (Adams and Lodge, 1964.)

example, because if the flow is momentarily stopped when the stress has reached a steady value and is then restarted, no maximum occurs; the changes of structure, if real, are reversible in the sense that if the rest period is increased to several hours the pressure maxima reappear when the flow is restarted, showing that the liquid regains its original properties. Presumably therefore no appreciable breaking of polymer molecules can occur; but the effect might be explicable if a network of polymer molecules were formed whose junctions consisted of entanglements which became more complicated (and therefore longer-lived) when the solution was at rest than when it was flowing. A single maximum might be explained in these terms, but it is not clear whether a double maximum could.

A few cases have been recorded in which the "viscosity" *increases* with prolonged stirring ("negative thixotropy" or "rheopexy"); Eliassaf, Silberberg and Katchalsky (1955) find that the viscosity of a 5% solution of polymethacrylic acid (DP $\simeq 10^4$) in water increased from 5 to 1750 poise after shearing for 1 min at a shear rate of 10 sec^{-1}.

Thixotropic effects are not accounted for, even qualitatively, by the theory for the rubberlike liquid given in Chapter 6: for it can readily be verified, from the results of Examples 6, No. 1, with the memory function given by (6.5), that $p_{11}-p_{22}$ and p_{21} increase steadily to their steady values when a constant shear rate is first applied. No maxima occur, and the steady values are attained in times of the order of the constants τ_s which occur in the exponential functions (6.5); these also determine the stress relaxation periods, as indicated above and in (6.31) and (6.37). Time constants of this type which are associated with polymethyl methacrylate solutions of concentration and molecular weight similar to those of solution A are at most of the order of 1 sec. (Toms and Strawbridge, 1953), whereas the times required to reach steady values of pressure, as shown in Fig. 10.11, are of the order of 10^3 sec. It would seem, therefore, that a radical change is necessary in the form of the rheological equations of state if the thixotropic properties of solution A are to be described.

Oscillatory Shear

The properties of polymeric materials subjected to sinusoidally varying oscillatory shear of very small amplitude have been extensively studied over wide ranges of frequency and temperature (Ferry, 1961). Since the strains are small, the response is effectively linear, and the quantities to be measured are the parts of the shear stress in phase and out of phase with the shear strain, represented by the terms in D and in A in (6.41), second equation. These are related to Fourier transforms of the memory function. (Any incompressible material, whether described by (6.9) or not, should lead to an equation of the form (6.41) in the limit of infinitesimally small strains.)

One of the most striking features of the properties of many polymer systems when studied in this way concerns the behaviour of the moduli A and D at different temperatures and frequencies; a change of temperature appears to be equivalent to a change of frequency in the sense that curves of the logarithm of modulus versus the logarithm of frequency obtained at different temperatures can be superposed so as to form a single "master curve" by means of suitable translations parallel to the axes. In assigning these translations for both moduli, only a single function of temperature needs to be determined empirically, and the resulting data often superpose well over as many as 12 decades of the "reduced frequency" (Ferry, 1961, p. 206). Moreover, under more limited ranges, the required function is found to be simply related to the solution viscosity and need not then be assigned empirically. Explanations of the success of this method of "reduced variables" have been given in terms of a molecular theory (in the first instance, for very dilute solutions) due to Rouse (1953).

Investigations of oscillatory shear with *finite* amplitudes are more limited. Weissenberg and Freeman (1948) pointed out that the normal stress component differences would be expected to vary at double the frequency of the shear strain (though higher harmonics of even order would also seem to be theoretically possible), and verified that the total thrust in a cone-and-plate apparatus did vary at double the frequency of rotation. The Weissenberg Rheogoniometer has provision to make similar measurements not only in oscillatory shear but also in oscillatory shear superposed on steady shear flow; no results of such measurements appear to have been published, however. Ward and Jenkins (1958) have published results for oscillatory shear (i.e. oscillatory torsion) in a parallel plate system, and find that the thrust varies at double the torsion frequency; their materials were viscoelastic solids rather than liquids, however.

Miscellaneous Properties

Three other properties of polymer solutions and polymer melts are worthy of mention. The first, known as *melt fracture*, is of some technical importance; it is found that when polymer melts are extruded through a die at a low enough rate, the emerging liquid stream is smooth but that at higher rates the stream becomes irregular (Nason, 1945; Spencer and Dillon, 1949; Tordella, 1956; Benbow, Brown and Howells, 1961). Since the Reynolds number is usually much below that at which turbulence would be expected in a Newtonian liquid, it is likely that the elastic properties of the polymer melts are in some way responsible, possibly giving rise to an instability of flow at the entrance to the die (Tordella). Although most investigations published so far refer to polymer melts or solutions of high concentration, the author found that a solution similar to solution A but with slightly higher concentration (4%) gave a noticeably irregular flow when subjected to the same conditions as the solutions shown in Fig. 10.8.

The second property is an unexplained curiosity, recently noted by Kaye (1963), who found that, on pouring solution B out of a flask into a dish of the same solution, every few seconds the falling liquid stream would, on reaching the liquid in the dish, rise up again and fall in an arc which reached the liquid surface in the dish at a distance of the order of a few centimetres from the starting point under the original falling stream (Fig. 10.12).

The third property concerns the stability of liquid jets. It is found that polymer solutions of concentrations of only a few per cent, and aluminium soap solutions of similar concentrations, when forced at high enough pressure through a horizontal tube continue for a considerable distance in the form of an unbroken jet before effects of surface tension cause the liquid to break up into separate drops. These effects were extensively studied during the last war (Garner, Nissan and Wood, 1950), and these studies led to the post-war investigation of the Weissenberg effects. Recent studies of jets of viscoelastic liquids have been made by Gill and Gavis (1956) and by Gaskins and Philippoff (1959).

The Stress–Strain Relation for Rubber

As we have seen in Chapter 8, the rheological properties of any isotropic perfectly elastic solid are determined when the free energy F is given as a function of three invariants of strain and the temperature. For isothermal strains in an incompressible solid, we can omit reference to the temperature and to the invariant J_3, whose value is unity when the volume is constant, and the factor $2\rho J_3 \dfrac{\partial F}{\partial J_3}$ in the stress–strain relation (8.14) must be replaced by a variable p, which is the magnitude of an additive isotropic contribution to the stress and is determined by boundary conditions and stress equations of equilibrium. This statement can be proved by pursuing an argument similar to that used in the derivation of (8.14), by taking the constant volume condition $J_3 = 1$ as an additional constraint on the values of the shape variables, and introducing the variable p as a Lagrange multiplier associated with this constraint; the transition from compressibility to incompressibility has been discussed in more detail by Oldroyd (1950b).

It then follows from (8.14) that the stress–strain relations for all possible types of strain in an isotropic incompressible perfectly elastic solid are determined by the two derivatives

$$\frac{\partial F(J_1, J_2)}{\partial J_1}, \quad \frac{\partial F(J_1, J_2)}{\partial J_2},$$

and their dependence on the two invariants J_1 and J_2, defined in terms of the principal elongation ratios by (8.3). The density ρ, a constant, may be assumed to be given.

FIG. 10.12. Liquid B is poured into a shallow dish filled with the same liquid (left). When the falling stream is thin enough, it rises again following a trajectory (right) which collapses in a fraction of a second. (Kaye, 1963; photos by D. G. Backhouse.)

A systematic series of measurements leading to the evaluation of these derivatives (or their equivalent) has been made by Rivlin and Saunders (1951) for a sample of natural rubber into which cross-links (i.e. chemical bonds between the long-chain molecules) had been introduced by a process known as "vulcanization". Natural rubber when unvulcanized behaves like a liquid, rather than a solid, at least for sufficiently long-term experiments, and exhibits hysteresis in the values of stress for increasing and decreasing cycles of strain. By suitable preparation, involving a certain degree of vulcanization, such effects can be minimized and a reasonable approximation to a perfectly elastic solid can be obtained.

Rivlin and Saunders subjected a sheet of rubber to simultaneous elongations in two mutually perpendicular directions in the plane of the sheet; the principal elongation ratios and the corresponding values of the principal stresses were measured in a central region of the sheet where the strain was sensibly uniform. It was reasonable to regard the material as being isotropic and incompressible. The foregoing measurements then suffice for the calculation of the required two derivatives and of the strain invariants. The results are given in Table 10.3; they have been calculated from the data given by Rivlin and Saunders, who present their results in terms of a strain-energy function W and strain invariants I_1, I_2, which are related to our quantities by the equations

$$\rho F(J_1, J_2) = W(I_1, I_2), \quad J_1 = I_1, \quad J_2 = I_1^2 - 2I_2.$$

It will be seen that these results are in reasonable agreement with the predictions

$$\frac{\partial F}{\partial J_1} = \text{constant}; \quad \frac{\partial F}{\partial J_2} = 0,$$

of the kinetic theory of rubberlike elasticity (cf. (4.40), (8.14)); for the values in the third column vary within $\pm 10\%$ of their central value, and the values in the fourth column are less than 5% of the values in the third column. The deviations from the kinetic theory, though small, are significant, and show up clearly enough in other types of stress–strain experiments, notably in simple elongation. Various other types of stress–strain experiment were also performed by Rivlin and Saunders, partly as a check on the results and theory already described and partly in order to obtain reliable data for smaller values of the strain invariants.

It is of particular interest to note that, in the torsion of a rubber cylinder between parallel circular plates, measurements of the radial distribution of pressure on one of the plates give an approximately parabolic distribution with the maximum at the axis of rotation and a

TABLE 10.3

Derivatives of the strain–energy function ρF for rubber for different values of the strain invariants J_1, J_2 (from the data of Rivlin and Saunders (1951, Tables 1 and 2)).

J_1	J_2	$\rho \frac{\partial F}{\partial J_1}$ (kg/cm²)	$-\rho \frac{\partial F}{\partial J_2}$ (kg/cm²)
5	14·6	2·77	0·10
5	13·0	3·04	0·11
5	11·1	3·06	0·10
7	34·3	3·05	0·09
7	30·8	2·99	0·09
7	27·8	2·92	0·09
7	25·7	2·98	0·10
7	24·5	2·86	0·09
9	62·5	3·32	0·09
9	55·6	3·17	0·09
9	50·6	3·05	0·08
9	46·3	3·03	0·08
9	42·7	2·88	0·07
9	41·5	2·84	0·07
11	71·5	2·72	0·05
11	67·0	2·56	0·04
11	63·4	2·57	0·03
11	60·9	2·51	0·03
5·92	25·0	3·20	0·13
5·49	30·1	3·19	0·14
5·19	16·9	2·92	0·11
4·92	14·2	3·11	0·14
4·69	12·0	2·74	0·10
9·10	62·8	3·16	0·08
8·63	54·5	3·16	0·09
8·13	46·1	3·09	0·09
7·82	41·1	2·93	0·09
7·46	35·7	3·01	0·09
7·14	31·0	2·99	0·10
6·85	26·9	2·87	0·09
6·62	23·8	2·98	0·11
10·39	68·0	2·81	0·05
10·00	60·0	2·78	0·05
9·80	56·0	2·67	0·05
9·40	48·4	2·71	0·05
9·20	44·6	2·61	0·05
11·6	75·5	2·74	0·04
11·4	70·0	2·62	0·04
11·2	64·5	2·61	0·04

positive intercept at the rim (Rivlin, 1947). A maximum at the centre is also obtained in the torsional shear flow of polymer solutions (e.g. Fig. 10.5); the effects in solid and liquid are comparable, as the discussion at the end of Chapter 9 indicates. The intercept at the rim depends on the term $\partial F/\partial J_2$ (which is zero according to the kinetic theory) and not on the term $\partial F/\partial J_1$, and may therefore afford a convenient direct method of investigating the nature of the observed deviations from the kinetic theory, in so far as the non-zero value of $\partial F/\partial J_2$ is concerned; the truth of this statement can be seen as follows.

In the usual notation, the pressure on the plate at the rim is equal to $-p_{22}(R)$; the value of pressure usually recorded is that relative to atmospheric pressure p_a as zero, and is thus equal to $-p_{22}(R)-p_a$. From the conditions at the free boundary when this is part of a sphere in the cone-and-plate system, we have seen that $p_a = -p_{33}(R)$ (9.56), and it is a straightforward matter to show that the same result is valid for a parallel plate system when the free boundary is part of a right circular cylinder coaxial with the axis of rotation (or torsion). Moreover, for the reasons indicated at the end of Chapter 9, these arguments are valid for shear of solids or shear flow of liquids. We see, therefore, that the pressure on the plate at the rim is given by

$$\begin{aligned} -p_{22}(R)-p_a &= p_{33}(R)-p_{22}(R) \\ &= -4\rho s^2 \frac{\partial F}{\partial J_2}, \qquad \text{by (8.15) and (8.20),} \end{aligned}$$

where s, the magnitude of the simple (rectilinear) shear on which the derivation of (8.20) was based, is equal to the magnitude of (curvilinear) shear at the rim in the torsional experiment. The validity of this step can be established by an appeal to (9.5) with G replaced by s; (9.5) is valid for an isotropic perfectly elastic solid, because (8.14) involves no spatial gradient of shape variables and hence rectilinear shear and curvilinear shear are equivalent for this material (Chapter 12).

Although the rubber samples were different in the torsion experiment and in the experiments leading to the data of Table 10.3, it is interesting to note that, according to the above equation, the positive sign of the pressure at the rim in the torsion experiment is consistent with the negative sign in the fourth column of Table 10.3.

From the point of view of testing the kinetic theory of rubberlike elasticity, it can be seen from the rheological equation of state (4.40) that, in addition to determining the form of the relation between stress and shape variables (as discussed above), the dependence of the shear modulus on temperature and on concentration of cross-links should be investigated. However, as our main concern in this book is with stress–strain relations rather than with questions of validity of molecular theories, we refer the reader to Treloar (1958) for information on these important points.

In view of the relation between the molecular theory for the rubberlike liquid, outlined in Chapter 6, and the theory for composite networks in a rubberlike solid, outlined in Chapter 4, it is worth while drawing attention to certain experimental investigations of composite networks which have been made. It was shown in Chapter 4 that if a rubberlike material is cross-linked in a stress-free state t_0, subjected to a pure strain $t_0 \rightarrow t_1$, and subjected to further cross-linking in the state t_1, then on removal of stress the material will deform to a state t_2 which is related to state t_0 by a strain which has a principal elongation ratio ($e_3(t_2)$ in (4.51) and Fig. 4.1) greater than unity, the corresponding elongation ratio for the pure strain being equal to unity. To investigate this rather unexpected prediction (which was made on the basis of the "two-network hypothesis" by Lodge (1958a)), Neubert and Saunders (1958) performed the appropriate experiments on samples of rubber, using a process of heating in air in state t_1 in order to introduce the second set of cross-links; this process also involves the removal of some of the original cross-links, however, so that the theory of Chapter 4 needs modification before it can be properly compared with the data. The data did, however, establish the reality of the predicted expansion in the $\mathbf{e}_3$ direction, although the values obtained for the quantity $e_3(t_2) - 1$ were some three times smaller than those predicted by (4.51).

The lateral expansion ($e_3(t_2) > 1$), found by Neubert and Saunders in their experiments on the permanent set of rubber, is of interest in connection with the lateral expansion in free recovery following steady shear flow in a rubberlike liquid which is predicted by the theory of Chapter 7; according to the network theory of the rubberlike liquid, there is a valid analogy between the two effects, which are both essentially due to the introduction into a Gaussian network of two or more sets of cross-links in states related to one another by finite strains. For this reason, the lateral expansion in the permanent set of rubber may bear a relation to the effect called "die swell" in the extrusion of polymers in a liquid state, if, as suggested earlier in the present chapter, the lateral expansion predicted by the theory for the rubberlike liquid (following steady shear flow) is a contributory cause of die swell.

CHAPTER 11

Solutions to Examples

Chapter 1

Example 1

Suppose, if possible, that $\mathbf{e}^i$ are linearly dependent; then numbers x_i (not all zero) exist such that

$$\sum_{i=1}^{3} x_i \mathbf{e}^i = 0.$$

Taking the scalar product of this equation with $\mathbf{e}_j$, it follows that

$$0 = \sum_i x_i \mathbf{e}^i . \mathbf{e}_j = \sum_i x_i \delta_{ij} = x_j, \qquad \text{by (1.16).}$$

Hence $x_j = 0$ for $j = 1, 2, 3$, which is contrary to our hypothesis, and therefore $\mathbf{e}^i$ are linearly independent.

Example 2

Since $\mathbf{e}_i$ are linearly independent, $v \neq 0$, and therefore $\mathbf{e}^i$ are linearly independent; by (1.10), we can write

$$\mathbf{r} = \sum_j x_j \mathbf{e}^j$$

for some values of x_j. Hence

$$0 = \mathbf{r} . \mathbf{e}_i = \sum_j x_j \delta_{ji} = x_i, \qquad \text{by (1.16),}$$

and therefore $\mathbf{r} = 0$.

Example 3

If possible, let $\mathbf{f}^i$ be a second set of vectors reciprocal to the given set $\mathbf{e}_i$, so that

$$\mathbf{f}^i . \mathbf{e}_j = \delta_{ij}, \quad \mathbf{e}^i . \mathbf{e}_j = \delta_{ij}.$$

On subtraction, it follows that

$$(\mathbf{f}^i - \mathbf{e}^i) . \mathbf{e}_j = 0.$$

By Example 2 above, taking $\mathbf{r} = \mathbf{f}^i - \mathbf{e}^i$, it follows that $\mathbf{f}^i - \mathbf{e}^i = 0$ $(i = 1, 2, 3)$, which proves the result.

Example 4

Since $\mathbf{e}_i$ are linearly independent, we may write

$$\mathbf{r} = \sum_i x_i \mathbf{e}_i$$

for some x_i, and hence

$$\mathbf{r}.\mathbf{e}^j = \sum_i x_i \delta_{ij} = x_j, \qquad \text{by (1.16).}$$

Thus
$$\mathbf{r} = \sum_i \mathbf{r}.\mathbf{e}^i \mathbf{e}_i.$$

Since $\mathbf{e}^i$ are linearly independent (by Example 1), a similar argument leads to the second result asked for.

Example 5

Case (*i*). Suppose that $\mathbf{v}$ and $\mathbf{w}$ are parallel. Then $\mathbf{v} = \lambda\mathbf{w}$ for some λ. The right-hand side of the given equation becomes

$$\mathbf{u}.\mathbf{w}\,\lambda\mathbf{w} - \mathbf{u}.(\lambda\mathbf{w})\,\mathbf{w} = 0,$$

while the left-hand side is zero because $\mathbf{v} \wedge \mathbf{w} = 0$.

Case (*ii*). Suppose that $\mathbf{v}$ and $\mathbf{w}$ are not parallel. Then $\mathbf{v}$ and $\mathbf{w}$, when represented by lines drawn from a common origin, define a plane, and we can introduce a right-handed *orthonormal* basis $\mathbf{e}_1$, $\mathbf{e}_2$, $\mathbf{e}_3$, where $\mathbf{e}_2$, $\mathbf{e}_3$ lie in the plane of $\mathbf{v}$, $\mathbf{w}$ and $\mathbf{e}_3$ is parallel to $\mathbf{w}$. We may then write

$$\begin{cases} \mathbf{w} = w_3\,\mathbf{e}_3, \\ \mathbf{v} = v_2\,\mathbf{e}_2 + v_3\,\mathbf{e}_3, \\ \mathbf{u} = u_1\,\mathbf{e}_1 + u_2\,\mathbf{e}_2 + u_3\,\mathbf{e}_3, \end{cases}$$

for suitable values of the coefficients.

Then
$$\mathbf{v} \wedge \mathbf{w} = w_3 v_2\,\mathbf{e}_2 \wedge \mathbf{e}_3 = w_3 v_2\,\mathbf{e}_1,$$

and
$$\mathbf{u} \wedge (\mathbf{v} \wedge \mathbf{w}) = w_3 v_2(-u_2\,\mathbf{e}_3 + u_3\,\mathbf{e}_2),$$

since
$$\mathbf{e}_2 \wedge \mathbf{e}_3 = \mathbf{e}_1, \quad \mathbf{e}_1 \wedge \mathbf{e}_1 = 0, \quad \text{etc.}$$

Also

$$\begin{aligned} \mathbf{u}.\mathbf{w}\,\mathbf{v} - \mathbf{u}.\mathbf{v}\,\mathbf{w} &= u_3 w_3(v_2\,\mathbf{e}_2 + v_3\,\mathbf{e}_3) - (u_2 v_2 + u_3 v_3)\,w_3\,\mathbf{e}_3 \\ &= w_3 v_2(u_3\,\mathbf{e}_2 - u_2\,\mathbf{e}_3) \\ &= \mathbf{u} \wedge (\mathbf{v} \wedge \mathbf{w}), \end{aligned}$$

which proves the result.

Example 6

Since $\mathbf{e}_i$ are linearly independent, the reciprocal set $\mathbf{e}^i$ are linearly independent, by Example 1. Hence $\bar{v} \neq 0$, and the vectors

$$\mathbf{f}_i \equiv \frac{1}{\bar{v}} \mathbf{e}^j \wedge \mathbf{e}^k \qquad (i, j, k = 1, 2, 3 \text{ in cyclic order})$$

form a set reciprocal to $\mathbf{e}^i$. But it follows from Example 3 that a given set of vectors has only one reciprocal set, and also that if $\mathbf{e}^i$ are reciprocal to $\mathbf{e}_i$, $\mathbf{e}_i$ are reciprocal to $\mathbf{e}^i$ (because the equations $\mathbf{e}^i . \mathbf{e}_j = \delta_{ij}$ defining the relation of reciprocality are symmetrical with respect to the interchange of $\mathbf{e}^i$ and $\mathbf{e}_i$).

Hence $\mathbf{e}_i$ and $\mathbf{f}_i$ are reciprocal to $\mathbf{e}^i$, and therefore $\mathbf{e}_i = \mathbf{f}_i$, which proves the result. To show that $\bar{v}v = 1$, we note that

$$\begin{aligned} \mathbf{e}^1 \wedge \mathbf{e}^2 &= v^{-1} \mathbf{e}^1 \wedge (\mathbf{e}_3 \wedge \mathbf{e}_1), && \text{by (1.15)} \\ &= v^{-1}(\mathbf{e}^1 . \mathbf{e}_1 \, \mathbf{e}_3 - \mathbf{e}^1 . \mathbf{e}_3 \, \mathbf{e}_1), && \text{by Example 5} \\ &= v^{-1} \mathbf{e}_3, && \text{by (1.16).} \end{aligned}$$

Hence $$\bar{v} \equiv \mathbf{e}^1 \wedge \mathbf{e}^2 . \mathbf{e}^3 = v^{-1} \mathbf{e}_3 . \mathbf{e}^3 = v^{-1}, \qquad \text{by (1.16).}$$

Example 7

Since $\mathbf{e}^i . \mathbf{e}^j = (e^i)^2 \delta_{ij}$, the vectors $\mathbf{e}^i$ are mutually perpendicular, and hence, in particular, $\mathbf{e}^2 \wedge \mathbf{e}^3$ is parallel to $\mathbf{e}^1$. But

$$\mathbf{e}^2 \wedge \mathbf{e}^3 = \bar{v} \, \mathbf{e}_1, \qquad \text{by Example 6,}$$

and therefore $\mathbf{e}_1 = b\mathbf{e}^1$ for some b. Now

$$\begin{aligned} 1 &= \mathbf{e}^1 . \mathbf{e}_1 \qquad \text{by (1.16)} \\ &= \mathbf{e}^1 . \mathbf{e}^1 \, b \\ &= (e^1)^2 b; \end{aligned}$$

hence $$\mathbf{e}_1 = (e^1)^{-2} \mathbf{e}^1,$$

and similarly $\mathbf{e}_i = (e^i)^{-2} \mathbf{e}^i$, which proves the first result. Equating the magnitudes of these vectors, we have

$$e_i = (e^i)^{-2} e^i = (e^i)^{-1},$$

and hence $\mathbf{e}_i = (e_i)^2 \mathbf{e}^i$, which completes the proof.

Example 8

Case (*i*). Suppose the vectors $\mathbf{e}_i$ are linearly dependent. Then there is a relation of the form $\sum x^i \mathbf{e}_i = 0$ in which at least one of the coefficients, x^1 say, is not zero. Dividing by x^1, it follows that

$$\mathbf{e}_1 = b\mathbf{e}_2 + c\mathbf{e}_3$$

for some b, c. On substituting this expression for $\mathbf{e}_1$ in the elements of the determinant on the right-hand side of the given equation, it can be seen that the first column is a sum of multiples of the other two columns and therefore the determinant is equal to zero. The left-hand side of the given equation is also zero in this case, because $\mathbf{e}_1 \wedge \mathbf{e}_2 . \mathbf{e}_3 = 0$.

Case (*ii*). Suppose $\mathbf{e}_i$ are linearly independent. Then the reciprocal vectors $\mathbf{e}^i$ are linearly independent, and we may express the vectors $\mathbf{f}_i$ in terms of $\mathbf{e}^i$ as follows:

$$\mathbf{f}_i = \sum_j \mathbf{f}_i . \mathbf{e}_j \, \mathbf{e}^j \qquad \text{(Example 4, with } \mathbf{r} = \mathbf{f}_i\text{)}.$$

Hence
$$\mathbf{f}_1 \wedge \mathbf{f}_2 = \left(\sum_j \mathbf{f}_1 . \mathbf{e}_j \mathbf{e}^j\right) \wedge \left(\sum_k \mathbf{f}_2 . \mathbf{e}_k \mathbf{e}^k\right)$$
$$= \sum_j \sum_k \mathbf{f}_1 . \mathbf{e}_j \, \mathbf{f}_2 . \mathbf{e}_k \, \mathbf{e}^j \wedge \mathbf{e}^k.$$

By Example 6,

$$v\mathbf{e}^j \wedge \mathbf{e}^k = \begin{cases} \mathbf{e}_i & (i, j, k = 1, 2, 3 \text{ in cyclic order}) \\ -\mathbf{e}_i & (i, j, k = 1, 2, 3 \text{ not in cyclic order}) \\ 0 & (\text{if two or three of } i, j, k \text{ are equal}). \end{cases}$$

Hence, on multiplying by v and evaluating the double sum by taking $j, k = 2, 3;\ 3, 2;\ 3, 1;\ 1, 3;\ 1, 2;\ 2, 1;$ in turn, we have

$$\begin{aligned} v\mathbf{f}_1 \wedge \mathbf{f}_2 = {} & (\mathbf{f}_1 . \mathbf{e}_2 \, \mathbf{f}_2 . \mathbf{e}_3 - \mathbf{f}_1 . \mathbf{e}_3 \, \mathbf{f}_2 . \mathbf{e}_2) \, \mathbf{e}_1 \\ & + (\mathbf{f}_1 . \mathbf{e}_3 \, \mathbf{f}_2 . \mathbf{e}_1 - \mathbf{f}_1 . \mathbf{e}_1 \, \mathbf{f}_2 . \mathbf{e}_3) \, \mathbf{e}_2 \\ & + (\mathbf{f}_1 . \mathbf{e}_1 \, \mathbf{f}_2 . \mathbf{e}_2 - \mathbf{f}_1 . \mathbf{e}_2 \, \mathbf{f}_2 . \mathbf{e}_1) \, \mathbf{e}_3. \end{aligned}$$

On taking the scalar product of each side of this equation with $\mathbf{f}_3$, it can be seen that the right-hand side of the equation so obtained is equal to the given determinant expanded by the elements of its third row; since $v = \mathbf{e}_1 \wedge \mathbf{e}_2 . \mathbf{e}_3$, we have

$$(\mathbf{e}_1 \wedge \mathbf{e}_2 . \mathbf{e}_3)(\mathbf{f} \wedge \mathbf{f}_2 . \mathbf{f}_3) = \det \mathbf{e}_i . \mathbf{f}_j,$$

which is the required result.

On putting $\mathbf{f}_i = \mathbf{e}_i$ in this equation, we see that

$$v^2 = \det \mathbf{e}_i . \mathbf{e}_j = \det \gamma_{ij},$$

which proves the second result asked for.

Example 9

The expansion of $\det \gamma_{ij}$ by the elements of row i may be written in the form

$$\gamma = \sum_{j=1}^{3} \gamma_{ij} \Gamma^{ji},$$

where Γ^{ji}, the cofactor of element γ_{ij} in the determinant, does not contain the particular element γ_{ij}.

On differentiating this equation with respect to the particular element γ_{ij}, the other elements being regarded as constants in the differentiation, we see that

$$\frac{\partial \gamma}{\partial \gamma_{ij}} = \Gamma^{ji} = \gamma \gamma^{ji}, \qquad \text{by (1.23)},$$

which is the first result asked for.

Example 10

In the given equation $\sum_j \gamma^{ij} \gamma_{jk} = \delta_{ik}$, the quantities γ^{ij} may be regarded as functions of the nine independent variables γ_{ij}. On differentiating with respect to any one of these variables, γ_{rs} say, we have

$$\sum_j \left(\frac{\partial \gamma^{ij}}{\partial \gamma_{rs}} \gamma_{jk} + \gamma^{ij} \frac{\partial \gamma_{jk}}{\partial \gamma_{rs}} \right) = 0.$$

Now

$$\frac{\partial \gamma_{jk}}{\partial \gamma_{rs}} = \begin{cases} 1 \text{ if } \gamma_{jk} \equiv \gamma_{rs}, \text{ i.e. if } j = r,\ k = s; \\ 0 \text{ otherwise, i.e. if } j \neq r \text{ and/or } k \neq s; \end{cases}$$

we may write this in the form

$$\frac{\partial \gamma_{jk}}{\partial \gamma_{rs}} = \delta_{jr} \delta_{ks}.$$

With this expression, the above equation becomes

$$\sum_j \frac{\partial \gamma^{ij}}{\partial \gamma_{rs}} \gamma_{jk} = - \sum_j \gamma^{ij} \delta_{jr} \delta_{ks} = -\gamma^{ir} \delta_{ks}.$$

Multiplying both sides by γ^{kl} and summing over k, we have

$$\sum_j \sum_k \frac{\partial \gamma^{ij}}{\partial \gamma_{rs}} \gamma_{jk} \gamma^{kl} = -\sum_k \gamma^{ir} \delta_{ks} \gamma^{kl}.$$

Therefore

$$\sum_j \frac{\partial \gamma^{ij}}{\partial \gamma_{rs}} \delta_{jl} = -\gamma^{ir} \gamma^{sl}, \qquad \text{using (1.21).†}$$

Therefore

$$\frac{\partial \gamma^{il}}{\partial \gamma_{rs}} = -\gamma^{ir} \gamma^{sl},$$

which gives the required result if j is written in place of l.

Chapter 2

Example 1

The value of any sum does not depend on the choice of letters used as summation suffixes; in the given double sum, therefore, the value is unaltered if the suffixes i, j be replaced by j, i;

i.e.
$$\begin{aligned} \sum_i \sum_j S_{ij} A_{ij} &= \sum_j \sum_i S_{ji} A_{ji} \\ &= \sum_j \sum_i (+S_{ij})(-A_{ij}) \\ &= -\sum_i \sum_j S_{ij} A_{ij}, \end{aligned}$$

since the order of summation can be interchanged in any finite sum. Therefore

$$\sum_i \sum_j S_{ij} A_{ij} = 0,$$

as stated.

Example 2

Part (*i*). In state t, the distance r between a particle P of coordinates ξ^i and the particle O at the origin of the basis $\mathbf{e}_i$ is given by the equation

$$r^2 = \sum \sum \gamma_{ij}(t) \xi^i \xi^j. \tag{11.1}$$

If the distance is unity in state t_0, then

$$1 = \sum \sum \gamma_{ij}(t_0) \xi^i \xi^j. \tag{11.2}$$

This may therefore be regarded as the equation, in convected coordinates, for particles lying on the surface of a sphere of centre O and unit radius in state t_0.

† (1.21) can be derived from the given equation $\Sigma \gamma^{ij} \gamma_{jk} = \delta_{ik}$ by an argument similar to that given at the top of p. 12.

In state t, these particles will lie in the surface of an ellipsoid whose main axes are determined by those sets of values of ξ^i for which r^2 (given by (11.1)) has an extreme value (maximum or minimum) for variations $\delta\xi^i$ in the variables ξ^i subject to the condition (11.2).

Using a Lagrange multiplier λ^2 in connection with (11.2), we have

$$\begin{aligned}\delta(r^2) &= \sum\sum \gamma_{ij}(t)\{(\delta\xi^i)\,\xi^j + \xi^i\,\delta\xi^j\}\\ &= 2\sum\sum \gamma_{ij}(t)\,\xi^i\,\delta\xi^j \qquad (\text{since } \gamma_{ij} = \gamma_{ji});\end{aligned}$$

similarly, $0 = \sum\sum\gamma_{ij}(t_0)\,\xi^i\delta\xi^j$, and so we may write

$$\delta(r^2) = 2\sum_i\sum_j [\gamma_{ij}(t) - \lambda^2\gamma_{ij}(t_0)]\,\xi^i\,\delta\xi^j,$$

where λ^2 (a Lagrange multiplier) is arbitrary.

For an extreme value of r^2, we must have $\delta(r^2) = 0$ to the first order in $\delta\xi^i$ for all values of $\delta\xi^i$ consistent with (11.2); $\delta\xi^1$ and $\delta\xi^2$ may therefore be given any values, and then $\delta\xi^3$ will be determined by the differential of (11.2). If in the equation $\delta(r^2) = 0$ we choose the value of λ^2 to make the coefficient of $\delta\xi^3$ vanish, it follows that the coefficients of $\delta\xi^1$ and $\delta\xi^2$ must also vanish. Hence, for a suitable value of λ^2, we must have

$$(11.3)\qquad \sum_{i=1}^{3} [\gamma_{ij}(t) - \lambda^2\gamma_{ij}(t_0)]\,\xi^i = 0 \qquad (j = 1, 2, 3).$$

These are three linear homogeneous equations in the three variables ξ^i; a necessary and sufficient condition for a solution other than $\xi^1 = \xi^2 = \xi^3 = 0$ is that the determinant of the coefficients vanish, i.e.

$$(11.4)\qquad \det[\gamma_{ij}(t) - \lambda^2\gamma_{ij}(t_0)] = 0.$$

This is a cubic equation in λ^2, and has three roots which we shall denote by λ_a^2, λ_b^2, λ_c^2. To any one root, λ_a^2 say, there corresponds a solution $\xi^i = \xi^i_{(a)}$ of the equation obtained by putting $\lambda^2 = \lambda_a^2$ in (11.3):

$$(11.5)\qquad \sum_i [\gamma_{ij}(t) - \lambda_a^2\gamma_{ij}(t_0)]\,\xi^i_{(a)} = 0.$$

This equation determines $\xi^i_{(a)}$ to within a constant factor, and hence determines the direction in the material of a main axis of the ellipsoid; the constant factor may be determined by using (11.2).

To prove that there are in fact three main axes, it is necessary to prove that the roots in λ^2 are all real, for it will then follow from (11.5) that the solutions for $\xi^i_{(a)}$, $\xi^i_{(b)}$, and $\xi^i_{(c)}$ are real.

Proof that the roots of (11.4) *are real.* The proof depends on the fact that the quantities γ_{ij} are symmetric, i.e. $\gamma_{ij} = \gamma_{ji}$.

Suppose if possible that one root is complex; then we may write $\lambda^2 = \mu + \iota\nu$, where μ and ν are real, and $\iota \equiv \sqrt{(-1)}$. Corresponding to this root, there will be a solution to the equations (11.3) which we may write in the form $\xi^i = x^i + \iota y^i$, where x^i and y^i are real. On substituting these expressions in (11.3), multiplying by the complex conjugate $\bar{\xi}^j = x^j - \iota y^j$, and summing over j, we obtain an equation which may be written in the form

$$\sum_i \sum_j [\gamma_{ij}(t) - (\mu + \iota\nu)\gamma_{ij}(t_0)][x^i x^j + y^i y^j + \iota(x^j y^i - x^i y^j)] = 0.$$

The term $x^j y^i - x^i y^j$ is antisymmetric in i and j, and hence, by Examples 2, No. 1, its double sum with the quantities $\gamma_{ij}(t)$, $\gamma_{ij}(t_0)$ is zero, since these are both symmetric. In the remaining terms, the coefficient of ι must vanish, i.e.

$$\nu \sum \sum \gamma_{ij}(t_0)(x^i x^j + y^i y^j) = 0.$$

Since the ξ^i are not all zero, x^i and y^i are not all zero; but $\sum\sum \gamma_{ij}(t_0) x^i x^j$ is the square of the length of the vector $\sum x^i \mathbf{e}_i(t_0)$, and is therefore greater than or equal to zero, and is equal to zero only if all x^i are zero. Hence the coefficient of ν is positive, and therefore $\nu = 0$, which proves that λ^2 is real. Since (11.4) has three roots in λ^2, they must all be real.

Part (ii). From (11.1), the length r_a of the semi-axis of the ellipsoid corresponding to the principal value $\lambda = \lambda_a$ is given by the equation

$$\begin{aligned} r_a^2 &= \sum_i \sum_j \gamma_{ij}(t)\, \xi^i_{(a)} \xi^j_{(b)} \\ &= \lambda_a^2 \sum_i \sum_j \gamma_{ij}(t_0)\, \xi^i_{(a)} \xi^j_{(b)}, \qquad \text{by (11.5)}, \\ &= \lambda_a^2, \qquad \text{by (11.2)}. \end{aligned}$$

Thus $r_a = \lambda_a$, since we may take λ_a to be positive without loss of generality. Similarly, $r_b = \lambda_b$ and $r_c = \lambda_c$.

The roots in λ of (11.4) therefore give the main semi-axes of that ellipsoid in state t which was a unit sphere in state t_0.

Part (iii). We now prove that, when $\lambda_a \neq \lambda_b$, the lines OP_a and OP_b are orthogonal, where P_a is the particle $\xi^i_{(a)}$, etc.

Multiplying (11.5) by $\xi^j_{(b)}$ and summing over j, we have

$$\sum_i \sum_j [\gamma_{ij}(t) - \lambda_a^2 \gamma_{ij}(t_0)]\, \xi^i_{(a)} \xi^j_{(b)} = 0.$$

Similarly,

$$\sum_i \sum_j [\gamma_{ij}(t) - \lambda_b^2 \gamma_{ij}(t_0)]\, \xi^i_{(b)} \xi^j_{(a)} = 0.$$

On subtracting one of these equations from the other, we obtain the result

$$(\lambda_a^2-\lambda_b^2)\sum_i\sum_j\gamma_{ij}(t_0)\,\xi^i_{(a)}\,\xi^j_{(b)} = 0,$$

when we use the fact that $\sum\sum\gamma_{ij}\,\xi^i_{(a)}\,\xi^j_{(b)} = \sum\sum\gamma_{ij}\,\xi^i_{(b)}\,\xi^j_{(a)}$, which follows from the symmetry of γ_{ij}.

It follows that, when $\lambda_a \neq \lambda_b$, we must have

$$\begin{aligned} 0 &= \sum_i\sum_j\gamma_{ij}(t_0)\,\xi^i_{(a)}\,\xi^j_{(b)} \\ &= \left[\sum_i \xi^i_{(a)}\,\mathbf{e}_i(t_0)\right].\left[\sum_j \xi^j_{(b)}\,\mathbf{e}_j(t_0)\right] \\ &= (\overrightarrow{\mathrm{OP}}_a.\overrightarrow{\mathrm{OP}}_b)_{t_0}, \end{aligned}$$

which proves that OP_a and OP_b are perpendicular in state t_0. The corresponding result for state t can be proved in a similar fashion if one starts by dividing (11.5) by λ_a^2; for one then evidently obtains an equation which is similar to that on which the above proof is based but has λ_a^{-2} and t in place of λ_a^2 and t_0.

A similar argument applies to any pair of roots; hence, when the roots λ_a, λ_b, and λ_c are all different, it follows that the principal axes OP_a, OP_b, and OP_c are mutually orthogonal in state t_0 and in state t.

For completeness, we consider the cases in which the roots are not all different.

The case $\lambda_a = \lambda_b = \lambda_c$

We shall prove that, when $\lambda_a = \lambda_b = \lambda_c$, the strain $t_0 \to t$ is a dilatation; by Example 5 below, it then follows that every set of material lines which are mutually orthogonal in state t_0 are mutually orthogonal in state t and are therefore principal axes, as stated in Chapter 2.

For simplicity, we may take the basis to be orthonormal in state t_0, without loss of generality. Then $\gamma_{ij}(t_0) = \delta_{ij}$, and writing

$$\gamma_{ij}(t) = \begin{pmatrix} a & h & g \\ h & b & f \\ g & f & c \end{pmatrix},$$

equation (11.4) becomes

$$\begin{vmatrix} a-\lambda^2 & h & g \\ h & b-\lambda^2 & f \\ g & f & c-\lambda^2 \end{vmatrix} = 0. \tag{11.6}$$

On expanding this determinant, we obtain the equation

$$-\lambda^6+A\lambda^4-B\lambda^2+\gamma = 0, \tag{11.7}$$

where $\gamma = \det\gamma_{ij}(t)$ and

$$\begin{cases} A = a+b+c \\ B = bc+ca+ab-f^2-g^2-h^2. \end{cases} \tag{11.8}$$

Since λ_a^2, λ_b^2, λ_c^2 are the roots in λ^2 of (11.7), we have

$$\begin{cases} A = \lambda_a^2+\lambda_b^2+\lambda_c^2 \\ B = \lambda_b^2\lambda_c^2+\lambda_c^2\lambda_a^2+\lambda_a^2\lambda_b^2. \end{cases} \tag{11.9}$$

When $\lambda_a = \lambda_b = \lambda_c$, it follows that $A = 3\lambda_a^2$, $B = 3\lambda_a^4$, and hence

$$\begin{aligned} 0 &= A^2-3B \\ &= \tfrac{1}{2}(b-c)^2+\tfrac{1}{2}(c-a)^2+\tfrac{1}{2}(a-b)^2+3f^2+3g^2+3h^2, \quad \text{by (11.8).} \end{aligned}$$

Every term in this sum of squares must therefore vanish; hence

$$f = g = h = 0,$$

and

$$a = b = c;$$

i.e.

$$\gamma_{ij}(t) = a\delta_{ij},$$

and

$$\gamma_{ij}(t_0) = \delta_{ij},$$

which proves that the deformation $t_0 \to t$ is a dilatation, by comparison with (2.40) and (2.56).

The case $\lambda_a = \lambda_b \neq \lambda_c$

In this case, the material lines OP_b and OP_c are perpendicular in states t_0 and t, by the proof given in the first case above. Let us now define P_a as being that particle which in state t_0 lies on the perpendicular through O to the plane $\mathrm{OP}_b\mathrm{P}_c$ at unit distance from O. We now show that the material line OP_a, so defined, is also perpendicular to OP_b and OP_c in state t.

The foregoing arguments are valid for any basis; let us now take base vectors $\mathbf{e}_1 = \overrightarrow{\mathrm{OP}}_a$, $\mathbf{e}_2 = \overrightarrow{\mathrm{OP}}_b$, $\mathbf{e}_3 = \overrightarrow{\mathrm{OP}}_c$. Then since $\overrightarrow{\mathrm{OP}}_b = \sum_i \xi^i_{(b)}\mathbf{e}_i$, we have

$\xi^i_{(b)} = (0,1,0)$; similarly, $\xi^1_{(c)} = \xi^2_{(c)} = 0$, $\xi^3_{(c)} = 1$. Moreover, the basis is orthonormal in state t_0, and therefore $\gamma_{ij}(t_0) = \delta_{ij}$. With these results, equations (11.3) applied to the principal axes OP_b and OP_c take the form

$$\left.\begin{aligned}\gamma_{2j}(t) - \lambda_b^2\,\delta_{2j} &= 0\\ \gamma_{3j}(t) - \lambda_c^2\,\delta_{3j} &= 0\end{aligned}\right\} \qquad (j = 1, 2, 3).$$

These determine all the quantities $\gamma_{ij}(t)$ except $\gamma_{11}(t)$ and we have in fact the result

$$\gamma_{ij}(t) = \begin{pmatrix}\gamma_{11}(t) & 0 & 0\\ 0 & \lambda_b^2 & 0\\ 0 & 0 & \lambda_c^2\end{pmatrix}. \tag{11.10}$$

Since this shows that $\gamma_{ij}(t) = 0$ $(i \neq j)$, it follows that the basis is orthogonal in state t.

We have thus shown that in every case there are three material lines through any given particle O which are mutually orthogonal in each of two states t_0 and t related by a uniform deformation. This completes the proof of Theorem (2.38).

In view of the fundamental importance of this theorem, we complete the treatment of this topic by proving the further result in the present case $(\lambda_a = \lambda_b \neq \lambda_c)$ that any two material lines, OP_α and OP_β say, lying in the plane OP_aP_b and perpendicular to one another in state t_0 are principal axes, i.e. that OP_α, OP_β, and OP_c (mutually orthogonal in state t_0, by definition) are mutually orthogonal in state t.

With the present basis, OP_α and OP_β lie in the plane of $\mathbf{e}_1$ and $\mathbf{e}_2$, and therefore we may write

$$\left.\begin{aligned}\overrightarrow{OP}_\alpha &= \xi^1_{(\alpha)}\,\mathbf{e}_1 + \xi^2_{(\alpha)}\,\mathbf{e}_2\\ \overrightarrow{OP}_\beta &= \xi^1_{(\beta)}\,\mathbf{e}_1 + \xi^2_{(\beta)}\,\mathbf{e}_2\end{aligned}\right\},$$

for suitable values of the coefficients $\xi^1_{(\alpha)}, \xi^2_{(\alpha)}, \xi^1_{(\beta)}, \xi^2_{(\beta)}$. It follows that

$$\overrightarrow{OP}_\alpha.\overrightarrow{OP}_\beta = \xi^1_{(\alpha)}\,\xi^1_{(\beta)}\,\gamma_{11} + (\xi^1_{(\alpha)}\,\xi^2_{(\beta)} + \xi^1_{(\beta)}\,\xi^2_{(\alpha)})\,\gamma_{12} + \xi^2_{(\alpha)}\,\xi^2_{(\beta)}\,\gamma_{22}, \tag{11.11}$$

on taking the scalar product of these equations and using (1.18); this equation is valid in both states, t_0 and t.

In state t_0, since $\gamma_{ij}(t_0) = \delta_{ij}$, the equation becomes

$$(\overrightarrow{OP}_\alpha.\overrightarrow{OP}_\beta)_{t_0} = \xi^1_{(\alpha)}\,\xi^1_{(\beta)} + \xi^2_{(\alpha)}\,\xi^2_{(\beta)}.$$

Using (11.10), (11.4) becomes

$$\begin{vmatrix} \gamma_{11}(t)-\lambda^2 & 0 & 0 \\ 0 & \lambda_b^2-\lambda^2 & 0 \\ 0 & 0 & \lambda_c^2-\lambda^2 \end{vmatrix} = 0,$$

and this must be identical with

$$(\lambda_b^2-\lambda^2)^2(\lambda_c^2-\lambda^2) = 0,$$

since the three principal values in the present case are λ_b, λ_b, and λ_c. It follows that

$$\gamma_{11}(t) = \lambda_b^2 = \gamma_{22}(t).$$

Using this result and (11.10), equation (11.11) applied to state t takes the form

$$(\overrightarrow{\mathrm{OP}}_\alpha . \overrightarrow{\mathrm{OP}}_\beta)_t = \lambda_b^2(\xi^1_{(\alpha)}\xi^1_{(\beta)} + \xi^2_{(\alpha)}\xi^2_{(\beta)}).$$

Hence

$$(\overrightarrow{\mathrm{OP}}_\alpha . \overrightarrow{\mathrm{OP}}_\beta)_t = \lambda_b^2(\overrightarrow{\mathrm{OP}}_\alpha . \overrightarrow{\mathrm{OP}}_\beta)_{t_0},$$

from which it follows that $\overrightarrow{\mathrm{OP}}_\alpha$ and $\overrightarrow{\mathrm{OP}}_\beta$ are perpendicular in state t because they are perpendicular in state t_0, by hypothesis. Since they lie in a material plane $\mathrm{OP}_a\mathrm{P}_b$ which is perpendicular to OP_c in both states, it follows that OP_α, OP_β, and OP_c are mutually orthogonal in state t_0 and in state t, as stated. This completes the discussion of principal axes of strain.

Example 3

Let R′ and S′ be any two particles in any given material plane α' which is parallel to the fixed plane α in state t_0. Let R′ and S′ occupy places A_0 and B_0 in state t_0 and A and B in state t (Fig. 11.1).

We may choose two particles R and S in the fixed plane α in such a way that $\mathrm{RSB_0A_0}$ is a parallelogram. Then from (2.5) it follows that RSBA is a parallelogram, and in particular that $\mathrm{AB} = \mathrm{RS} = \mathrm{A_0B_0}$ and that AB is parallel to $\mathrm{A_0B_0}$ for both are parallel to RS. Hence $\mathrm{A_0B_0BA}$ is a parallelogram, and therefore $\mathrm{A_0B_0} = \mathrm{AB}$ and $\overrightarrow{\mathrm{A_0A}} = \overrightarrow{\mathrm{B_0B}}$, i.e. the separation of an arbitrary pair of particles in α' does not change and the displacement of every particle in α' is represented by the same vector; thus α' moves rigidly without rotation.

Let C be any closed material curve in the fixed plane α bounding a region of area Y, say; in state t_0, let the perpendiculars from all points of C to α' meet α' in a material curve C′. The right circular cylinder so formed will have volume Yh_0, where h_0 is the separation of α and α' in state t_0. In state t, the generators of the new cylinder formed with the same particles are parallel to one another, by (2.5); the area of either end of the cylinder is Y, and the ends are parallel by (2.4); the volume is therefore Yh, where h is the separation of α and α' in state t. Since the volume is constant, by hypothesis, it follows that $h_0 = h$, i.e. that α' moves at constant separation from α. This completes the proof of (i).

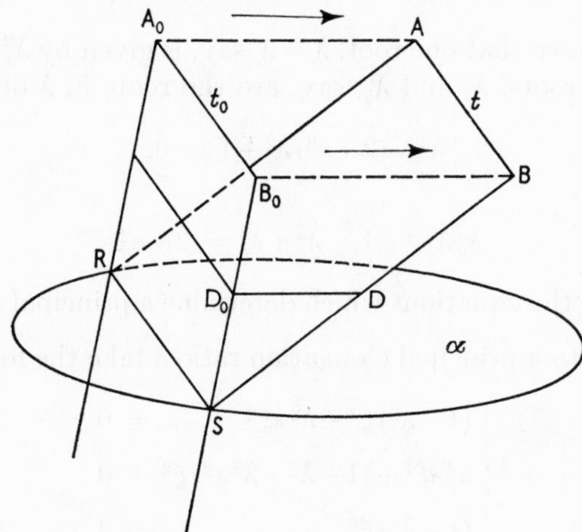

FIG. 11.1.

Let any other material plane α'' parallel to α and lying on the same side of α as α' meet B_0S in D_0. Let the particle at D_0 in state t_0 move to a place D in state t. Then in the deformation $t_0 \to t$, the material line lying along SD_0B_0 moves to coincide with SDB, showing that D must lie on the line SB. Moreover, $\overrightarrow{D_0D}$ must be parallel to $\overrightarrow{B_0B}$, for they are the intersections of parallel planes α'' and α' with a single plane SB_0B. Hence $\overrightarrow{D_0D}$ is parallel to $\overrightarrow{B_0B}$, and therefore the displacements of α'' and α' are parallel. Further, since the triangles SD_0D and SB_0B are similar, it follows that $D_0D : B_0B = SD_0 :: SB_0 = h'' : h$, where h'' is the distance between α'' and α. If α'' lies on the side of α opposite to α', it is clear that a similar argument will apply, the only difference being that the displacement of α'' will be in the opposite direction to that of α'. This completes the proof of (ii).

Example 4

From (2.62), (2.64), and (11.4), the equation whose roots in λ are the principal elongation ratios takes the form

$$\begin{vmatrix} 1-\lambda^2 & \lambda^2 s & 0 \\ \lambda^2 s & 1-\lambda^2-\lambda^2 s^2 & 0 \\ 0 & 0 & 1-\lambda^2 \end{vmatrix} = 0$$

for a simple shear of magnitude s; this reduces to

$$(\lambda^2-1)[\lambda^4-(2+s^2)\lambda^2+1] = 0,$$

from which we see that one root, $\lambda = \lambda_c$ say, is given by $\lambda_c^2 = 1$, and that the other two roots, λ_a and λ_b, say, are the roots in λ of the equation

$$\lambda^4-(2+s^2)\lambda^2+1 = 0.$$

Hence

$$\text{(11.12)} \qquad \lambda_a^2\lambda_b^2 = 1, \quad \lambda_a^2+\lambda_b^2 = 2+s^2.$$

From (11.3), the equations which determine a principal axis $\mathbf{r} = \sum_i \xi^i \mathbf{e}_i$ corresponding to a principal elongation ratio λ take the form

$$\text{(11.13)} \qquad \begin{cases} (1-\lambda^2)\xi^1+\lambda^2 s\xi^2 = 0 \\ \lambda^2 s\xi^1+(1-\lambda^2-\lambda^2 s^2)\xi^2 = 0 \\ (1-\lambda^2)\xi^3 = 0. \end{cases}$$

$\lambda = \lambda_c = 1$. In this case, (11.13) are satisfied by $\xi^1_{(c)} = \xi^2_{(c)} = 0$; hence $\mathbf{r}_{(c)} = \xi^3_{(c)}\mathbf{e}_3$, showing that this principal axis is parallel to $\mathbf{e}_3$, as expected.

$\lambda = \lambda_a$. Since $s \neq 0$, $\lambda_a \neq 1$, and hence from the last of equations (11.13) we have $\xi^3_{(a)} = 0$, which shows that the corresponding principal axis lies in the plane of $\mathbf{e}_1$ and $\mathbf{e}_2$. Let χ be its inclination to $\mathbf{e}_1$ in state t (Fig. 11.2). Then

$$\mathbf{r}_{(a)} = \xi^1_{(a)}\mathbf{e}_1+\xi^2_{(a)}\mathbf{e}_2$$
$$= \lambda_a\cos\chi\mathbf{e}_1+\lambda_a\sin\chi\mathbf{e}_2,$$

since $\mathbf{e}_1$ and $\mathbf{e}_2$ are orthonormal in state t. Hence

$$\tan\chi = -\frac{\xi^2_{(a)}}{\xi^1_{(a)}} = \frac{\lambda_a^2-1}{\lambda_a^2 s}, \qquad \text{by (11.13)};$$

i.e.

$$\text{(11.14)} \qquad 1-\lambda_a^{-2} = s\tan\chi.$$

$\lambda = \lambda_b$. Since the principal values are all different, the principal axes are mutually orthogonal, and in particular the principal axis $\mathbf{r}_b$ lies in the plane of $\mathbf{e}_1$ and $\mathbf{e}_2$ making an angle $\chi + \frac{\pi}{2}$ with $\mathbf{e}_1$. The argument leading to (11.14) may be repeated if we replace λ_a and χ by λ_b and $\chi + \frac{\pi}{2}$; in place of (11.14) we thus obtain the result

$$1 - \lambda_b^{-2} = s \tan\left(\chi + \frac{\pi}{2}\right) = -s \cot \chi. \tag{11.15}$$

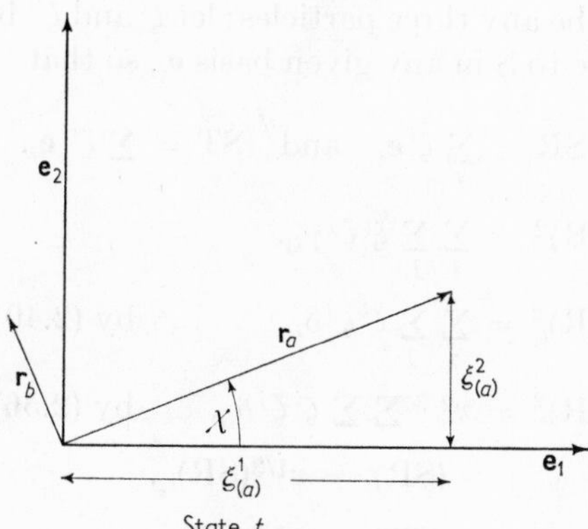

FIG. 11.2.

Adding (11.14) and (11.15) and substituting the expressions for the sum and product of the roots given in (11.12), we obtain the required result

$$s = \cot \chi - \tan \chi = 2 \cot 2\chi. \tag{2.67}$$

Substituting this value for s in (11.14), we see that

$$1 - \lambda_a^{-2} = 1 - \tan^2 \chi,$$

from which it follows that $\lambda_a = |\cot \chi|$. Without loss of generality, we may take $0 \leqslant \chi \leqslant \frac{\pi}{2}$ (as given in the question); then $\cot \chi \geqslant 0$, and hence $\lambda_a = \cot \chi$. It then follows from (11.12) that $\lambda_b = \tan \chi$, which completes the proof of (2.68).

Finally, when $s > 0$, we have $\tan 2\chi = 2/s > 0$, from (2.67), and therefore

$$0 < \chi < \frac{\pi}{4} \quad \text{or} \quad \frac{\pi}{2} < \chi < \frac{3\pi}{4};$$

the second possibility is excluded by the given inequality $0 \leqslant \chi \leqslant \frac{\pi}{2}$, and therefore $0 < \chi < \frac{\pi}{4}$, $\lambda_b = \tan\chi < 1$, and $\lambda_a = \cot\chi > 1$, which completes the proof.

Example 5

Let R, S, and T be any three particles; let ζ^i and ζ'^i be the coordinates of R and T relative to S in any given basis $\mathbf{e}_i$, so that

$$\overrightarrow{\mathrm{SR}} = \sum_i \zeta^i \mathbf{e}_i \quad \text{and} \quad \overrightarrow{\mathrm{ST}} = \sum_i \zeta'^i \mathbf{e}_i.$$

We have $$(\mathrm{SR})^2 = \sum_i \sum_j \zeta^i \zeta^j \gamma_{ij},$$

and hence $$(\mathrm{SR})^2_{t_0} = \sum_i \sum_j \zeta^i \zeta^j \delta_{ij}, \qquad \text{by (2.40)};$$

$$(\mathrm{SR})^2_t = v^{2/3} \sum \sum \zeta^i \zeta^j \delta_{ij}, \qquad \text{by (2.56)};$$

thus $$(\mathrm{SR})_t = v^{1/3} (\mathrm{SR})_{t_0},$$

and similarly $$(\mathrm{ST})_t = v^{1/3} (\mathrm{ST})_{t_0}.$$

If θ denotes the angle between the material lines SR and ST, we have

$$(\mathrm{SR\,ST}\cos\theta)_t = \overrightarrow{\mathrm{SR}}.\overrightarrow{\mathrm{ST}} = \sum_i \sum_j \zeta^i \zeta'^j \gamma_{ij}(t)$$

$$= v^{2/3} \sum_i \sum_j \zeta^i \zeta'^j \delta_{ij}, \qquad \text{by (2.56)};$$

also

$$(\mathrm{SR\,ST}\cos\theta)_{t_0} = \sum_i \sum_j \zeta^i \zeta'^j \delta_{ij}, \qquad \text{by (2.40)}.$$

Hence $$(\mathrm{SR\,ST}\cos\theta)_t = v^{2/3} (\mathrm{SR\,ST}\cos\theta)_{t_0};$$

on substituting the values obtained above for SR and ST in the two states, we see that $(\cos\theta)_t = (\cos\theta)_{t_0}$, which proves the required result.

Example 6

Using (1.22), the condition for constancy of volume may be written in the form

$$\gamma \equiv \det \gamma_{ij} = \text{constant}.$$

Assuming that the flow is such that the quantities γ_{ij} are differentiable functions of time t, this leads to the result

$$0 = \frac{d\gamma}{dt} = \sum_i \sum_j \frac{\partial\gamma}{\partial\gamma_{ij}} \frac{d\gamma_{ij}}{dt}$$

$$= \sum_i \sum_j \gamma\gamma^{ij} \frac{d\gamma_{ij}}{dt}, \qquad \text{by Examples 1, No. 9 and (1.19);}$$

in differentiating the determinant, each element in turn has to be differentiated so that γ_{ij} and γ_{ji} $(i \neq j)$ must be treated as independent functions of t (irrespective of the fact that $\gamma_{ij} = \gamma_{ji}$); the result of Examples 1, No. 9, is therefore applicable.

Since $\gamma \neq 0$, it follows that $\sum\sum \gamma^{ij} d\gamma_{ij}/dt = 0$, as stated. To deduce the second result stated, we differentiate equation (1.21) and obtain the equation

$$\sum_j \left(\frac{d\gamma_{ij}}{dt} \gamma^{jk} + \gamma_{ij} \frac{d\gamma^{jk}}{dt} \right) = 0 \qquad (i, k = 1, 2, 3).$$

Putting $k = i$ in this equation and summing over the values $i = 1, 2, 3$, we see that

$$\sum_i \sum_j \gamma_{ij} \frac{d\gamma^{ji}}{dt} = -\sum\sum \gamma^{ji} \frac{d\gamma_{ij}}{dt},$$

which proves the second required result, since $\gamma^{ji} = \gamma^{ij}$.

Example 7

The proof of this example and of the following example depends essentially on the identity

$$\sum_{\mathbf{n}} \mathbf{r}.\mathbf{nn} = \mathbf{r}, \tag{11.16}$$

which holds for any vector $\mathbf{r}$ when the summation extends over any three mutually orthogonal unit vectors $\mathbf{n}$. The truth of this result is evident from Examples 1, No. 4, if we take the linearly independent vectors $\mathbf{e}_j$ to be orthonormal and remember that in this case they are self-reciprocal, i.e. that $\mathbf{e}_j = \mathbf{e}^j (= \mathbf{n})$.

Let us now use $\mathbf{e}_i$ to denote any embedded basis in the material. By (2.37), we have for any planes of unit normal $\mathbf{n}$ (in state t) the result

$$\left(\frac{h}{h_0}\right)^2 = \sum_i \sum_j \gamma^{ij}(t_0)\, l_i l_j \qquad (l_i \text{ in state } t)$$

$$= \sum_i \sum_j \gamma^{ij}(t_0)\, \mathbf{e}_i.\mathbf{nn}.\mathbf{e}_j, \qquad \text{by (2.20).}$$

On summing this equation over three mutually orthogonal **n**-vectors, we have

$$J_1(t_0, t) = \sum_i \sum_j \gamma^{ij}(t_0)\, \mathbf{e}_i . \sum_{\mathbf{n}} \mathbf{nn}.\mathbf{e}_j;$$

here, the summation over **n** can be carried out in the position indicated because $\gamma^{ij}(t_0)$ and $\mathbf{e}_i$ are independent of **n**.

Applying (11.16) with $\mathbf{r} = \mathbf{e}_j$, this equation becomes

$$J_1(t_0, t) = \sum_i \sum_j \gamma^{ij}(t_0)\, \mathbf{e}_i . \mathbf{e}_j = \sum_i \sum_j \gamma^{ij}(t_0)\, \gamma_{ij}(t), \tag{11.17}$$

because the vectors $\mathbf{e}_i$ refer to the state t since the quantities l_i do.

Since γ^{ij} and γ_{ij} are independent of **n**, it follows from (11.17) that $J_1(t_0, t)$ has the same value for every set of three mutually orthogonal unit vectors **n**, which proves (i).

Furthermore, the definition of J_1 (in terms of separation ratios) makes no reference to any basis, and therefore the value of J_1 and of the right-hand side of (11.17) must be independent of the choice of base vectors used in the definition of γ^{ij} and γ_{ij}; this proves (iii).

Finally, by Theorem (2.38), we can choose a particular basis $\mathbf{e}_i$ which is orthonormal in state t_0 and coincides in direction with the principal axes for the given deformation $t_0 \to t$. Substituting the appropriate values for γ^{ij} and γ_{ij} from (2.45) and (2.41) in (11.17), we obtain the required result (ii), which must be valid whatever basis is used because of (iii).

Example 8

With the notation as given in the question, we may write

$$(\overrightarrow{\mathrm{OP}})_t \equiv \mathbf{r} = \sum_j \xi^j \mathbf{e}_j \qquad \text{(in state } t)$$

where the coordinates ξ^j are constant. In state t_0, we therefore have

$$(\overrightarrow{\mathrm{OP}})_{t_0} = \sum_j \xi^j \mathbf{e}_j(t_0) = h_0 \mathbf{n}_0 \qquad \text{(by definition)},$$

where h_0 and $\mathbf{n}_0$ denote the planes' separation and unit normal in state t_0 (Fig. 11.3).

Hence $\qquad \xi^j = h_0 \mathbf{n}_0 . \mathbf{e}^j(t_0) \qquad$ by (1.16)

$$= h_0 \sum_i (l_i \mathbf{e}^i . \mathbf{e}^j)_{t_0} \qquad \text{by (2.19)},$$

where the notation $(\ldots)_{t_0}$ means that all quantities within the brackets refer to state t_0.

By (2.24) and the fact that η_i in (2.24) are constant, it follows that $(l_i/h)_{t_0} = (l_i/h)_t$ and hence that

$$\xi^j = \frac{h_0^2}{h} \sum_i l_i \gamma^{ij}(t_0) \qquad \text{by (1.18)},$$

and that
$$\mathbf{r} = \frac{h_0^2}{h} \sum_i \sum_j \gamma^{ij}(t_0)\, l_i\, \mathbf{e}_j,$$

as stated.

In this expression, three quantities, h, h_0 and l_i, depend on $\mathbf{n}$; in order to apply a method similar to that used in the previous example, we therefore consider the vector

$$\mathbf{u} \equiv \frac{h}{h_0^2}\mathbf{r} = \sum_i \sum_j \gamma^{ij}(t_0)\,(\mathbf{e}_i.\mathbf{n})\,\mathbf{e}_j \qquad \text{by (2.20)}$$

$$= \sum_k \sum_m \mathbf{e}_k(\mathbf{e}_m.\mathbf{n})\,\gamma^{km}(t_0);$$

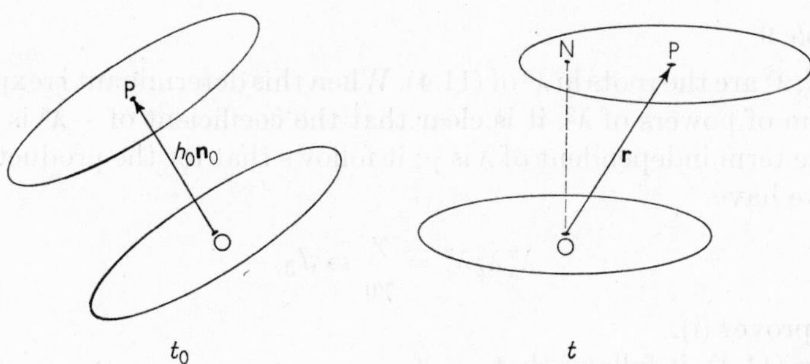

FIG. 11.3.

the last step is taken simply by changing the dummy suffixes from i, j to k, m and altering the order of the factors. In the right-hand side of this equation, the vector $\mathbf{n}$ occurs only once, and we may now proceed as in the proof of the previous example, after taking the scalar product of $\mathbf{u}$ with itself:

$$\frac{h^2 r^2}{h_0^4} = \mathbf{u}.\mathbf{u}$$

$$= \left\{\sum_i \sum_j \gamma^{ij}(t_0)\,(\mathbf{e}_i.\mathbf{n})\,\mathbf{e}_j\right\} . \left\{\sum_k \sum_m \mathbf{e}_k(\mathbf{e}_m.\mathbf{n})\,\gamma^{km}(t_0)\right\}$$

$$= \sum_i \sum_j \sum_k \sum_m \gamma^{ij}(t_0)\,\gamma_{jk}(t)\,\gamma^{km}(t_0)\,\mathbf{e}_m.\mathbf{nn}.\mathbf{e}_i, \qquad \text{by (1.18)}.$$

Summing this equation over any three mutually orthogonal unit vectors $\mathbf{n}$ and then using the result $\sum_{\mathbf{n}} \mathbf{nn}.\mathbf{e}_i = \mathbf{e}_i$, we obtain the equation

$$J_2(t_0, t) = \sum_i \sum_j \sum_k \sum_m \gamma^{ij}(t_0)\gamma_{jk}(t)\gamma^{km}(t_0)\gamma_{mi}(t), \qquad \text{by (1.18).} \tag{11.18}$$

The right-hand side is independent of $\mathbf{n}$; therefore J_2 has the same value for every orthonormal set of $\mathbf{n}$-vectors, which proves (i). The quantity J_2 is defined without reference to any set of base vectors; therefore the value of the right-hand side of the above equation is independent of the choice of base vectors used in the definition of γ^{ij} and γ_{ij}, which proves (iii).

Since the value of J_2 is independent of the basis, we may determine the value in particular in that basis $\mathbf{e}_i$ which is orthonormal in state t_0 and coincides in direction with the principal axes for the given deformation $t_0 \to t$; when the appropriate values for γ^{ij} and γ_{ij} are substituted from (2.45) and (2.41) in the above equation, the right-hand side reduces to $\lambda_a^4 + \lambda_b^4 + \lambda_c^4$, which proves (ii).

Example 9

$\lambda_a^2, \lambda_b^2, \lambda_c^2$ are the roots in λ^2 of (11.4). When this determinant is expressed as a sum of powers of λ^2, it is clear that the coefficient of $-\lambda^6$ is γ_0 and that the term independent of λ is γ; it follows that for the product of the roots we have

$$\lambda_a^2\lambda_b^2\lambda_c^2 = \frac{\gamma}{\gamma_0} \equiv J_3,$$

which proves (i).

From (11.4), it follows that

$$\begin{aligned} 0 &= \{\det \gamma^{ki}(t)\}\{\det [\gamma_{ij}(t) - \lambda^2\gamma_{ij}(t_0)]\}\{\det \gamma^{jm}(t_0)\} \\ &= \det\left\{\sum_i \sum_j \gamma^{ki}(t)\,[\gamma_{ij}(t) - \lambda^2\gamma_{ij}(t_0)]\,\gamma^{jm}(t_0)\right\} \quad \text{(by the rule for the multiplication of determinants)} \\ &= \det\left\{\sum_j \delta_{kj}\gamma^{jm}(t_0) - \sum_i \lambda^2\gamma^{ki}(t)\,\delta_{im}\right\} \quad \text{by (1.21), (1.19)} \\ &= \det\{\gamma^{km}(t_0) - \lambda^2\gamma^{km}(t)\}, \end{aligned}$$

which may be written in the form

$$\det[\Delta^{km} - (\lambda^2 - 1)\gamma^{km}(t)] = 0, \tag{11.19}$$

which proves (ii).

This equation is similar in form to (11.4) with Δ^{km}, λ^2-1, and $\gamma^{km}(t)$ taking the place of $\gamma_{ij}(t)$, λ^2, and $\gamma_{ij}(t_0)$; by making these changes, the argument which led from (11.4) to (i) above will evidently lead from (11.19) to the equation

$$(\lambda_a^2-1)(\lambda_b^2-1)(\lambda_c^2-1) = \frac{\det \Delta^{km}}{\det \gamma^{km}(t)}$$

$$= \gamma \det \Delta^{km}, \qquad \text{by (1.22).}$$

This proves (iii).

Example 10

Part (*i*). From (2.69) and (2.64) with t_0 replaced by t', we see that

$$\frac{d\gamma_{ij}}{dt} \equiv \lim_{t'\to t} \frac{d\gamma_{ij}(t')}{dt'} = \begin{pmatrix} 0 & G & 0 \\ G & 0 & 0 \\ 0 & 0 & 0 \end{pmatrix},$$

and also that

$$\gamma_{ij} \equiv \gamma_{ij}(t) = \begin{pmatrix} 1 & 0 & 0 \\ 0 & 1 & 0 \\ 0 & 0 & 1 \end{pmatrix}.$$

The given equation for determining the principal values in the case $n = 1$ therefore takes the form

$$\det\left(\frac{d\gamma_{ij}}{dt} - \omega_1 \gamma_{ij}\right) = \begin{vmatrix} -\omega_1 & G & 0 \\ G & -\omega_1 & 0 \\ 0 & 0 & -\omega_1 \end{vmatrix} = 0,$$

which reduces to

$$\omega_1(\omega_1^2 - G^2) = 0,$$

which has roots $\omega_1 = 0, G, -G$, as stated.

Part (*ii*). With any embedded basis $\mathbf{e}_i$, let $\mathbf{u} = \sum_i \xi^i \mathbf{e}_i$ (ξ^i constant) be a material line parallel to the given principal axis of $d\gamma_{ij}/dt$, and let ω_1 be the corresponding principal value; then

$$\sum_j \left(\frac{d\gamma_{ij}}{dt} - \omega_1 \gamma_{ij}\right) \xi^j = 0 \qquad (i = 1, 2, 3). \tag{11.20}$$

Suppose that the stated result that **u** is parallel to a principal axis of $d^n\gamma_{ij}/dt^n$ is true for some value of $n \geqslant 1$; then

$$\sum_j \left(\frac{d^n\gamma_{ij}}{dt^n} - \omega_n \gamma_{ij}\right)\xi^j = 0 \qquad (i = 1, 2, 3).$$

On differentiating this equation (remembering that $d\xi^j/dt = 0$), we have

$$\sum_j \left(\frac{d^{n+1}\gamma_{ij}}{dt^{n+1}} - \frac{d\omega_n}{dt}\gamma_{ij}\right)\xi^j = \sum_j \omega_n \frac{d\gamma_{ij}}{dt}\xi^j$$

$$= \omega_1 \omega_n \sum_j \gamma_{ij}\xi^j, \qquad \text{by (11.20);}$$

this equation may be written in the form

$$\sum_j \left(\frac{d^{n+1}\gamma_{ij}}{dt^{n+1}} - \omega_{n+1}\gamma_{ij}\right)\xi^j = 0,$$

where $\omega_{n+1} = d\omega_n/dt + \omega_1\omega_n$. But this proves that **u** is a principal axis of $d^{n+1}\gamma_{ij}/dt^{n+1}$ and that the corresponding principal value is ω_{n+1}, which is related to ω_n and ω_1 by the equation we are required to establish. The required result is therefore true for a value $n+1$ if it is true for the value n. It is true for the value $n = 1$, by (11.20); it is therefore true, by induction, for any positive integral value of n, which completes the required proof.

Example 11

Part (*i*). If **n** is the unit normal drawn from O to the required plane, we have

$$h\mathbf{n} = \overrightarrow{\mathrm{OP}} = \sum_j \xi^j \mathbf{e}_j, \tag{11.21}$$

since $h = \mathrm{OP}$. The coordinates η_i of the plane are given by the equations

$$\eta_i = \frac{l_i}{h} = \frac{1}{h}\mathbf{n}\,.\,\mathbf{e}_i \qquad \text{by (2.24) and (2.20)}$$

$$= \frac{1}{h^2}\sum_j \xi^j \mathbf{e}_j\,.\,\mathbf{e}_i \qquad \text{by (11.21);}$$

hence

$$\eta_i = \frac{1}{h^2}\sum_j \xi^j \gamma_{ji} \qquad \text{by (1.18),} \tag{11.22}$$

which proves (i).

Part (ii). We may apply the above formalism to that material plane through particle P which is perpendicular to OP in state t. Multiplying (11.22) by $h^2\gamma^{ik}$ and summing over i, we see that

$$(11.23) \qquad h^2 \sum_i \eta_i \gamma^{ik} = \sum_i \sum_j \xi^j \gamma_{ji} \gamma^{ik} = \xi^k, \qquad \text{by (1.21)}.$$

Since it is given that OP is a principal axis for the deformation $t_0 \to t$ and that λ is the corresponding principal elongation ratio, it follows from (11.3) (by changing the dummy suffixes) that the coordinates ξ^k of P satisfy the equations

$$\sum_k [\gamma_{mk} - \lambda^2 \gamma_{mk}(t_0)]\, \xi^k = 0 \qquad (m = 1, 2, 3).$$

Substituting the expression (11.23) for ξ^k in these equations and dividing by h^2, which is not zero, we obtain the result

$$\sum_k \sum_i [\gamma_{mk} - \lambda^2 \gamma_{mk}(t_0)]\, \eta_i \gamma^{ik} = 0.$$

Here and elsewhere in this solution we write $\gamma_{ij}(t) = \gamma_{ij}$ for brevity.

Multiplying this equation by $\gamma^{jm}(t_0)$ and summing over m, we see that

$$\sum_m \sum_k \sum_i \{\gamma^{jm}(t_0)\,\gamma_{mk}\gamma^{ki} - \lambda^2 \gamma^{jm}(t_0)\,\gamma_{mk}(t_0)\,\gamma^{ki}\}\, \eta_i = 0,$$

and hence, from (1.21), that

$$\sum_i \left\{ \sum_m \gamma^{jm}(t_0)\,\delta_{mi} - \lambda^2 \sum_k \delta_{jk}\gamma^{ki} \right\} \eta_i = 0$$

which reduces to

$$(11.24) \qquad \sum_i \{\gamma^{ji}(t_0) - \lambda^2 \gamma^{ji}(t)\}\, \eta_i = 0,$$

which proves the first part of (ii).

The similarity of form between these equations for a principal plane η_i and equations (11.3) for a principal axis ξ^i should be noted.

Using a suffix t_0 or 0 to label quantities referring to state t_0, we have for the unit normal to the plane η_i in state t_0 the equation

$$\begin{aligned}
\mathbf{n}_0 &= h_0 \sum_i \eta_i \mathbf{e}^i(t_0) && \text{by (2.19) and (2.24)} \\
&= h_0 \sum_j \sum_i \eta_i \gamma^{ij}(t_0)\, \mathbf{e}_j(t_0) && \text{by (1.20)} \\
&= h_0 \lambda^2 \sum_j \sum_i \eta_i \gamma^{ij}(t)\, \mathbf{e}_j(t_0) && \text{by (11.24)} \\
&= \frac{h_0 \lambda^2}{h^2} \sum_j \xi^j\, \mathbf{e}_j(t_0) && \text{by (11.23)}.
\end{aligned}$$

It follows that

$$h_0\,\mathbf{n}_0 = \left(\frac{h_0\lambda}{h}\right)^2 (\overrightarrow{\mathrm{OP}})_{t_0}, \qquad \text{by (11.21) applied to state } t_0.$$

Therefore $(\overrightarrow{\mathrm{OP}})_{t_0}$ is parallel to $\mathbf{n}_0$ and perpendicular to the plane η_i in state t_0, which is the required result.

It follows, in particular, that parallel principal planes undergo no relative tangential displacement.

Chapter 3

Example 1

If $\mathbf{n}$ is a principal axis of stress and σ is the corresponding principal value, the traction across the corresponding principal plane must equal $\sigma\mathbf{n}$, and hence we have

$$\sum_i \sum_j \pi^{ij} l_i \mathbf{e}_j = \sigma\mathbf{n} \qquad \text{by (3.7).}$$

Taking the scalar product of each side of this equation with $\mathbf{e}_k$, we have

$$\sum_i \sum_j \pi^{ij} l_i \gamma_{jk} = \sigma l_k \qquad \text{by (1.18) and (2.20).}$$

Multiplying throughout by γ^{km} and summing over k, we have

$$\sum_i \sum_j \pi^{ij} l_i \delta_{jm} = \sigma \sum_k \gamma^{km} l_k \qquad \text{by (1.21).}$$

Changing the dummy suffix from k to i, we may write this equation in the required form

$$(11.25) \qquad \sum_i (\pi^{im} - \sigma\gamma^{im})\, l_i = 0 \qquad (m = 1, 2, 3),$$

which proves (i).

For a given state of stress and a given basis, these are three simultaneous equations linear and homogeneous in the three unknown quantities l_i; a necessary and sufficient condition for a solution in which not all l_i are zero is that the determinant of the coefficients should vanish, i.e. that

$$(11.26) \qquad \det(\pi^{im} - \sigma\gamma^{im}) = 0.$$

This is a cubic equation in σ and therefore has three roots. The equation is of the same form as (11.4), whose roots (in λ^2) were shown to be real by a proof which made use of the symmetry of the quantities γ_{ij}. Since the corresponding quantities π^{im} and γ^{im} in (11.26) are symmetric, it follows that the roots in σ are all real. To each root there corresponds a solution for l_i of (11.25). Let σ and σ' be any two distinct roots of (11.26), and let l_i and l'_i be the corresponding solutions of (11.25) (they are determined only to within a constant factor by (11.25); this factor is itself determined by the normalizing condition (2.21)); let $\mathbf{n}$ and $\mathbf{n}'$ be the corresponding unit vectors along the principal axes.

Then we have

$$\mathbf{n}.\mathbf{n}' = \left(\sum_i l_i \mathbf{e}^i\right) \cdot \left(\sum_j l'_j \mathbf{e}^j\right) \qquad \text{from (2.19)}$$

$$= \sum_i \sum_j \gamma^{ij} l_i l'_j \qquad \text{from (1.18).}$$

Multiplying (11.25) by l'_m and summing over m, we have

$$\sum_i \sum_m (\pi^{im} - \sigma\gamma^{im})\, l_i l'_m = 0.$$

Similarly,

$$\sum_i \sum_m (\pi^{im} - \sigma'\gamma^{im})\, l'_i l_m = 0.$$

Since $\pi^{im} = \pi^{mi}$ and $\gamma^{im} = \gamma^{mi}$, on subtracting one of these equations from the other, we obtain the result

$$(\sigma - \sigma') \sum_i \sum_m \gamma^{im} l_i l'_m = 0.$$

Since $\sigma \neq \sigma'$, by hypothesis, it follows that

$$\mathbf{n}.\mathbf{n}' = \sum_i \sum_m \gamma^{im} l_i l'_m = 0,$$

which proves that the principal axes belonging to two distinct principal values of stress are orthogonal. When all three principal values are different from one another, it follows that the three principal axes are mutually orthogonal, which proves (ii).

Example 2

Since the basis used in (3.27) is orthonormal, we have $\pi^{ij} = p_{ij}$ and $\gamma^{ij} = \delta_{ij}$, and hence (11.26) becomes

$$\begin{vmatrix} p_{11} - \sigma & p_{12} & 0 \\ p_{21} & p_{22} - \sigma & 0 \\ 0 & 0 & p_{33} - \sigma \end{vmatrix} = 0,$$

i.e.

$$(p_{33} - \sigma)\{\sigma^2 - (p_{11} + p_{22})\,\sigma - p_{21}^2 + p_{11}p_{22}\} = 0.$$

The roots of this equation, σ_a, σ_b and σ_c say, are

(11.27)
$$\left.\begin{array}{l}\left.\begin{array}{l}\sigma_a\\ \sigma_b\end{array}\right\} = \frac{1}{2}(p_{11}+p_{22})\pm\{\frac{1}{4}(p_{11}-p_{22})^2+p_{21}^2\}^{1/2},\\ \sigma_c\ = p_{33}.\end{array}\right.$$

Equations (11.25) take the form

(11.28)
$$\left.\begin{array}{rl}(p_{11}-\sigma)\,l_1+p_{12}\,l_2 &= 0\\ p_{21}\,l_1+(p_{22}-\sigma)\,l_2 &= 0\\ (p_{33}-\sigma)\,l_3 \qquad\qquad &= 0\end{array}\right\}.$$

For general values of p_{ij}, the roots (11.27) will all be different from one another. Then neither σ_a nor σ_b can equal p_{33}, and therefore for these roots we must have $l_3 = 0$, from (11.28); the corresponding principal axes must therefore lie in the plane of $\mathbf{e}_1$ and $\mathbf{e}_2$.

Since the basis $\mathbf{e}_i$ is orthonormal, the quantities l_i are actual direction cosines of a principal axis; for a principal axis lying in the plane of $\mathbf{e}_1$ and $\mathbf{e}_2$ making an angle χ with $\mathbf{e}_1$, we therefore have

(11.29)
$$l_1 = \cos\chi, \quad l_2 = \sin\chi, \quad l_3 = 0.$$

Eliminating σ between the first two of equations (11.28), we have

$$(p_{11}-p_{22})\,l_1\,l_2+p_{21}(l_2^2-l_1^2) = 0.$$

Substituting the values for l_i from (11.29) in this equation, we obtain the required result

(11.30)
$$2\cot 2\chi = \frac{p_{11}-p_{22}}{p_{21}}.$$

In fact, the angle $\chi+\dfrac{\pi}{2}$ which the other principal axis in the plane of $\mathbf{e}_1$ and $\mathbf{e}_2$ makes with $\mathbf{e}_1$ also satisfies this equation, because

$$\cot 2\left(\chi+\frac{\pi}{2}\right) = \cot 2\chi.$$

Substituting for $p_{11}-p_{22}$ from (11.30) in (11.27), we have

(11.31)
$$\left.\begin{array}{l}\sigma_a\\ \sigma_b\end{array}\right\} = \tfrac{1}{2}(p_{11}+p_{22})\pm p_{21}\operatorname{cosec} 2\chi,$$

and hence $\sigma_a-\sigma_b = 2p_{21}\operatorname{cosec} 2\chi$, as stated.

To show that the principal axis corresponding to σ_a lies in the positive quadrant, we have from (11.28), (11.27), and (11.29) the result

$$\tan\chi = \frac{l_2}{l_1} = \frac{\sigma_a - p_{11}}{p_{21}} = \frac{p_{22}-p_{11}}{2p_{21}} + \left\{\left(\frac{p_{11}-p_{22}}{2p_{21}}\right)^2 + 1\right\}^{1/2}$$

$$= -x + \sqrt{(x^2+1)}$$

where $x \equiv (p_{11}-p_{22})/(2p_{21})$; since $\sqrt{(x^2+1)} > x$, it follows that $\tan\chi > 0$, and therefore that

$$0 < \chi < \frac{\pi}{2} \quad \left(\text{or } \pi < \chi < \frac{3\pi}{2}\right)$$

which proves the required result.

Example 3

Let us consider any pair of parallel faces of the basic parallelepiped, say those which are parallel to $\mathbf{e}_1$ and $\mathbf{e}_3$, and therefore have $\mathbf{e}^2$ as normal. External material exerts across the upper face (Fig. 11.4) a resultant

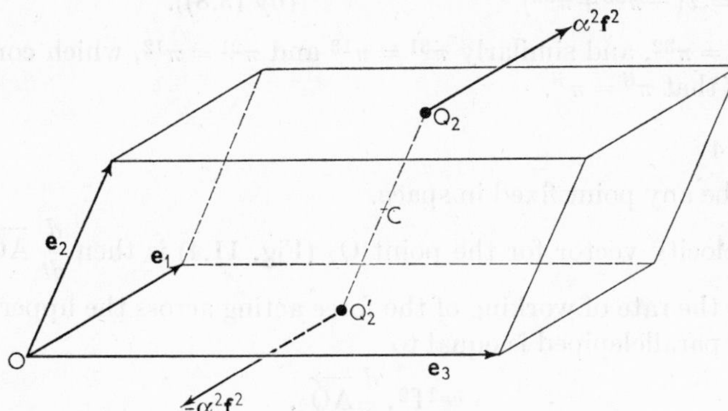

FIG. 11.4.

force $\alpha^2\mathbf{f}^2$, where α^2 is the area of the face and $\mathbf{f}^2$ is the traction, and the line of action passes through the centre Q_2 of the face. The moment of this force about the centre C of the parallelepiped is

$$\overrightarrow{CQ_2} \wedge (\alpha^2\mathbf{f}^2) = \tfrac{1}{2}\alpha^2\mathbf{e}_2 \wedge \mathbf{f}^2,$$

since $\overrightarrow{CQ_2} = \frac{1}{2}\mathbf{e}_2$. The corresponding moment of the force acting on the lower face is $\overrightarrow{CQ_2'} \wedge (-\alpha^2\mathbf{f}^2) = \frac{1}{2}\alpha^2\mathbf{e}_2 \wedge \mathbf{f}^2$, since $\overrightarrow{CQ_2'} = -\frac{1}{2}\mathbf{e}_2$, and therefore the sum of these two moments is $\alpha^2\mathbf{e}_2 \wedge \mathbf{f}^2$. It follows from (1.5) and (1.15) that $v\mathbf{e}^2$ is the areal vector for either of these faces, and hence that $ve^2 = \alpha^2$ and therefore the sum of the moments is $ve^2\mathbf{e}_2 \wedge \mathbf{f}^2$.

Adding this and two similar expressions which arise from the contributions from the other two pairs of faces, we thus obtain the required result

$$\sum_i e^i \mathbf{f}^i \wedge \mathbf{e}_i = 0, \tag{11.32}$$

(on dividing throughout by v, the volume of the parallelepiped) since the sum of the moments of all the external forces must be zero (there being no body couples acting on the material inside the parallelepiped, by hypothesis).

Taking the scalar product of this equation with $\mathbf{e}_1$, we have

$$\begin{aligned} 0 &= \sum_i e^i \mathbf{f}^i \wedge \mathbf{e}_i . \mathbf{e}_1 \\ &= \sum_i e^i \mathbf{f}^i . \mathbf{e}_i \wedge \mathbf{e}_1 && \text{(since . and } \wedge \text{ are interchangeable)} \\ &= e^2 \mathbf{f}^2 . \mathbf{e}_2 \wedge \mathbf{e}_1 + e^3 \mathbf{f}^3 . \mathbf{e}_3 \wedge \mathbf{e}_1 && (\text{since } \mathbf{e}_1 \wedge \mathbf{e}_1 = 0) \\ &= e^2 \mathbf{f}^2 . (-v\mathbf{e}^3) + e^3 \mathbf{f}^3 . (v\mathbf{e}^2) && \text{(by (1.15))} \\ &= v(-\pi^{23} + \pi^{32}) && \text{(by (3.8)).} \end{aligned}$$

Thus $\pi^{23} = \pi^{32}$, and similarly $\pi^{31} = \pi^{13}$ and $\pi^{21} = \pi^{12}$, which completes the proof that $\pi^{ij} = \pi^{ji}$.

Example 4

Let A be any point fixed in space.

The velocity vector for the point Q_2 (Fig. 11.4) is then $\frac{d}{dt}\overrightarrow{AQ_2}$, and therefore the rate of working of the force acting across the upper face of the basic parallelepiped is equal to

$$ve^2 \mathbf{f}^2 . \frac{d}{dt}\overrightarrow{AQ_2}.$$

Similarly, the rate of working of the force acting across the lower face is equal to

$$ve^2(-\mathbf{f}^2) . \frac{d}{dt}\overrightarrow{AQ_2'}.$$

The sum of these two rates is

$$\begin{aligned} ve^2 \mathbf{f}^2 . \frac{d}{dt}(\overrightarrow{AQ_2} - \overrightarrow{AQ_2'}) &= ve^2 \mathbf{f}^2 . \frac{d}{dt}\overrightarrow{Q_2'Q_2} \\ &= ve^2 \mathbf{f}^2 . \frac{d\mathbf{e}_2}{dt}, \end{aligned}$$

since $\overrightarrow{Q_2'Q_2} = \mathbf{e}_2$.

Since the mass of material in the parallelepiped is ρv, the rate of working of all the external forces per unit mass is equal to

$$\frac{1}{\rho v}\sum_i v e^i \mathbf{f}^i.\frac{d\mathbf{e}_i}{dt} = \frac{1}{\rho}\sum_j\sum_i e^i \mathbf{f}^i.\mathbf{e}^j \mathbf{e}_j.\frac{d\mathbf{e}_i}{dt} \quad \text{(by Examples 1, No. 4)}$$

$$= \frac{1}{\rho}\sum_j\sum_i \pi^{ij}\mathbf{e}_j.\frac{d\mathbf{e}_i}{dt} \quad \text{(by (3.8))}$$

$$= \frac{1}{2\rho}\sum_j\sum_i \pi^{ij}\left(\mathbf{e}_j.\frac{d\mathbf{e}_i}{dt}+\mathbf{e}_i.\frac{d\mathbf{e}_j}{dt}\right) \quad (\text{since } \pi^{ij} = \pi^{ji})$$

$$= \frac{1}{2\rho}\sum_j\sum_i \pi^{ij}\frac{d}{dt}(\mathbf{e}_j.\mathbf{e}_i)$$

$$= \frac{1}{2\rho}\sum_j\sum_i \pi^{ij}\frac{d\gamma_{ij}}{dt} \quad \text{(by (1.18))};$$

this proves the required result.

Example 5

The normal component of traction is given by (3.17) in terms of π^{ij}. Dividing this equation by h^2 and using (2.24), we obtain the equation

$$\frac{\mathbf{f}.\mathbf{n}}{h^2} = \sum_i\sum_j \pi^{ij}\eta_i\eta_j,$$

where η_i are independent of time. Therefore

$$\frac{d}{dt}\frac{\mathbf{f}.\mathbf{n}}{h^2} = \sum_i\sum_j \frac{d\pi^{ij}}{dt}\eta_i\eta_j,$$

and hence, on multiplying by h^2 and using (2.24) again, we obtain the required result.

Example 6

From (3.17) and (2.20), we obtain the equation

$$\mathbf{f}.\mathbf{n} = \sum_i\sum_j \pi^{ij}\mathbf{e}_i.\mathbf{nn}.\mathbf{e}_j.$$

Summing this equation for three mutually perpendicular unit vectors $\mathbf{n}$, we have

$$\sum_{\mathbf{n}} \mathbf{f}.\mathbf{n} = \sum_i\sum_j \pi^{ij}\mathbf{e}_i.\mathbf{e}_j \quad (\text{by (11.16) with } \mathbf{r} = \mathbf{e}_j)$$

$$= \sum_i\sum_j \pi^{ij}\gamma_{ij} \quad \text{(by (1.18))}.$$

The right-hand side is independent of the vectors **n**; therefore the left-hand side has the same value for every set of orthonormal **n**-vectors, which was to be proved. Further, the left-hand side is independent of the choice of base vectors $\mathbf{e}_i$ used in the definition of π^{ij} and γ_{ij}, and therefore the right-hand side is also independent of this choice, which was to be proved.

To show that the value of $\sum\sum\pi^{ij}\gamma^{ij}$ does depend on the choice of base vectors, let us consider a simple tension T on planes of unit normal **n**, and use an orthogonal basis $\mathbf{e}_i$ with $\mathbf{e}_1$ parallel to **n**. Then the tractions across the planes of normal **n** and across two mutually orthogonal planes are

$$\mathbf{f}^1 = T\mathbf{n} = T\frac{\mathbf{e}^1}{e^1}, \quad \mathbf{f}^2 = \mathbf{f}^3 = 0.$$

From (3.8), it follows that the only non-zero stress component is

$$\pi^{11} = e^1\mathbf{f}^1.\mathbf{e}^1 = T\mathbf{e}^1.\mathbf{e}^1 = T(e^1)^2.$$

Since $\gamma^{11} = (e^1)^2$, it follows that

$$\sum\sum\pi^{ij}\gamma^{ij} = \pi^{11}\gamma^{11} = T(e^1)^4.$$

This depends on the value of e^1, and therefore on the choice of base vectors, as stated.

We may note that, in this case, we have

$$\sum\sum\pi^{ij}\gamma_{ij} = \pi^{11}\gamma_{11} = T(e^1)^2(e_1)^2 = T,$$

since $e^1e_1 = 1$, by Examples 1, No. 7; this verifies that the value of this expression is independent of the choice of base vectors.

Example 7

We have

$$\overrightarrow{\mathrm{OP}} = \sum_i x_i\mathbf{e}^i = (\mathbf{f}.\mathbf{n})^{-1/2}\mathbf{n},$$

and therefore, on taking the scalar product of this equation with $\mathbf{e}_j$, we have

$$x_j = (\mathbf{f}.\mathbf{n})^{-1/2}\mathbf{n}.\mathbf{e}_j = (\mathbf{f}.\mathbf{n})^{-1/2}l_j \qquad \text{by (2.20).}$$

Hence

$$\sum_i\sum_j\pi^{ij}x_ix_j = (\mathbf{f}.\mathbf{n})^{-1}\sum_i\sum_j\pi^{ij}l_il_j$$
$$= 1 \qquad \text{by (3.17),}$$

which is the required equation for the polar diagram.

Let $\mathbf{e}_1$, $\mathbf{e}_2$, and $\mathbf{e}_3$ be unit vectors coinciding with the principal axes of stress, and let σ_a, σ_b, and σ_c be the corresponding principal values. Then $\mathbf{e}^1$ is the unit normal to one principal plane, and the corresponding values of l_i are given by

$$\begin{aligned} l_i &= \mathbf{e}^1 . \mathbf{e}_i && \text{by (2.20)} \\ &= \delta_{1i} && \text{by (1.16).} \end{aligned}$$

Hence (11.25) become

$$\sum_i (\pi^{im} - \sigma_a \delta_{im}) \delta_{1i} = 0$$

since $\gamma^{im} = \delta_{im}$, which reduces to

$$\pi^{1m} = \sigma_a \delta_{1m} \qquad (m = 1, 2, 3).$$

Similarly, $\pi^{2m} = \sigma_b \delta_{2m}$ and $\pi^{3m} = \sigma_c \delta_{3m}$, so that

$$\pi^{ij} = \begin{pmatrix} \sigma_a & 0 & 0 \\ 0 & \sigma_b & 0 \\ 0 & 0 & \sigma_c \end{pmatrix}.$$

With these values for π^{ij}, we see that

$$\sum_i \sum_j \pi^{ij} x_i x_j = \sigma_a (x_1)^2 + \sigma_b (x_2)^2 + \sigma_c (x_3)^2,$$

which completes the required proof.

Example 8

We have

$$\sum_i x^i \mathbf{e}_i = \mathbf{f} = \sum_i \sum_k \pi^{ik} l_i \mathbf{e}_k \qquad \text{by (3.7).}$$

Taking the scalar product with $\mathbf{e}^j$, we have

$$x^j = \sum_i \pi^{ij} l_i = \sum_i \pi^{ji} l_i \qquad \text{by (1.16).}$$

Multiplying by $\bar{\pi}_{kj}$ and summing over j, we have

$$\begin{aligned} \sum_j \bar{\pi}_{kj} x^j &= \sum_i \sum_j \bar{\pi}_{kj} \pi^{ji} l_i \\ &= \sum_i \delta_{ki} l_i = l_k, \end{aligned}$$

since

(11.33) $$\sum_j \bar{\pi}_{kj} \pi^{ji} = \delta_{ki}$$

by definition. Hence

$$1 = \sum_m \sum_k \gamma^{mk} l_m l_k \qquad \text{by (2.21)}$$

$$= \sum_m \sum_k \gamma^{mk} \left(\sum_i \bar{\pi}_{mi} x^i\right)\left(\sum_j \bar{\pi}_{kj} x^j\right)$$

on substituting for l_k (and l_m) from the above equation. On rearranging the factors and taking the summation signs outside, this is seen to be the equation asked for.

When the base vectors are orthonormal and coincide with the principal axes of stress, the values of π^{ij} are given in the previous example; in particular, $\pi^{1j} = \pi^{j1} = \sigma_a \delta_{1j}$, and when this is substituted in (11.33) with $i = 1$ we obtain the result $\bar{\pi}_{i1} = \sigma_a^{-1}\delta_{i1}$. Similarly, we have

$$\bar{\pi}_{i2} = \sigma_b^{-1}\delta_{i2} \quad \text{and} \quad \bar{\pi}_{i3} = \sigma_c^{-1}\delta_{i3};$$

thus

$$\bar{\pi}_{ij} = \begin{pmatrix} \sigma_a^{-1} & 0 & 0 \\ 0 & \sigma_b^{-1} & 0 \\ 0 & 0 & \sigma_c^{-1} \end{pmatrix}.$$

Using these results together with the equation $\gamma^{mk} = \delta_{mk}$ the equation for the stress ellipsoid simplifies to give the form stated.

Chapter 4

Example 1

For the present proof, it is convenient to change the notation as follows:

$$\xi^i = (x, y, z), \qquad \gamma_{ij} = \begin{pmatrix} a & h & g \\ h & b & f \\ g & f & c \end{pmatrix}.$$

The quadratic form becomes

$$Q = ax^2 + by^2 + cz^2 + 2(fyz + gzx + hxy),$$

and the stated conditions become

(i) $$a > 0,$$

(ii) $$ab - h^2 > 0,$$

(iii) $$\gamma \equiv a(bc - f^2) + h(fg - ch) + g(hf - bg) > 0.$$

The conditions are *necessary*, because if $Q > 0$ for all values of x, y, and z, not all zero, we may first take $x = 1$, $y = z = 0$; then $Q = a > 0$, which proves (i).

We may now rewrite Q in the following form, by collecting together the terms in x and completing their square: thus

$$Q = a\left(x+\frac{gz+hy}{a}\right)^2+\frac{ab-h^2}{a}y^2+2\frac{af-gh}{a}yz+\frac{ac-g^2}{a}z^2.$$

We may now take $y = 1$, $z = 0$, and $x = -h/a$, so that all terms except the second vanish: then $Q = (ab-h^2)/a > 0$, and therefore $ab-h^2 > 0$, by (i), which proves (ii).

Finally, on completing the square of the terms in y in the second and third terms in the last expression, we find after some reduction that Q may be written in the form

$$\text{(11.34)} \quad Q = a\left(x+\frac{gz+hy}{a}\right)^2+\frac{ab-h^2}{a}\left(y+\frac{af-gh}{ab-h^2}z\right)^2+\frac{\gamma}{ab-h^2}z^2;$$

division by $ab-h^2$ here is legitimate because (ii) has been proved. Putting $z = 1$ in this expression, we can evidently choose values for x and y to make the first two terms vanish; then $Q = \gamma/(ab-h^2) > 0$, and therefore $\gamma > 0$, which proves (iii).

The conditions are *sufficient*, for if (i) and (ii) hold, the steps leading to (11.34) are permissible; if, in addition, (iii) holds, then (11.34) is a sum of squares with all coefficients positive, and therefore $Q \geqslant 0$.

Moreover, $Q = 0$ if and only if each term is zero, i.e. if and only if

$$\left.\begin{aligned} x+\frac{gz+hy}{a} &= 0 \\ y+\frac{af-gh}{ab-h^2}z &= 0 \\ z &= 0 \end{aligned}\right\}.$$

The last two equations give $y = z = 0$, and then the first gives $x = 0$. Therefore $Q > 0$ unless $x = y = z = 0$, which proves that (i), (ii), and (iii) are sufficient to ensure that Q is positive definite.

Example 2

The condition is *necessary*, for if linearly independent vectors $\mathbf{e}_i$ exist which satisfy the given equations

$$\text{(11.35)} \qquad \mathbf{e}_i \cdot \mathbf{e}_j = \gamma_{ij} \qquad (i, j = 1, 2, 3),$$

then it follows that $\mathbf{u} \equiv \sum_i \xi^i \mathbf{e}_i$ is a vector whose squared magnitude is positive or zero, and is zero if and only if the vector $\mathbf{u}$ is zero, i.e. if and only if all the coefficients ξ^i are zero (since $\mathbf{e}_i$ are linearly independent). It follows that

$$Q \equiv \Big(\sum_i \xi^i \mathbf{e}_i\Big).\Big(\sum_j \xi^j \mathbf{e}_j\Big) = \sum_i \sum_j \xi^i \xi^j \gamma_{ij}$$

is a positive definite form in ξ^i, as stated.

The condition is *sufficient*, for if Q is positive definite, then by (i) in the previous example we have $\gamma_{11} > 0$, and we may choose a vector $\mathbf{e}_1$ of any orientation and of magnitude $e_1 = \sqrt{\gamma_{11}}$, so that (11.35) with $i = j = 1$ is satisfied.

Can we now choose a vector $\mathbf{e}_2$ so that (11.35) with $i = j = 2$ and with $i = 2$, $j = 1$ are satisfied, i.e. so that $\mathbf{e}_2.\mathbf{e}_2 = \gamma_{22}$ and $\mathbf{e}_2.\mathbf{e}_1 = \gamma_{21}$? The first of these equations can be satisfied if we choose the length of $\mathbf{e}_2$ so that $e_2 = \sqrt{\gamma_{22}}$; this is possible, for conditions analogous to (i), (ii), and (iii) must hold in which a cyclic interchange of the suffixes 1, 2, and 3 is made, so that in particular we have $\gamma_{22} > 0$. If θ is the angle between $\mathbf{e}_1$ and $\mathbf{e}_2$ (supposed for the moment to exist), then the second equation becomes $e_2 e_1 \cos\theta = \gamma_{21}$. A vector $\mathbf{e}_2$ not linearly dependent on $\mathbf{e}_1$ will therefore exist if and only if a solution for θ not equal to 0 or π exists, i.e. if and only if

$$\cos^2\theta < 1,$$

i.e.
$$(e_1 e_2 \cos\theta)^2 < (e_1 e_2)^2,$$

i.e.
$$(\gamma_{21})^2 < \gamma_{11}\gamma_{22};$$

but this condition is satisfied because of (ii) in the previous example. A vector $\mathbf{e}_2$ can therefore be chosen satisfying the required conditions.

Finally, we have to show that a third vector $\mathbf{e}_3$ can be found, not coplanar with $\mathbf{e}_1$ and $\mathbf{e}_2$, such that the remaining equations (11.35) can be satisfied. Having chosen $\mathbf{e}_1$ and $\mathbf{e}_2$, let us introduce an orthonormal set of vectors $\mathbf{u}$, $\mathbf{v}$, and $\mathbf{w}$ with $\mathbf{u}$ parallel to $\mathbf{e}_1$; $\mathbf{v}$ lying in the plane of $\mathbf{e}_1$ and $\mathbf{e}_2$; and $\mathbf{w}$ perpendicular to this plane. Then we have

$$\mathbf{e}_1 = e_1 \mathbf{u},$$

$$\mathbf{e}_2 = e_2(\mathbf{u}\cos\theta + \mathbf{v}\sin\theta), \qquad \text{(since } \theta \text{ is the angle between } \mathbf{e}_1 \text{ and } \mathbf{e}_2\text{)}$$

and if $\mathbf{e}_3$ exists, it may be expressed in the form

$$\mathbf{e}_3 = x\mathbf{u} + y\mathbf{v} + z\mathbf{w},$$

for suitable values of the coefficients x, y, and z. The vectors $\mathbf{e}_i$ will be linearly independent if $z \neq 0$, for then $\mathbf{e}_3$ will lie outside the plane of $\mathbf{e}_1$ and $\mathbf{e}_2$. The remaining equations of (11.35) then take the form

$$\begin{cases} \gamma_{13} = \mathbf{e}_1 . \mathbf{e}_3 = x e_1 \\ \gamma_{23} = \mathbf{e}_2 . \mathbf{e}_3 = e_2(x\cos\theta + y\sin\theta) \\ \gamma_{33} = \mathbf{e}_3 . \mathbf{e}_3 = x^2 + y^2 + z^2. \end{cases}$$

All that remains therefore is to show that these equations have a real solution for x, y, and z such that $z \neq 0$.

The first two equations evidently give real solutions for x and y, namely

$$x = \gamma_{13}/e_1 \quad \text{and} \quad y = (\gamma_{23} - e_2 x \cos\theta)/(e_2 \sin\theta).$$

($\sin\theta \neq 0$ because we have shown that $\mathbf{e}_1$ and $\mathbf{e}_2$ are linearly independent). From these expressions, we find that

$$x^2 + y^2 = \frac{(\gamma_{13})^2}{\gamma_{11}} + \frac{(\gamma_{11}\gamma_{23} - \gamma_{12}\gamma_{13})^2}{\gamma_{11}[\gamma_{11}\gamma_{22} - (\gamma_{12})^2]},$$

when we use the results

$$e_1 = \sqrt{\gamma_{11}}, \quad e_2 = \sqrt{\gamma_{22}},$$

$$(e_1 e_2 \sin\theta)^2 = (e_1 e_2)^2 - (e_1 e_2 \cos\theta)^2 = \gamma_{11}\gamma_{22} - (\gamma_{21})^2.$$

When this expression is inserted in the third of the above equations, it is found after some lengthy reduction that this equation may be expressed in the form

$$z^2 = \gamma_{33} - (x^2 + y^2)$$

$$= \frac{\gamma}{\gamma_{11}\gamma_{22} - (\gamma_{12})^2} > 0, \quad \text{by (ii) and (iii) of Examples 4, No. 1, solution.}$$

This shows that a real non-zero solution for z exists, and this completes the required proof.

For use in the next example, we may note here that the above equation defines two values for z, differing only in sign; the corresponding vectors $\mathbf{e}_3$ will therefore lie one on each side of the plane defined by $\mathbf{e}_1$ and $\mathbf{e}_2$, and with these vectors will therefore give one right-handed system and one left-handed system. It can also be seen from the foregoing argument that, apart from this choice of hand, the set of vectors $\mathbf{e}_i$ which satisfy (11.35) (for given values of γ_{ij}) is determined to within a rigid rotation of the set; for the lengths and mutual inclinations of the vectors $\mathbf{e}_i$ are evidently determined by (11.35).

Example 3

Since C_0 and C_1 are positive, and $\gamma_{ij}(t_0)$ and $\gamma_{ij}(t_1)$ are each coefficients of positive definite forms (by Examples 4, No. 2), it is clear that $\gamma_{ij}(t_2)$ are also coefficients of a positive definite form. From Examples 4, No. 2, it therefore follows that the equations

$$\mathbf{e}_i \cdot \mathbf{e}_j = \gamma_{ij}(t_2)$$

are satisfied by some linearly independent set of vectors $\mathbf{e}_i = \mathbf{e}_i(t_2)$, say, which can be chosen to be right-handed and which are then determined to within a rigid rotation. We may then identify these vectors with those material lines which coincided in state t_0 with the vectors $\mathbf{e}_i(t_0)$ and in state t_1 with the vectors $\mathbf{e}_i(t_1)$; the stipulation that the three sets of vectors should all be right-handed is made in order to exclude the physically unrealizable "turning inside-out" of the material which would be implied if one of the sets was left-handed. The quantities $\gamma_{ij}(t_2)$, therefore, define a shape of the material, and this shape is unique.

Example 4

Let η_i be any three numbers, not all zero.

Write
$$\sum_j \gamma^{ij} \eta_j = \xi^i.$$

Multiplying by γ_{ki} and summing over i, we obtain the result

$$\eta_k = \sum_i \gamma_{ki} \xi^i \qquad \text{by (1.21).}$$

Thus not all of the three numbers ξ^i can be zero, for if they were, then $\eta_k = 0$ $(k = 1, 2, 3)$, which would contradict our hypothesis.

Since the given form is positive definite, it follows that

$$\begin{aligned} 0 &< \sum_k \left(\sum_i \gamma_{ki} \xi^i \right) \xi^k \\ &= \sum_k \eta_k \xi^k \\ &= \sum_k \eta_k \left(\sum_j \gamma^{kj} \eta_j \right) = \sum_j \sum_k \gamma^{kj} \eta_k \eta_j, \end{aligned}$$

which proves that this form is positive definite, as stated.

The converse may be readily proved by a similar argument, in which upper suffix quantities and lower suffix quantities are interchanged.

It follows therefore that, in the context of Examples 4, No. 3, the quantities $\gamma^{ij}(t_0)$ and $\gamma^{ij}(t_1)$ are coefficients of positive definite forms, because $\gamma_{ij}(t_0)$ and $\gamma_{ij}(t_1)$ are. Hence $C_0 \gamma^{ij}(t_0) + C_1 \gamma^{ij}(t_1) \equiv \gamma^{ij}(t_2)$ say, are coefficients of a positive definite form, and so also are $\gamma_{ij}(t_2)$ (defined in terms of $\gamma^{ij}(t_2)$ by (1.21)), by the first part of the present example. Hence $\gamma_{ij}(t_2)$ define a unique shape, by the result of Examples 4, No. 3, which completes the required proof.

Example 5

Part (*i*). Relative to a basis which is orthonormal in state t_0, the shape variables are given by the expressions

$$\gamma_{ij}(t_0) = \begin{pmatrix} 1 & 0 & 0 \\ 0 & 1 & 0 \\ 0 & 0 & 1 \end{pmatrix}, \quad \gamma^{ij}(t) = \begin{pmatrix} \lambda_a^{-2} & 0 & 0 \\ 0 & \lambda_b^{-2} & 0 \\ 0 & 0 & \lambda_c^{-2} \end{pmatrix} \qquad \text{from (2.39), (2.40), and (2.46).}$$

Since this basis is orthogonal in state t, we have

$$p_{ij} = e_i e_j \pi^{ij} \qquad \text{by (3.15)}$$

$$= -p \begin{pmatrix} 1 & 0 & 0 \\ 0 & 1 & 0 \\ 0 & 0 & 1 \end{pmatrix} + \mu_0 \begin{pmatrix} \lambda_a^{2} & 0 & 0 \\ 0 & \lambda_b^{2} & 0 \\ 0 & 0 & \lambda_c^{2} \end{pmatrix}.$$

Part (*ii*). Let us now take a basis which is orthonormal in state t, and therefore orthogonal in state t_0. Then $\lambda_a e_1(t_0) = e_1(t) = 1$, etc., so that $\gamma_{11}(t_0) = [e_1(t_0)]^2 = \lambda_a^{-2}$, etc., and hence

$$\gamma_{ij}(t_0) = \begin{pmatrix} \lambda_a^{-2} & 0 & 0 \\ 0 & \lambda_b^{-2} & 0 \\ 0 & 0 & \lambda_c^{-2} \end{pmatrix}; \quad \gamma^{ij}(t) = \begin{pmatrix} 1 & 0 & 0 \\ 0 & 1 & 0 \\ 0 & 0 & 1 \end{pmatrix}.$$

Hence

$$p_{ij} = \pi^{ij} \qquad \text{by (3.14)}$$

$$= -p \begin{pmatrix} 1 & 0 & 0 \\ 0 & 1 & 0 \\ 0 & 0 & 1 \end{pmatrix} + \mu_0 \begin{pmatrix} \lambda_a^{-2} & 0 & 0 \\ 0 & \lambda_b^{-2} & 0 \\ 0 & 0 & \lambda_c^{-2} \end{pmatrix}.$$

Thus the values of the cartesian stress components p_{ij} in state t depend on the choice of base vectors used in the calculation, which is absurd. The proposed equations are not therefore possible rheological equations of state for any actual material.

Chapter 5

Example 1

The rate of working of the external tractions on the basic parallelepiped is

$$\frac{dw}{dt} = \tfrac{1}{2}\sum_i \sum_j \pi^{ij}\frac{d\gamma_{ij}}{dt}$$

per unit volume, by Examples 3, No. 4. For a Newtonian liquid, using the expression (5.4) for π^{ij}, this becomes

$$\frac{dw}{dt} = -\tfrac{1}{2}\sum_i \sum_j \left(p\gamma^{ij} + \eta\frac{d\gamma^{ij}}{dt}\right)\frac{d\gamma_{ij}}{dt}$$

$$= +\tfrac{1}{2}\eta\sum_i \sum_j \sum_k \sum_l \frac{d\gamma^{ij}}{dt}\frac{d\gamma^{kl}}{dt}\gamma_{jk}\gamma_{il},$$

because the coefficient of p is zero, by Examples 2, No. 6, and $d\gamma_{ij}/dt$ can be expressed in terms of $d\gamma^{ij}/dt$ by the equation obtained when upper and lower suffixes are interchanged in (2.35).

When the basic parallelepiped is instantaneously a unit cube at time t, we have $\gamma_{jk} = \delta_{jk}$, and hence the above equation simplifies to

$$\frac{dw}{dt} = \tfrac{1}{2}\eta\sum_i \sum_j \left(\frac{d\gamma^{ij}}{dt}\right)^2.$$

Since $\eta > 0$, it follows that $dw/dt \geqslant 0$, and that the case $dw/dt = 0$ occurs if and only if

$$\frac{d\gamma^{ij}}{dt} = 0 \qquad (i, j = 1, 2, 3),$$

i.e. if and only if the material is moving as a rigid body (Theorem (2.34)).

Example 2

From (2.80) with $G = 0$ and (2.65) with $t_0 = t'$, we have

$$\gamma^{ij}(t') = \begin{pmatrix} 1+s^2 & s & 0 \\ s & 1 & 0 \\ 0 & 0 & 1 \end{pmatrix},$$

where $s = \alpha(\sin\omega t - \sin\omega t')$

and the basis is orthonormal in state t.

Hence

$$\frac{d\gamma^{ij}(t')}{dt'} = -\alpha\omega\cos\omega t'\begin{pmatrix}2s & 1 & 0\\ 1 & 0 & 0\\ 0 & 0 & 0\end{pmatrix},$$

and

$$\frac{d\gamma^{ij}}{dt} = \lim_{t'\to t}\frac{d\gamma^{ij}(t')}{dt'} = -\alpha\omega\cos\omega t\begin{pmatrix}0 & 1 & 0\\ 1 & 0 & 0\\ 0 & 0 & 0\end{pmatrix}.$$

Substituting these expressions in (5.4) and using (3.14), we have

$$p_{ij} = \pi^{ij} = -p\begin{pmatrix}1 & 0 & 0\\ 0 & 1 & 0\\ 0 & 0 & 1\end{pmatrix} + \eta\alpha\omega\cos\omega t\begin{pmatrix}0 & 1 & 0\\ 1 & 0 & 0\\ 0 & 0 & 0\end{pmatrix}.$$

Thus

$$p_{21} = \eta\alpha\omega\cos\omega t,$$

which is 90° out of phase with the motion when this is described by the magnitude of shear

$$s = \alpha\sin\omega t$$

measured from a state at a reference time $t' = 0$.

Example 3

We have

$$\begin{aligned}\mathbf{u}.\mathbf{u} &= \sum_i\sum_j\sum_k\sum_m (\dot{\gamma}^{ij}l_i\mathbf{e}_j).(\mathbf{e}_k l_m\dot{\gamma}^{mk})\\ &= \sum_i\sum_j\sum_k\sum_m \dot{\gamma}^{ij}l_i\gamma_{jk}l_m\dot{\gamma}^{mk}, \qquad \text{by (1.18).}\end{aligned}$$

Now

$$\begin{aligned}\sum_{\mathbf{n}} l_i l_m &= \sum_{\mathbf{n}} \mathbf{e}_i.\mathbf{nn}.\mathbf{e}_m \qquad \text{by (2.20)}\\ &= \mathbf{e}_i.\mathbf{e}_m \qquad \text{by Examples 1, No. 4, with } \mathbf{r} = \mathbf{e}_i \text{ and } \mathbf{e}^j = \mathbf{e}_j = \mathbf{n}.\end{aligned}$$

The summation here is over any three mutually perpendicular unit vectors $\mathbf{n}$.

Hence

$$\begin{aligned}\sum_{\mathbf{n}} u^2 &= \sum_i\sum_j\sum_k\sum_m \dot{\gamma}^{ij}\dot{\gamma}^{mk}\gamma_{jk}\gamma_{im}\\ &\equiv \dot{\kappa}_2,\ \text{say.}\end{aligned}$$

But the left-hand side is positive or zero and does not contain the base vectors $\mathbf{e}_i$; hence $\dot{\kappa}_2 \geqslant 0$ and the value of $\dot{\kappa}_2$ is independent of the choice of base vectors.

If the material is moving rigidly, then $\dot{\gamma}^{ij} = 0$ and hence $\dot{\kappa}_2 = 0$. To prove the converse, we may, since the value of $\dot{\kappa}_2$ is independent of the choice of basis, choose a basis which is instantaneously orthonormal at time t; then $\gamma_{jk} = \delta_{jk}$ and hence

$$\dot{\kappa}_2 = \sum_i \sum_j (\dot{\gamma}^{ij})^2.$$

From this expression, it follows that if $\dot{\kappa}_2 = 0$ then $\dot{\gamma}^{ij} = 0$ $(i,j = 1,2,3)$ and so the material is moving rigidly.

Finally, it follows from the results obtained in the solution to Example 1 above that the rate of working of the external tractions on an arbitrary parallelepiped of a Newtonian liquid is given by the equation

$$\frac{dw}{dt} = \tfrac{1}{2}\eta\dot{\kappa}_2.$$

From the results just proved for $\dot{\kappa}_2$, it follows that $dw/dt \geqslant 0$ and that $dw/dt = 0$ if and only if the material is moving rigidly.

Example 4

On multiplying (5.4) by γ_{ij} and summing over i and j, since

$$\sum \sum \gamma_{ij}\gamma^{ij} = \sum \delta_{ii} = 3, \qquad \text{by (1.21)},$$

and $$\sum \sum \gamma_{ij}\, d\gamma^{ij}/dt = 0, \qquad \text{by Examples 2, No. 6},$$

we obtain the result

$$\sum \sum \gamma_{ij}\pi^{ij} + 3p = 0,$$

which was to be proved.

When the basis is orthonormal, $\gamma_{ij} = \delta_{ij}$ and $\pi^{ij} = p_{ij}$, by (3.14); hence

$$p = -\tfrac{1}{3}\sum_i p_{ii} = -\tfrac{1}{3}(p_{11}+p_{22}+p_{33}).$$

This result is not generally valid for materials other than Newtonian liquids.

Example 5

Let us rewrite (5.4) with suffixes l, m in place of i, j; multiply throughout by $\gamma_{il}\gamma_{jm}$ and sum over l, m. The first term is just π_{ij}, by definition; the second term reduces to $p\gamma_{ij}$, by (1.21); the third term reduces to $-\eta\, d\gamma_{ij}/dt$, when the equation obtained from (2.35) by interchange of upper and lower suffixes is used. The resulting equation is that which is required.

Chapter 6

Example 1

Let us take a basis $\mathbf{e}_i$ which is orthonormal in the state t in which the stress is to be calculated ($t \geqslant t_1$). As usual, $\mathbf{e}_1$ is parallel to the lines of shear and, at time t, $\mathbf{e}_2$ is instantaneously normal to the shearing planes.

For $t_1 \leqslant t' \leqslant t$, we have a steady shear flow of shear rate G, and therefore the difference of shape variables is given by

$$\gamma^{ij}(t') - \gamma^{ij}(t) = \begin{pmatrix} G^2(t-t')^2 & G(t-t') & 0 \\ G(t-t') & 0 & 0 \\ 0 & 0 & 0 \end{pmatrix} \qquad (t_1 \leqslant t' \leqslant t),$$

from (2.70) and (2.62).

For $t' \leqslant t_1$, the liquid is at rest (or is rigid); hence $\gamma^{ij}(t') = \gamma^{ij}(t_1)$ and therefore

$$\begin{aligned}\gamma^{ij}(t') - \gamma^{ij}(t) &= \gamma^{ij}(t_1) - \gamma^{ij}(t) \\ &= \begin{pmatrix} G^2(t-t_1)^2 & G(t-t_1) & 0 \\ G(t-t_1) & 0 & 0 \\ 0 & 0 & 0 \end{pmatrix} \qquad (t' \leqslant t_1 \leqslant t),\end{aligned}$$

which is obtained from the last equation by putting $t' = t_1$.

We now use these expressions in the rheological equations of state (6.8), dividing the range of integration into two parts, $(-\infty, t_1)$ and (t_1, t); since the basis is orthonormal at time t, we have $p_{ij} = \pi^{ij}$, by (3.14), and hence

$$\begin{aligned}p_{ij} + p_0\,\delta_{ij} = \int_{-\infty}^{t_1} \mu(t-t')\,dt' &\begin{pmatrix} G^2(t-t_1^2) & G(t-t_1) & 0 \\ G(t-t_1) & 0 & 0 \\ 0 & 0 & 0 \end{pmatrix} \\ + \int_{t_1}^{t} \mu(t-t')\,dt' &\begin{pmatrix} G^2(t-t')^2 & G(t-t') & 0 \\ G(t-t') & 0 & 0 \\ 0 & 0 & 0 \end{pmatrix}.\end{aligned}$$

Let us change the variable of integration from t' to $\tau = t - t'$. The first integrals on the right-hand side of this equation are of the form

$$G^r(t-t_1)^r \int_{t-t_1}^{\infty} \mu(\tau)\,d\tau \qquad (r = 1, 2).$$

The second integrals are of the form

$$G^r \int_0^{t-t_1} \mu(\tau)\,\tau^r\,d\tau = G^r\left\{\int_0^{\infty} - \int_{t-t_1}^{\infty}\right\}\mu(\tau)\,\tau^r\,d\tau$$

$$= G^r \mu_r - G^r \int_{t-t_1}^{\infty} \mu(\tau)\,\tau^r\,d\tau, \qquad \text{by (6.3).}$$

Hence the sum of the first and second integrals may be written in the form

$$G^r \mu_r - G^r \int_{t-t_1}^{\infty} \mu(\tau)\,[\tau^r - (t-t_1)^r]\,d\tau.$$

When $r = 1$, we therefore have the required result

$$p_{21}(t) = G\mu_1 - GI_1(t-t_1), \qquad \text{by (6.32).}$$

When $r = 2$, we use the identity

$$\tau^2 - (t-t_1)^2 = [\tau-(t-t_1)]^2 + 2(t-t_1)\,[\tau-(t-t_1)]$$

in the above equations to obtain the second required result

$$p_{11} - p_{22} = G^2\{\mu_2 - I_2(t-t_1) - 2(t-t_1)\,I_1(t-t_1)\}.$$

Using these results, together with the definition of β given in (6.35), we see that, at time $t \geqslant t_1$,

$$\beta p_{21} - (p_{11} - p_{22}) = \frac{G^2}{\mu_1}(\mu_1 I_2 - \mu_2 I_1) + 2G^2(t-t_1)\,I_1.$$

In the argument associated with equation (6.38), we proved that, when μ is a sum of exponential functions of the form (6.5), the inequality

$$\mu_1 I_2 - \mu_2 I_1 \geqslant 0$$

holds; moreover, I_1 is evidently positive from its definition (6.32), since the integrand is positive over the range of integration except for the lower limit where it is zero. It follows that $\beta p_{21} > p_{11} - p_{22}$, as stated. This completes the required proof.

Example 2

If the shape is kept constant from time t_1, we have

$$\gamma^{ij}(t_1) = \gamma^{ij}(t') = \gamma^{ij}(t) \qquad (t_1 \leqslant t' \leqslant t)$$

and

$$\gamma^{ij}(t') - \gamma^{ij}(t) = \gamma^{ij}(t') - \gamma^{ij}(t_1)$$

$$= \begin{pmatrix} s^2 & s & 0 \\ s & 0 & 0 \\ 0 & 0 & 0 \end{pmatrix} \qquad (t' \leqslant t_1 \leqslant t),$$

where $s = \alpha[\sin \omega t_1 - \sin \omega t']$.

Thus s is independent of the current time t at which we evaluate the stress components. The above results are obtained from (2.66) with t' in place of t_0 and from (2.80) with $G = 0$. The basis $\mathbf{e}_i$ is orthonormal at the current time t.

On substituting these expressions in (6.8) and using (3.14), we see that the integrand is zero for $t_1 \leqslant t' \leqslant t$ and that we obtain the results

$$p_{11} - p_{22} = \int_{-\infty}^{t_1} \mu(t-t')\, s^2\, dt',$$

$$p_{21} = \int_{-\infty}^{t_1} \mu(t-t')\, s\, dt'.$$

When μ is given by (6.7), the factor $\exp(-t/\tau_1)$ can be taken outside each of these integrals, and the integrals then remaining do not depend on t. It follows that $p_{11} - p_{22}$ and p_{21} decrease steadily without oscillation as t increases. It is easy to see that the argument can be extended to cover the case in which μ is given by (6.5).

Example 3

On differentiating the rheological equation of state (6.9), we have

$$\frac{d\Pi^{ij}}{dt} = \int_{-\infty}^{t} \frac{d\mu(t-t')}{dt}\, \gamma^{ij}(t')\, dt' + \mu(0)\, \gamma^{ij}(t);$$

the second term on the right-hand side comes from differentiating the upper limit of integration.

When μ is given by (6.7), we have

$$\frac{d\mu(t-t')}{dt} = -\frac{1}{\tau_1}\mu(t-t'),$$

and hence the above equation becomes

$$\frac{d\Pi^{ij}}{dt} = -\frac{1}{\tau_1}\Pi^{ij} + \mu(0)\,\gamma^{ij} \qquad \text{(by (6.9))},$$

which is the required form.

Example 4

In an orthonormal basis, we have $\pi_{ij} = \pi^{ij} = p_{ij}$, from (1.12), (1.18) and (3.14). Hence, using our usual basis for shear flow (which is orthonormal at time t), we obtain the following expression for the cartesian stress components at time t:

$$p_{ij} + p\begin{pmatrix} 1 & 0 & 0 \\ 0 & 1 & 0 \\ 0 & 0 & 1 \end{pmatrix} = -\int_{-\infty}^{t} \mu(t-t')\begin{pmatrix} 0 & -G(t-t') & 0 \\ -G(t-t') & G^2(t-t')^2 & 0 \\ 0 & 0 & 0 \end{pmatrix} dt';$$

this is obtained from (2.66) with t_0 replaced by t' and from (2.69). The integrals here are evidently of the form (6.3), and we see that

$$p_{11} - p_{33} = 0,$$

$$p_{22} - p_{33} = -G^2\mu_2,$$

as stated. We may note also that $p_{21} = G\mu_1$.

Example 5

When the basis is (instantaneously) orthonormal, we have $\gamma_{jk} = \delta_{jk}$ (from (1.12) and (1.18)), and hence $L_2 = \sum_i \sum_k \dot{\gamma}^{ik}\dot{\gamma}^{ki}$. For steady shear flow, $\dot{\gamma}^{ik} \equiv d\gamma^{ik}/dt$ is given by (2.73) relative to a basis which is instantaneously orthonormal, and hence $L_2 = 2G^2$ since only two terms in the sum are non-zero.

It follows that, in steady shear flow, $\mu = \mu[t-t', 2G^2]$ which has the same dependence on t and t' as μ has in (6.9); the stated results therefore follow from the corresponding results (6.22) and (6.3) appropriate to (6.9).

Chapter 7

Example 1

The given rheological equations of state differ from those (i.e. from (6.9)) for the rubberlike liquid in having lower suffixes in place of upper suffixes and $-\mu$ in place of μ. Equations (7.2) and (7.3) determine the instantaneously recoverable state for the rubberlike liquid when the stress is suddenly made zero following any given flow history, i.e. when one puts $\pi^{ij} = 0$. From the definition of π_{ij}, it is clear that $\pi_{ij} = 0$ whenever $\pi^{ij} = 0$ and hence, from the nature of the argument leading from (6.9) to (7.2) and (7.3), it can be seen that a similar argument will lead from the given rheological equations of state to the following equations:

$$\mu_0^* \gamma_{ij}(t_1^*) = -\int_{-\infty}^{t_1} \mu(t_1 - t')\, \gamma_{ij}(t')\, dt',$$

$$\det \gamma_{ij}(t_1^*) = \det \gamma_{ij}(t_1)$$

these determine the instantaneously recoverable state t_1^*, which can be described by the shape variables $\gamma_{ij}(t_1^*)$ or by their associated variables $\gamma^{ij}(t_1^*)$ which were used with the rubberlike liquid. μ_0^* is a constant to be determined by the solution of the above simultaneous equations.

These equations are valid for any given flow history prior to the removal of stress at a time t_1. When this flow history is a steady shear flow of shear rate G, the appropriate values of $\gamma_{ij}(t')$ may be obtained from (2.64) with $t_0 = t'$ and from (2.69) with $t = t_1$, the basis being chosen to be orthonormal in state t_1 immediately before the removal of stress. With these values for $\gamma_{ij}(t')$, the above equations become

$$\mu_0^* \gamma_{ij}(t_1^*) = -\int_{-\infty}^{t_1} \mu(t_1 - t') \begin{pmatrix} 1 & -G(t_1 - t') & 0 \\ -G(t_1 - t') & 1 + G^2(t_1 - t')^2 & 0 \\ 0 & 0 & 1 \end{pmatrix} dt'$$

$$= \begin{pmatrix} -\mu_0 & G\mu_1 & 0 \\ G\mu_1 & -\mu_0 - G^2 \mu_2 & 0 \\ 0 & 0 & -\mu_0 \end{pmatrix}, \quad \text{by (6.3) with } t = t_1.$$

Taking the determinant of each side of this equation, we have

$$\mu_0^{*3} \det \gamma_{ij}(t_1^*) = -\mu_0[\mu_0(\mu_0 + G^2 \mu_2) - G^2 \mu_1^2];$$

but $\det \gamma_{ij}(t_1^*) = \det \gamma_{ij}(t_1) = 1$, since the basis is orthonormal in state t_1, and hence

$$\mu_0^* = -\mu_0 \lambda^2,$$

where λ is given by (7.16). With this expression for μ_0^*, the above equations for the required instantaneously recoverable state become

$$\gamma_{ij}(t_1^*) = \mathbf{e}_i^* . \mathbf{e}_j^* = \begin{pmatrix} \lambda^{-2} & -\lambda^{-2} G \dfrac{\mu_1}{\mu_0} & 0 \\ -\lambda^{-2} G \dfrac{\mu_1}{\mu_0} & \lambda^{-2}\left(1 + G^2 \dfrac{\mu_2}{\mu_0}\right) & 0 \\ 0 & 0 & \lambda^{-2} \end{pmatrix}.$$

(They may be compared with the corresponding equations (7.18) for the rubberlike liquid.)

The interpretation of this result can be made in the same way as that of (7.18). With the notation $\mathbf{e}_i^* \equiv \mathbf{e}_i(t_1^*)$, we have $\mathbf{e}_1^*.\mathbf{e}_3^* = \mathbf{e}_2^*.\mathbf{e}_3^* = 0$, showing that $\mathbf{e}_3^*$ is perpendicular to $\mathbf{e}_1^*$ and $\mathbf{e}_2^*$. Furthermore,

$$\mathbf{e}_1^*.\mathbf{e}_1^* = \mathbf{e}_3^*.\mathbf{e}_3^* = \lambda^{-2},$$

and hence $e_1^* = e_3^* = \lambda^{-1}$; since $e_1(t_1) = e_3(t_1) = 1$, it follows that material lines parallel to $\mathbf{e}_1$ decrease in length by a factor λ^{-1} and that material lines parallel to $\mathbf{e}_3$ also decrease in length by the factor λ^{-1} on instantaneous recovery (cf. the corresponding factors λ^{-2} and λ for the rubberlike liquid). The area of the plane defined by $\mathbf{e}_1$ and $\mathbf{e}_3$ therefore decreases by a factor λ^{-2}, and thus the separation of this plane and any parallel material plane must increase by a factor λ^2, since the volume is to remain constant.

The shear recovery angle ϵ^*, defined in Fig. 7.3, is determined by the equation

$$\gamma_{12}(t_1^*) = e_1^* e_2^* \cos\left(\frac{\pi}{2} + \epsilon^*\right)$$

which becomes

$$-\lambda^{-2} G \frac{\mu_1}{\mu_0} = \lambda^{-1}\left[\lambda^{-1}\left(1 + G^2 \frac{\mu_2}{\mu_0}\right)^{1/2}\right] \quad (-\sin\epsilon^*)$$

when the above values for $\gamma_{12}(t_1^*)$, e_1^* and e_2^* are used; this equation immediately reduces to the equation (7.22), which determines the shear recovery angle for the rubberlike liquid. This completes the proof of the results stated.

CHAPTER 12

Non-uniform Stress and Strain

The treatment of Chapters 1–8, which is restricted to uniform states of stress and strain, has sufficed to illustrate the process of formulating rheological equations of state for various kinds of idealized materials, and has enabled us to calculate many of the basic properties of these materials; using the rules stated in Chapter 8, the reader should be able to repeat the process for other forms of equations which he may wish to consider in relation to the observed properties of actual visco-elastic materials of interest. If so, the main object of the book will have been achieved.

The restriction of uniformity was introduced partly to enable an elementary treatment (involving vectors but not tensors) to be developed, and partly because a premature treatment of non-uniform stress and strain may obscure the basic points of physical interest with which we have been concerned. The restriction must be raised, however, if the theories are to be applied in detail to problems of practical importance, for non-uniformity of stress and strain arises in most engineering applications and also in the fundamental experiments for determining the differences of normal stress components in shear flow, as described in Chapter 9.

In the present chapter, we remove the restriction of uniformity and develop a formalism which is applicable to all states of stress and strain, non-uniform or uniform, and which reduces to the formalism of Chapters 1 to 8 in the particular case of uniform stress and strain. In particular applications of the general formalism, we prove the validity of the rules governing admissible combinations of the variables π^{ij} and γ_{ij}, as stated in Chapter 8, and of various statements concerning curvilinear shear flow made in Chapter 9.

The equations and methods given in this chapter are largely due to Oldroyd (1950a), Green and Zerna (1954), and Green and Adkins (1960); the terminology, which involves the explicit recognition and use of the distinction between body fields and space fields, has been given in rheological applications by Lodge (1951).

The present chapter is unavoidably of a more advanced nature than the previous chapters. A knowledge of general tensor analysis, such as is contained in McConnell (1931), will be assumed, and the treatment will be concise in view of the extensive ground which has to be covered.

Coordinate Systems and Tensor Fields

Since the term "tensor" is used in slightly different senses in the literature, it is first necessary to state how we shall use this and other related terms in the present treatment of continuous manifolds.

The *undefined elements* and assumed concepts in our logical structure are point, aggregate, class, correspondence, order, number, and the usual processes of analysis of functions of real variables.

A *manifold* is defined as an aggregate of points. (We retain the more familiar word *space* for that particular manifold in which we live and in which the points will be called *places*.)

A *coordinate system* is a one–one correspondence between points of a manifold and ordered sets of three real numbers. We shall say that a point P has coordinates (x^1, x^2, x^3) or x^i ($i = 1, 2, 3$ understood), where in this context x^1, x^2, and x^3 stand for three definite numbers. We shall also refer to "the coordinate system x^i", and in this context x^i stands for the ordered set of three variables all of whose allowable values correspond to the points of the manifold. Coordinates are thus pure numbers (without dimensions, such as length) which serve as labels for points of a given manifold. How in practice a coordinate system is to be set up for a given manifold does not matter here; that it can be done is in fact a property of the manifold.

We shall suppose that a coordinate system exists such that points of the manifold exist corresponding to all coordinate values in some finite intervals $a^i \leqslant x^i \leqslant b^i$ where $a^i < b^i$. Such a manifold is said to be *three-dimensional*, because three and only three coordinates are required to label a typical point. (The formalism can be readily extended to n-dimensional manifolds.)

If one coordinate system exists, an unlimited number exist; for let $\bar{x}^i$ be three variables related to x^i by three one-valued functional relations

$$\bar{x}^i = \bar{x}^i(x^1, x^2, x^3) \qquad (i = 1, 2, 3) \tag{12.1}$$

which have a unique (one-valued) inverse

$$x^i = x^i(\bar{x}^1, \bar{x}^2, \bar{x}^3) \qquad (i = 1, 2, 3). \tag{12.2}$$

Then because the correspondence $\mathrm{P} \rightleftharpoons x^i$ is one–one (since x^i is a coordinate system) and the correspondence $x^i \rightleftharpoons \bar{x}^i$ is one–one, it follows that there is a one–one correspondence $\mathrm{P} \rightleftharpoons \bar{x}^i$, which is therefore a coordinate system. We shall restrict our "allowable" coordinate systems to those obtainable from any one by means of *coordinate transformations* (12.1) and (12.2) which are continuous and "sufficiently differentiable" (i.e. differentiable as many times as may be required in subsequent use).

The aggregate of all points of a manifold for which one coordinate (in a given coordinate system) is constant is a two-dimensional manifold, or *coordinate surface*; if two coordinates are constant, the aggregate is a one-dimensional manifold, or *coordinate line*. The coordinate surfaces $x^1 = \lambda^1$ obtained by giving the parameter λ^1 all allowable values will include all points of the manifold once and only once. A coördinate system may be regarded as a three-parameter family of coordinate surfaces $x^1 = \lambda^1$, $x^2 = \lambda^2$, $x^3 = \lambda^3$. (The familiar picture of a coordinate system as a set of three lines or planes drawn from a special point, or origin, is not in general appropriate.) Each point is the intersection of three coordinate surfaces, one from each family, and the coordinates of the point are equal to the parameter values for those surfaces.

It should be noted that what is often referred to as a "moving coordinate system" in space is (in the present terminology) a succession of different coordinate systems, one for each instant of time; what is often referred to as "a coordinate system fixed in space" will here be called a space coordinate system, when it is necessary to emphasize what manifold it is associated with.

A *scalar* at a point is a number associated with that point; a *scalar field* defined over a given manifold is a correspondence between numbers and points of the manifold, there being one number attached to each point; since the numbers attached to different points may be equal, the correspondence is, in general, one-many. Scalar fields (e.g. temperature, density) usually have physical dimensions, so that the value of the field at any point depends on the units chosen; we shall not consider changes of units here. The value of a scalar field at any point, from its definition, is evidently not dependent in any way on a coordinate system. If ρ denotes the value of a scalar field at a typical point P, we may represent the field symbolically by the relation

$$\rho = \rho(\mathrm{P}).$$

If P has coordinates x^i and $\bar{x}^i$ in any two given coordinate systems, then the scalar field will be represented by two different functions,

$$\rho = s(x) \quad \text{and} \quad \rho = \bar{s}(\bar{x}) \text{ say.}$$

We therefore have the relation

$$\bar{s}(\bar{x}) = s(x) \tag{12.3}$$

between these functions, and this may be called the *transformation law* for a scalar field.

Here and elsewhere we write x for x^1, x^2, x^3 when these (or other similar variables) occur in the argument of a function; thus, for example, $s(x)$ stands for $s(x^1, x^2, x^3)$.

In order to specify a scalar field completely, it is evidently necessary to know (i) the manifold over which the field is defined, and (ii) the value of the field at each point, or, what is equivalent, the function $s(x)$ which represents the field in any one given coordinate system.

In extending these ideas to vector and tensor fields, we wish to draw a clear distinction between a vector (or tensor) and its components. The latter will be defined before the former.

We first consider a single point P of a given manifold. With the point P and a coordinate system x^i let there be associated an ordered set of three numbers (v^1, v^2, v^3), or v^i, for short; with P and any other allowable coordinate system $\bar{x}^i$ let there be associated a second such set $\bar{v}^i$; and so on, for all allowable coordinate systems. Then the sets v^i, $\bar{v}^i$, ..., are sets of *components of a contravariant vector at* P, referred to, or in, the coordinate systems x^i, $\bar{x}^i$, ..., if the components referred to each pair of coordinate systems are related like the corresponding coordinate differentials at P, i.e. if

$$\bar{v}^i = \left(\frac{\partial \bar{x}^i}{\partial x^j}\right)_{\mathrm{P}} v^j \qquad (i = 1, 2, 3). \tag{12.4}$$

The suffix P is used here to emphasize that the partial derivatives are to be evaluated at the point P. The repeated suffix j (or any letter suffix occurring in a term once in an upper and once in a lower position) means that the sum over the values 1, 2, 3 is to be taken.

The components v^i may be said to *represent* the vector in the coordinate system x^i; $\bar{v}^i$ in $\bar{x}^i$, etc. The *vector* itself may be defined as the *class of all sets of components that represent the vector*.

Taking the "class" of sets of components in this way is a process of logical abstraction (Milne, 1948) analogous to the process that has been used by Whitehead and Russell (1927) in their definition of cardinal number: any set of three objects is a representation of the number 3; the number 3 is the *class* of all sets of three objects—it is what they all have in common—their "three-ness", so to speak.

The vector defined above is a *contravariant vector at* P. A *contravariant vector field* is a correspondence between contravariant vectors and points of a manifold such that at each point one vector is defined. Relative to any given coordinate system x^i, such a field will give rise to three one-valued functions $v^i(x)$ which are related to the corresponding functions

$\bar{v}^i(\bar{x})$ in any other coordinate system $\bar{x}^i$ by equations of the form (12.4) in which the components v^i, $\bar{v}^i$ and the partial derivatives are evaluated at the same point. Equations (12.4) represent the transformation law for a contravariant vector field.

When no ambiguity is likely to arise, we shall for brevity use the conventional phrase "a contravariant vector v^i" when we mean "a contravariant vector field, defined over a given manifold, having components $v^i(x)$ relative to a given coordinate system x^i for the manifold". The word "field" can usually be omitted, once the basic terms have been defined, because we almost always deal with fields rather than with a single vector at a point.

A *covariant vector field* v_i is defined in a similar way, the only difference being that components in different coordinate systems are related like the gradient of a scalar field, i.e. the transformation law (in place of (12.4)) is

$$\bar{v}_i = \frac{\partial x^j}{\partial \bar{x}^i} v_j \qquad (i = 1, 2, 3). \tag{12.5}$$

Tensor fields of various types are defined in a similar way, with components transforming like outer (or direct) products of vector components. Thus, for example, the transformation law for the components T^{ij} of a *contravariant tensor field of second rank* is

$$\bar{T}^{ij}(\bar{x}) = \frac{\partial \bar{x}^i}{\partial x^r}\frac{\partial \bar{x}^j}{\partial x^s} T^{rs}(x) \qquad (i, j = 1, 2, 3); \tag{12.6}$$

for a *covariant tensor field of second rank* is

$$\bar{T}_{ij}(\bar{x}) = \frac{\partial x^r}{\partial \bar{x}^i}\frac{\partial x^s}{\partial \bar{x}^j} T_{rs}(x) \qquad (i, j = 1, 2, 3); \tag{12.7}$$

and for a *mixed tensor field of second rank* is

$$\bar{T}^i{}_j(\bar{x}) = \frac{\partial \bar{x}^i}{\partial x^r}\frac{\partial x^s}{\partial \bar{x}^j} T^r{}_s(x) \qquad (i, j = 1, 2, 3). \tag{12.8}$$

Tensor fields of nth rank ($n > 2$) are defined similarly, with components transforming like the outer product of n vectors. Scalar fields and vector fields may thus be regarded as tensor fields of rank zero and of rank unity, respectively. If the rank is not stated, the term tensor will usually be used for a tensor of rank two, especially where particular applications of the formalism are involved; in general discussion, on the other hand, the term tensor may be used to mean a tensor field of any rank.

In order to specify a tensor field completely, it is evidently necessary to be given the following information, or its equivalent:

(i) the manifold over which the field is defined;
(ii) the transformation law for an arbitrary coordinate transformation; and
(iii) the values of the tensor components, referred to any one given coordinate system, at all points of the manifold.

From (ii) and (iii), the values of the components in any allowable coordinate system can be calculated.

From given tensor fields, new fields can be formed by the processes of addition, multiplication by a scalar, contraction, and formation of the reciprocal (in the case of a non-singular second rank tensor). In each case, tensors *at the same point* are involved; the sum of tensors at different points is not defined, because if, for example, $T^{ij}(\mathrm{P})$ is a tensor at P and $S^{ij}(\mathrm{Q})$ is a tensor at another point Q, then

$$\bar{T}^{ij}(\mathrm{P})+\bar{S}^{ij}(\mathrm{Q}) = \left(\frac{\partial\bar{x}^i}{\partial x^r}\frac{\partial\bar{x}^j}{\partial x^s}\right)_{\mathrm{P}} T^{rs}(\mathrm{P})+\left(\frac{\partial\bar{x}^i}{\partial x^r}\frac{\partial\bar{x}^j}{\partial x^s}\right)_{\mathrm{Q}} S^{rs}(\mathrm{Q}),$$

and this is not equal to

$$\frac{\partial\bar{x}^i}{\partial x^r}\frac{\partial\bar{x}^j}{\partial x^s}(T^{rs}+S^{rs})$$

unless the partial derivatives have the same values at the two points; this will in general be the case only if the coordinate transformation (12.1) is linear.

The coordinate transformations could be restricted to be linear (and often are), but this restriction would be inconvenient for our present application to non-uniform states of stress and strain. One of the main points in the use of body fields (defined below) in rheological applications is in fact that it renders unnecessary the addition or comparison of tensors associated with two or more distinct points of the same manifold (although it is still necessary to compare tensors at *neighbouring* points, since this is involved in covariant differentiation).

Tensors at a point may be *compared* with one another, provided only that they are of the same type (e.g. both contravariant, second rank); by this we mean that (for example) we can assign a meaning to the statement that two such tensors are equal: they will be equal if corresponding components are equal in any one coordinate system; for then we have $T^{ij}-S^{ij}=0$ $(i,j=1,2,3)$, say, and hence, since the transformation equations (12.6) are linear and homogeneous in the tensor components, we have in any other coordinate system the result $\bar{T}^{ij}-\bar{S}^{ij}=0$.

Two points $P = x^i$ and $Q = x^i + dx^i$ are said to be *neighbouring points* if their coordinate differences dx^i in any given coordinate system are infinitesimally small; this definition does not depend on the choice of coordinate system, because the corresponding differences

$$d\bar{x}^i = \frac{\partial \bar{x}^i}{\partial x_r} dx^r$$

in any other allowable coordinate system will be infinitesimals of the same order of smallness, since the assumed differentiability of (12.1) means that the partial derivatives $\partial \bar{x}^i / \partial x^r$ are bounded.

A manifold is said to possess a *metric* if there exists a correspondence between neighbouring pairs of points and positive real numbers; to any given pair of neighbouring points corresponds one and only one number, called the *separation* of, or distance between, the points. If the separation, ds say, can be expressed as the positive root of a quadratic form in the coordinate differences dx^i, so that

$$(ds)^2 = g_{ij}(x)\, dx^i\, dx^j, \tag{12.9}$$

the manifold is said to be *Riemannian*. The coefficients g_{ij}, in general functions of x^1, x^2, and x^3, can be taken to be *symmetric* (i.e. $g_{ij} = g_{ji}$) without loss of generality, and can then be readily shown to be components of a covariant tensor field of second rank, called the *metric tensor*.

In the manifolds that we shall consider, the quadratic form (12.9) is positive definite (so that ds is always real). At any point, a coordinate system can always be chosen so that

$$g_{ij}(x) = \delta_{ij} \tag{12.10}$$

at that point; if a coordinate system can be chosen so that this relation holds at all points of the manifold, the manifold is said to be *Euclidean*, and the coordinate system *rectangular cartesian*; in such a manifold, *oblique* or *cartesian* coordinate systems exist such that g_{ij} are independent of x^i.

Since the form (12.9) is positive definite, it follows that $\det g_{ij} > 0$ and hence that the reciprocal matrix, of elements g^{ij} say, exists and is symmetric, so that we have

$$g_{ij}(x)\, g^{jk}(x) = \delta_i^{\,k}. \tag{12.11}$$

It can be shown that δ_i^k ($= 1$ or 0 according as $i = k$ or $i \neq k$) are components of a mixed second rank tensor, and that g^{ij} are components of a contravariant second rank tensor.

In manifolds of interest in physics, the separation has dimensions of length and the number ds depends on the choice of the unit of length. This means that a particular pair of neighbouring points (on a measuring rod) is arbitrarily chosen as a standard, and is assigned a separation of unity (e.g. 1 cm); the unit (cm) is a name for the particular pair chosen. The essential feature of a manifold with a metric is that it is measurable in the sense that a process of measurement can be assigned in which the separation of any given pair of neighbouring points can be compared with, and expressed in terms of, the separation of the standard pair of points. It will be recalled that the coordinates x^i, and therefore also their differentials dx^i, are pure numbers, not dependent on the choice of any unit of length; a change of this unit will alter the value of g_{ij}, which, from (12.9), must have the dimension (length)^2.

Body and Space Manifolds in Continuum Mechanics

The flow or deformation of a continuous material through space can most naturally be described mathematically in terms of two physically distinct manifolds:

(i) the *body manifold*, consisting of the material under consideration, in which the points are *particles*; and
(ii) the *space manifold*, through which the body moves, in which the points are *places*.

The assumptions made in replacing actual solids and liquids by idealized continuous materials are just such as ensure that the idealized material is a continuous three-dimensional manifold as defined above. We can therefore make two distinct applications of the above formalism: we can define coordinate systems and tensor fields for the body manifold, and coordinate systems and tensor fields for the space manifold. We shall call these "body" and "space" coordinate systems and fields, and shall where possible use Greek letters for symbols associated with the body manifold and the corresponding Roman letters for symbols associated with the space manifold.

It will usually be sufficient to use one space coordinate system x^i and one body coordinate system ξ^i in applications of the formalism, but it should be borne in mind that the use of body fields and space fields carries with it the implication that whole families of allowable coordinate systems (for each manifold) exist, because their existence is implicit in the definition of tensor fields given above.

It will be noticed that the symbol ξ^i, used here for the coordinates of a particle referred to a given body coordinate system, is the same as that used in earlier chapters, e.g. in (1.10), apparently in a different connection. In fact, the two uses agree in special circumstances, as we shall show later. For the present, however, we use the symbols as defined in the present chapter. Similar statements are true of other symbols, γ_{ij}, γ^{ij} and π^{ij}, defined below.

Relative to a given body coordinate system, *a given particle always has the same coordinates* ξ^i, say, which therefore serve as a label for that particle throughout the motion. A body coordinate surface, $\xi^1 = \text{constant}$, say, always contains the same particles, and may therefore be pictured as a surface imprinted in or convected with the moving material. A body coordinate system may therefore be called a *convected* coordinate system (Oldroyd, 1950a), but this terminology implies that the space manifold is singled out for special attention; a space coordinate system is then said to be a coordinate system fixed in space.

It is a curious fact that, in many rheological treatments, the space manifold has been singled out for special attention, sometimes explicitly but usually implicitly. For this reason, the reader may find some initial difficulty in picturing body coordinate systems and body fields. It is not in fact necessary to say how a body coordinate system can be set up (that it can be set up is a property of the idealized material), but it should be noted that in some experimental investigations of the deformation of solids and the flow of liquids, the material is marked by lines or by streams of coloured inks which constitute a body coordinate system, or part of one.

A *configuration*, or *state*, of the body is a one–one correspondence between particles of the body and places in a region of space; one place x^i is occupied by one and only one particle ξ^i, and therefore a state may be described by functions $x^i = f^i(\xi^1, \xi^2, \xi^3)$ which have a unique inverse, $\xi^i = \phi^i(x^1, x^2, x^3)$ say, for all places x^i that are occupied by particles. In dealing with more than one state, it is convenient to use a variable t to label the states, since we only need to consider in practice a one-parameter family of states. The values of t can be discrete, or continuous in a flow when t will represent time. We may therefore write

$$x^i = f^i(\xi, t), \quad \xi^i = \phi^i(x, t) \tag{12.12}$$

for the description of a flow referred to specified space and body coordinate systems x^i, ξ^i.

Equations (12.12) are formally similar to equations (12.1) and (12.2), which describe relations between two coordinate systems for one manifold, but have a different interpretation.

A flow is *continuous* if any pair of particles which occupy neighbouring places in one state occupy neighbouring places in every state. We shall confine our attention to such continuous changes of state; this means that phenomena such as fracture and self-diffusion are excluded. It is then convenient, having chosen any space coordinate system, to choose a body coordinate system in such a way as to ensure that the functions (12.12) are continuous and sufficiently differentiable. When t takes on a continuous range of values, it will usually be assumed that the functions (12.12) are also differentiable with respect to t, although important exceptions (associated with instantaneous elastic recovery) arise when the functions have finite discontinuities at particular values of t. It is clear that the velocity of the material (relative to space) can be represented by the contravariant space vector field whose components v^i are given by

$$v^i = \frac{\partial x^i}{\partial t} \equiv \frac{\partial f^i(\xi, t)}{\partial t}, \tag{12.13}$$

since these represent the "rate of change of place" of a given particle ξ^i. Here and elsewhere, the partial derivatives $\partial x^i/\partial t$ and $\partial x^i/\partial \xi^k$ mean $\partial f^i/\partial t$ and $\partial f^i/\partial \xi^k$, i.e. are formed from the functions (12.12); v^i (so defined) is a contravariant vector because it evidently has the same transformation properties as the coordinate differential dx^i.

The space metric tensor field will be denoted by g_{ij}; it is independent of time (effects considered in general relativity being neglected), and satisfies the condition that the Riemann curvature tensor formed from g_{ij} vanishes everywhere, since the space we consider is Euclidean. The separation of a pair of neighbouring places is given by (12.9).

The existence of a metric in space gives rise to a metric in the body in any given configuration t. For the space metric is a correspondence between positive numbers and neighbouring pairs of places, and a configuration is a correspondence which assigns one particle to each place, and neighbouring particles to neighbouring places; the two correspondences together therefore give rise to a correspondence between positive numbers and pairs of neighbouring particles. (More briefly: two neighbouring particles have a separation equal to the separation of the places they occupy in state t.)

The body metric will vary whenever the shape of the body changes, because the separations of pairs of neighbouring particles will then change. Moreover, on substituting the differentials

$$dx^i = \frac{\partial x^i}{\partial \xi^r} d\xi^r \tag{12.14}$$

in (12.9), it follows that the body metric is described by a quadratic differential form

$$(ds)^2 = \gamma_{rs}(\xi, t)\, d\xi^r\, d\xi^s, \tag{12.15}$$

where

$$\gamma_{rs} = \gamma_{sr} = \left(\frac{\partial x^i}{\partial \xi^r}\frac{\partial x^j}{\partial \xi^s}\right)_t g_{ij}(x). \tag{12.16}$$

The body manifold is therefore also Riemannian, and γ_{rs} are components of a symmetric covariant *body* tensor field of second rank. The form (12.15), being obtained by a real non-singular transformation (12.14) from a positive definite form (12.9), must also be positive definite.

In the foregoing argument, we have an example of a space field giving rise to, or inducing, a field in the body in a given configuration. This is an important example of a general process of this type, which we now consider.

Field Transfer between Body and Space Manifolds

According to the definitions given above, if we are given any continuous manifold and its associated family of allowable coordinate systems, tensor fields may be defined over the manifold; any such field consists of a correspondence between tensors of given type and points of the manifold, and conversely any such correspondence defines a tensor field over the manifold.

A configuration t gives rise to a one–one correspondence between the allowable coordinate systems for space and those for the body, and determines an isomorphism between space fields and body fields, as the following argument shows.

A space coordinate system x^i is a one–one correspondence $\mathrm{Q} \rightleftharpoons x^i$ between places Q and ordered sets of three numbers x^i; a configuration t is a one–one correspondence $\mathrm{Q} \rightleftharpoons \mathrm{P}$ between places Q and particles P; the two together therefore generate a one–one correspondence $\mathrm{P} \rightleftharpoons x^i$, which constitutes a coordinate system ξ'^i for the body, where $\xi'^i = x^i$. All allowable body coordinate systems can be obtained from the corresponding space systems in this way, because we have agreed to choose body coordinate systems which are such that the functions (12.12) are sufficiently differentiable. In other words, the coordinate surfaces of any allowable space system coincide (in any one given configuration) with the coordinate surfaces of one of the allowable body systems, and conversely. For a given state t, the equations (12.12) may therefore be interpreted as a body coordinate transformation $\xi^i \to \xi'^i = x^i = f^i(\xi, t)$, or as a space coordinate transformation $x^i \to x'^i \equiv \xi^i = \phi^i(x, t)$ (since the terms space and body are interchangeable throughout the above argument). Thus a configuration gives rise to a one–one correspondence between the allowable coordinate systems for the two manifolds. This correspondence changes as the configuration changes, so that during flow a given body coordinate system coincides with a succession of space coordinate systems.

The corresponding isomorphism between space fields and body fields is defined as follows. For definiteness, let us consider any given contravariant second rank space tensor field, having components $F^{ij}(x)$, say, relative to a given space coordinate system x^i. In state t, let ξ'^i be that body coordinate system which coincides with the space system x^i, so that $\xi'^i = x^i$. We now define a body field Φ^{ij} as follows:

(i) Φ^{ij} is a field defined over the body manifold;

(ii) this field is of the same type (in this case, a contravariant second rank tensor field) as the given space field; and

(iii) in a common coordinate system for the two manifolds, corresponding components of the two fields are equal, i.e.

$$\Phi'^{ij}(\xi') = F^{ij}(x), \tag{12.17}$$

where $\Phi'^{ij}(\xi')$ denote the components of the body field relative to the coordinate system ξ'^i, and evaluated at the particle ξ'^i which in the given state t occupies the place x^i at which the components $F^{ij}(x)$ are evaluated.

If $\Phi^{ij}(\xi)$ denote the components of this body field when referred to an arbitrary body coordinate system ξ^i, then the relation between Φ^{ij} and Φ'^{ij} is that for a coordinate transformation $\xi^i \to \xi'^i$ applied to the components of a contravariant second rank tensor, namely

$$\Phi^{ij}(\xi) = \frac{\partial \xi^i}{\partial \xi'^r}\frac{\partial \xi^j}{\partial \xi'^s}\Phi'^{rs}(\xi'). \tag{12.18}$$

We see therefore that a given space field $F^{ij}(x)$ induces, in state t, a field $\Phi^{ij}(\xi)$ in the body, where

$$F^{ij}(x) \overset{t}{\to} \Phi^{ij}(\xi) = \left(\frac{\partial \xi^i}{\partial x^r}\frac{\partial \xi^j}{\partial x^s}\right)_t F^{rs}(x). \tag{12.19}$$

This equation follows at once from (12.18) when we use (12.17) and the equations $\xi'^r = x^r$. We introduce the arrow symbol $\overset{t}{\to}$ for the isomorphism generated between space fields and body fields by a configuration t; since the two manifolds are on an equal footing, however, it would be more accurate to use a two-way symbol $\overset{t}{\rightleftharpoons}$ for this isomorphism, but in practice it may be convenient to use the one-way symbol $\overset{t}{\rightarrow}$ when it is necessary to emphasize that one field in a given context is defined in terms of the other. The partial derivatives in (12.19) are obtained from (12.12) and mean $\partial\phi^i/\partial x^r$, etc. Associated with the equations (12.19) are the equations

$$\Phi^{ij}(\xi) \overset{t}{\rightarrow} F^{ij}(x) = \left(\frac{\partial x^i}{\partial \xi^r}\frac{\partial x^j}{\partial \xi^s}\right)_t \Phi^{rs}(\xi), \tag{12.20}$$

which are evidently obtained if one pursues an argument similar to the above but with the manifolds interchanged.

The corresponding equations for covariant fields of second rank are readily found to be

$$F_{ij}(x) \overset{t}{\rightarrow} \Phi_{ij}(\xi) = \frac{\partial x^r}{\partial \xi^i}\frac{\partial x^s}{\partial \xi^j} F_{rs}(x), \tag{12.21}$$

$$\Phi_{ij}(\xi) \overset{t}{\rightarrow} F_{ij}(x) = \frac{\partial \xi^r}{\partial x^i}\frac{\partial \xi^s}{\partial x^j} \Phi_{rs}(\xi), \tag{12.22}$$

and the corresponding equations for any other type of tensor field can be written down if required; they are of the same form as the equations relating tensor components referred to two coordinate systems for the same manifold.

An important property of the isomorphism $\overset{t}{\rightarrow}$ (between fields) is that it *reproduces invariant relations*. For example, let $F^{ij}_{(1)}$, $F^{ij}_{(2)}$ and $F^{ij}_{(3)}$ be three space fields (contravariant second rank tensors, as indicated by the letter suffixes) which satisfy the invariant relation

$$F^{ij}_{(1)}(x) - F^{ij}_{(2)}(x) + F^{ij}_{(3)}(x) = 0$$

(which is invariant in form under a coordinate transformation). If $\Phi^{ij}_{(1)}$, $\Phi^{ij}_{(2)}$ and $\Phi^{ij}_{(3)}$ are the corresponding body fields defined under the isomorphism $\overset{t}{\rightarrow}$, then from (12.19) it follows that

$$\Phi^{ij}_{(1)}(\xi) - \Phi^{ij}_{(2)}(\xi) + \Phi^{ij}_{(3)}(\xi) = \left(\frac{\partial \xi^i}{\partial x^r}\frac{\partial \xi^j}{\partial x^s}\right)_t [F^{rs}_{(1)}(x) - F^{rs}_{(2)}(x) + F^{rs}_{(3)}(x)] = 0,$$

showing that a relation of the same form between the body tensors is valid.

This property of the isomorphism arises from the fact that the equations defining the isomorphism are formally similar to the equations relating components of the same tensor field referred to two coordinate systems, and from this it can be seen that the isomorphism does reproduce invariant relations of all types, whether they involve addition, subtraction, contraction, covariant differentiation, or the formation of outer products of tensor fields. It is this reproductive property which justifies the use of the term *isomorphism* for the one–one correspondence $\overset{t}{\rightleftharpoons}$ between body fields and space fields.

As an example, which we have already encountered, we may note that $d\xi^i \overset{t}{\rightarrow} dx^i$ (by (12.14)), and that

$$g_{ij}(x) \overset{t}{\rightarrow} \gamma_{ij}(\xi, t) \tag{12.23}$$

(cf. (12.16) and (12.21)), showing that *the space metric field induces at time t the metric field* $\gamma_{ij}(\xi,t)$ *in the body*; *the body metric field varies with time* when the configuration changes, although the space metric g_{ij} does not. Since a scalar field is unchanged in value under the isomorphism, we see that equation (12.9) is of the same form as the corresponding equation (12.15) which relates the quantities ds, γ_{ij}, and $d\xi^i$ obtained from the corresponding quantities ds, g_{ij}, and dx^i by the isomorphism $\overset{t}{\rightarrow}$.

We may also regard the isomorphism $\overset{t}{\rightarrow}$ as a process or operation which "transfers" a field from one manifold to the other; from the argument just given, we may say that the transfer operation $\overset{t}{\rightarrow}$ *commutes* with the various tensor operations of addition, contraction, covariant differentiation, etc., provided only that these refer to a single configuration t of the system. The operation $\overset{t}{\rightarrow}$ does not commute (for example) with the operations $\partial/\partial t$ and $\int \ldots dt$. We shall see below what happens with these operations; here it is enough to remark that the whole argument concerning the isomorphism as set out above is based on the consideration of a single configuration of the body in space, and that it is not surprising that complications arise when more than one configuration is involved. It is in fact just those cases in which more than one configuration is involved that are of particular interest in continuum mechanics and for which the introduction of the concept of body fields is worth while; if we never had to consider more than one configuration, then the distinction between body fields and space fields would not be worth making; indeed, since the two types of fields are isomorphic, they are in a sense mathematically indistinguishable so long as only one configuration is involved.

Descriptions of Shape and Strain Using Body Fields

The body metric tensor γ_{ij} describes the shape of the body, and changes when and only when the shape changes. A change of shape, or strain, in the neighbourhood of any given particle ξ^i, when the material moves from any one configuration t_1 to any other t_2, may be described by the difference of body metric tensors at ξ^i, namely

$$\gamma_{ij}(\xi, t_1) - \gamma_{ij}(\xi, t_2) \equiv \Delta_{ij}(\xi; t_1, t_2) \text{ say.} \tag{12.24}$$

This difference is itself a body tensor, since it involves tensors defined at the same point of the manifold concerned. It should perhaps be remarked that (12.24) are not components of any space tensor field, because the two tensors $\gamma_{ij}(\xi, t_1)$ and $\gamma_{ij}(\xi, t_2)$ are "attached" to one particle which will (in general) occupy different places in space in the two states.

It is perhaps instructive to compare the two equations

$$\begin{cases} (ds)^2 = \gamma_{ij}(\xi, t)\, d\xi^i d\xi^j & (12.15), \\ (ds)^2 = g_{ij}(x)\, dx^i dx^j & (12.9), \end{cases}$$

which are alternative ways of describing the changing separation ds of a given pair of neighbouring particles in a flowing material according to the body formalism and the space formalism. In the body formalism, the relative coordinates $d\xi^i$ of the particles are independent of time but the (body) metric tensor changes with time. In the space formalism, the relative coordinates of the places, x^i and $x^i + dx^i$, which the particles occupy, change with time but the (space) metric tensor g_{ij} is independent of time.

We may note that *the body field Δ_{ij}*, defined by (12.24), *is an additive measure of strain* in the sense that, for *any* three states t_1, t_2, and t_3, we evidently have the relation

$$\Delta_{ij}(\xi; t_1, t_2) + \Delta_{ij}(\xi; t_2, t_3) = \Delta_{ij}(\xi; t_1, t_3). \tag{12.25}$$

Strain fields of this type have been used by Oldroyd (1950a) and by Green and Zerna (1954, p. 57); Oldroyd calls γ_{ij} the *convected components* of the *space* metric tensor (i.e. the components referred to a coordinate system convected with the moving material) and does not explicitly introduce the concept of a body field. The terminology of Green and Zerna can be understood in terms of body fields and space fields as defined above.

The fundamental property of the strain tensor Δ_{ij} is expressed by the equation

$$[ds(t_1)]^2 - [ds(t_2)]^2 = \Delta_{ij}(\xi; t_1, t_2)\, d\xi^i d\xi^j \tag{12.26}$$

which follows at once from (12.15) and (12.24). Here $ds(t)$ denotes the separation at time t of a pair of neighbouring particles ξ^i, $\xi^i + d\xi^i$. By taking the limit as $t_2 \to t_1$ of (12.26) divided by $t_1 - t_2$, or, more generally, by differentiating (12.15) n times at constant ξ^i, we obtain the result

$$\frac{d^n}{dt^n}[ds(t)]^2 = \frac{\partial^n \gamma_{ij}(\xi,t)}{\partial t^n}\,d\xi^i\,d\xi^j. \tag{12.27}$$

Since it is formed by a limiting process involving only tensors associated with a given particle, it follows that $\partial^n\gamma_{ij}/\partial t^n$ is also a body tensor; it is sometimes called the "nth rate-of-strain tensor". $\partial\gamma_{ij}/\partial t$ is called the *rate-of-strain tensor*.

The above arguments can evidently be repeated using the contravariant body field $\gamma^{ij}(\xi,t)$ (i.e. the field reciprocal to $\gamma_{ij}(\xi,t)$) in place of $\gamma_{ij}(\xi,t)$. The only result which is not self-evident is that which corresponds to (12.15): *if $\sigma(\xi) = c$ is any one-parameter family of body surfaces, the separation δh at time t of neighbouring members, of parameter values c and $c+\delta c$, is given by the equation*

$$\left(\frac{\delta c}{\delta h}\right)^2 = \gamma^{ij}(\xi,t)\frac{\partial\sigma}{\partial\xi^i}\frac{\partial\sigma}{\partial\xi^j}. \tag{12.28}$$

Proof. If ξ^i is any particle on the surface c and $\xi^i+\delta\xi^i$ is a neighbouring particle on the surface $c+\delta c$, then $\sigma(\xi) = c$ and $\sigma(\xi+\delta\xi) = c+\delta c$, and hence, on subtraction, we have

$$\frac{\partial\sigma}{\partial\xi^i}\,\delta\xi^i = \delta c. \tag{12.29}$$

The normal to the surface c is represented by the covariant vector $\partial\sigma/\partial\xi^i$ or by the associated contravariant vector $\gamma^{ij}\,\partial\sigma/\partial\xi^j$, where γ^{ij} is the reciprocal metric tensor in the state under consideration; if the particle $\xi^i+\delta\xi^i$ lies on the normal at ξ^i, then we may write $\delta\xi^i = \epsilon\gamma^{ij}\,\partial\sigma/\partial\xi^j$, for some value of ϵ which may be expressed in terms of δc by substituting this expression for $\delta\xi^i$ in (12.29); using the expression for ϵ obtained in this way, the equation for $\delta\xi^i$ becomes

$$\delta\xi^i = \delta c\left(\gamma^{rs}\frac{\partial\sigma}{\partial\xi^r}\frac{\partial\sigma}{\partial\xi^s}\right);$$

the separation of the surfaces at ξ^i is equal to the separation of the two particles:

$$(\delta h)^2 = \gamma_{ij}\,\delta\xi^i\,\delta\xi^j;$$

when the above expression for $\delta\xi^i$ is substituted in this equation, the required result (12.28) is obtained on simplification.

The covariant metric tensor γ_{ij} is simply associated with separations of neighbouring particles; the contravariant metric tensor γ^{ij} with separations of neighbouring material surfaces belonging to the same one-parameter family.

Since δc and σ are independent of t, it follows that

$$\frac{d^n}{dt^n}\left[\frac{\delta c}{\delta h(t)}\right]^2 = \frac{\partial^n \gamma^{ij}(\xi,t)}{\partial t^n}\frac{\partial \sigma}{\partial \xi^i}\frac{\partial \sigma}{\partial \xi^j}, \tag{12.30}$$

which gives an interpretation to the nth rate-of-strain contravariant tensor $\partial^n \gamma^{ij}/\partial t^n$. We may also define a contravariant (finite-strain) body tensor

$$\gamma^{ij}(\xi,t_1)-\gamma^{ij}(\xi,t_2) \equiv \Delta^{ij}(\xi;t_1,t_2), \tag{12.31}$$

which is similar to (12.24).

Descriptions of Strain using Space Fields

We have seen that the change of shape which a material undergoes in a motion $t_0 \to t$ can be described by either of two *body* tensor fields, Δ_{ij} and Δ^{ij}, which represent the difference of the covariant metric tensors and the difference of the contravariant metric tensors in the two states t_0, t; there is in fact an unlimited number of body fields which can be constructed out of these two and which can be used to describe strain, but these two do arise naturally at an early stage in the present formalism.

In using *space* fields as an alternative method of describing strain, we are faced with an increase in the number of possible fields which may be regarded *a priori* as being equally simple, because in addition to the choice between covariant and contravariant fields there is a further choice arising from the fact that the space fields may be obtained from the above body fields by transferring them from the body manifold to the space manifold in either of the two states t_0, t; since in many applications the two states have a different significance (e.g. in dealing with a perfectly elastic solid, it is convenient to take one state t_0 as the unstressed state and the other state t as an arbitrary stressed state) this choice gives a significant increase in the number of possible simple descriptions.

The various space fields have been conveniently described by Prager (1961) (Chapter IX), and their definitions may be represented by the following equations:

$$[ds(t_0)]^2 = C_{ij}(x)\,dx^i\,dx^j \qquad \text{(Cauchy)}; \tag{12.32}$$

$$[ds(t)]^2 = \bar{C}_{ij}(a)\,da^i\,da^j \qquad \text{(Cauchy)}; \tag{12.33}$$

$$\delta_i^k = C_{ij}(x)\,B^{jk}(x) \qquad \text{(Finger)}; \tag{12.34}$$

(12.35) $$\delta_i^k = \bar{C}_{ij}(a)\,\bar{B}^{jk}(a) \qquad \text{(Finger)};$$

(12.36) $$2U_{ij}(x) = g_{ij}(x) - C_{ij}(x) \qquad \text{(Almansi)};$$

(12.37) $$2\bar{U}_{ij}(a) = \bar{C}_{ij}(a) - g_{ij}(a) \qquad \text{(Green)}.$$

The notation is as follows: relative to a single coordinate system fixed in space, a typical particle P of the material moves from a place of coordinates a^i in state t_0 to a place of coordinates x^i in state t; a neighbouring particle Q moves from a place $a^i + da^i$ to a place $x^i + dx^i$; the separation of P and Q is equal to $ds(t_0)$ in state t_0 and to $ds(t)$ in state t. The quantities C_{ij}, $\bar{C}_{ij}$, B^{jk}, $\bar{B}^{jk}$, U_{ij}, $\bar{U}_{ij}$ denote components of symmetric tensors representing strain fields which are associated with the people whose names are given in parenthesis. The above equations are obtained from Prager's equations (1.5), (1.6), (2.7), (3.1), (3.2), (3.5), (3.8), (3.12), and (3.24) which are valid in rectangular cartesian coordinate systems; in order to obtain our equations, valid in arbitrary coordinate systems, we have replaced δ_{ij} by g_{ij} where appropriate and have used upper and lower suffixes to indicate contravariant and covariant tensors, respectively. In other respects, our notation agrees with Prager's.

We shall now show that the above space fields are obtainable from the body metric fields in the following manner:

(12.38) $$\gamma_{ij}(\xi, t_0) \xrightarrow{t} C_{ij}(x),$$

(12.39) $$\gamma_{ij}(\xi, t) \xrightarrow{t_0} \bar{C}_{ij}(a),$$

(12.40) $$\gamma^{ij}(\xi, t_0) \xrightarrow{t} B^{ij}(x),$$

(12.41) $$\gamma^{ij}(\xi, t) \xrightarrow{t_0} \bar{B}^{ij}(a),$$

(12.42) $$\gamma_{ij}(\xi, t) - \gamma_{ij}(\xi, t_0) \xrightarrow{t} 2U_{ij}(x),$$

(12.43) $$\gamma_{ij}(\xi, t) - \gamma_{ij}(\xi, t_0) \xrightarrow{t_0} 2\bar{U}_{ij}(a).$$

Proof of (12.38). From (12.15) applied to state t_0, we have

$$[ds(t_0)]^2 = \gamma_{ij}(\xi, t_0)\, d\xi^i\, d\xi^j.$$

Let $\gamma_{ij}(\xi, t_0) \xrightarrow{t} C'_{ij}(x)$ (defining $C'_{ij}(x)$). Since $d\xi^i \xrightarrow{t} dx^i$ and $ds(t_0) \xrightarrow{t} ds(t_0)$, it follows that this equation induces the following equation in space in state t: $[ds(t_0)]^2 = C'_{ij}(x)\, dx^i dx^j$. On subtracting (12.32), we therefore have $[C'_{ij}(x) - C_{ij}(x)]\, dx^i dx^j = 0$ for all values of dx^i. Since the coefficients are symmetric, it follows that $C'_{ij}(x) - C_{ij}(x) = 0$, which proves (12.38). The *proof of* (12.39) may be obtained in a similar way, with t and t_0 interchanged.

Proof of (12.40). Let us define a body field β^{jk} by the relation $B^{jk}(x) \xrightarrow{t} \beta^{jk}$; we then require to show that $\beta^{jk} = \gamma^{jk}(\xi, t_0)$. Since δ_i^k are components of a mixed tensor whose components have the same numerical values in every coordinate system, it follows that the equations analogous to (12.19) for a mixed tensor become in this case

$$\delta_i^k \xrightarrow{t} \delta_i^k. \tag{12.44}$$

Hence, using (12.38), it follows that (12.34) induces the equation $\delta_i^k = \gamma_{ij}(\xi, t_0)\beta^{jk}$ in the body in state t. Multiplying both sides of this equation by $\gamma^{li}(\xi, t_0)$ and carrying out the implied summation over i, we see that

$$\gamma^{lk}(\xi, t_0) = \gamma^{li}(\xi, t_0)\,\delta_i^k = \gamma^{li}(\xi, t_0)\,\gamma_{ij}(\xi, t_0)\,\beta^{jk} = \delta_j^l \beta^{jk} = \beta^{lk},$$

which proves (12.40). The *proof of* (12.41) may be obtained in a similar way, with t and t_0 interchanged.

Proof of (12.42). From (12.23) and (12.38), it follows that

$$\begin{aligned} \gamma_{ij}(\xi, t) - \gamma_{ij}(\xi, t_0) &\xrightarrow{t} g_{ij}(x) - C_{ij}(x) \\ &= 2U_{ij}(x) \qquad \text{by (12.36).} \end{aligned}$$

Proof of (12.43). From (12.23), applied to state t_0, and (12.39), it follows that

$$\begin{aligned} \gamma_{ij}(\xi, t) - \gamma_{ij}(\xi, t_0) &\xrightarrow{t_0} \bar{C}_{ij}(a) - g_{ij}(a) \\ &= 2\bar{U}_{ij}(a), \qquad \text{by (12.37).} \end{aligned}$$

Time Derivatives of Body Fields

In describing rheological properties of a moving material, we may need to be able to describe the rates at which various field quantities (such as density, shape, and stress) change *at a given particle*, or, more precisely, in an infinitesimally small material element which includes a given particle; for the properties of a given element are (by hypothesis) determined by the rates of change and by the history of changes of the relevant field variables at that element, and are not in any way dependent on the positions in or motions through space of that element. For this reason, *body fields give a simpler and more natural description of rheological properties than do space fields.*

Time derivatives of body fields (i.e. partial derivatives with respect to t, at constant ξ^i) can therefore enter rheological equations of state without introducing any (unwanted) dependence on motion relative to axes fixed in space. It is natural to ask what happens when such time derivatives of body fields are transferred to the space manifold at time t, in view of the extensive use made of space fields in the literature. We have already stated that the operations $\partial/\partial t$ and $\overset{t}{\rightarrow}$ do not commute; we shall now show that the commutator

$$\left(\frac{\partial}{\partial t}\overset{t}{\rightarrow}-\overset{t}{\rightarrow}\frac{\partial}{\partial t}\right)$$

for these operations involves terms which depend on the vorticity and on the rate of strain in the element concerned. The results have been given by Oldroyd (1950a).

Scalar field. Let $\sigma(\xi,t)$ be a time-dependent body scalar field, and let $s(x,t)$ be the space scalar field isomorphic to this field at time t. Then

$$s(x,t) \rightleftharpoons \sigma(\xi,t) = [s(x,t)]_{x^i=f^i(\xi,t)} \tag{12.45}$$

The particle coordinates ξ^i and the coordinates x^i of the place which this particle occupies at time t are related by equations of the form (12.12).

Differentiating (12.45) with respect to t at constant ξ^i, we have

$$\frac{\partial\sigma(\xi,t)}{\partial t} = \frac{\partial s(x,t)}{\partial t}+\frac{\partial s(x,t)}{\partial x^i}\frac{\partial x^i}{\partial t} = \frac{\partial s(x,t)}{\partial t}+\frac{\partial s(x,t)}{\partial x^i}v^i(x,t), \tag{12.46}$$

where v^i is the velocity of the material relative to space (cf. (12.13)). This equation may be written in the form

$$\frac{\partial\sigma(\xi,t)}{\partial t}\overset{t}{\rightarrow}\frac{Ds(x,t)}{Dt}, \tag{12.47}$$

where

$$\frac{D}{Dt} \equiv \frac{\partial}{\partial t}+v^i(x,t)\frac{\partial}{\partial x^i} \tag{12.48}$$

denotes the "hydrodynamic derivative" or the "time derivative following the motion represented by a velocity field v^i".

It should perhaps be stated that the meaning of a partial derivative is to be understood from the context when applied to a function whose argument is given explicitly: thus $\partial\sigma(\xi,t)/\partial t$ is a time derivative with ξ^i constant, $\partial s(x,t)/\partial t$ is a time derivative with x^i constant, and $\partial s(x,t)/\partial x^1$ is a spatial derivative with x^2, x^3, t constant. If the argument of a function is not given explicitly, the meaning of a derivative will be stated when ambiguity might otherwise occur.

Vector fields. Let $\Phi_i(\xi,t)$ be a time-dependent covariant body vector field, and let $F_i(x,t)$ be the space field isomorphic to this field at time t.

From an equation similar to (12.21), it follows that

$$\Phi_i(\xi, t) = F_r(x, t)\frac{\partial x^r}{\partial \xi^i}. \tag{12.49}$$

On differentiating this equation with respect to t at constant ξ^i, the derivative of the second factor on the right-hand side will be (putting s in place of r)

$$\frac{\partial}{\partial t}\frac{\partial x^s}{\partial \xi^i} = \frac{\partial}{\partial \xi^i}\left(\frac{\partial x^s}{\partial t}\right)_{\text{const. }\xi^i} = \frac{\partial v^s}{\partial \xi^i} = \frac{\partial v^s}{\partial x^r}\frac{\partial x^r}{\partial \xi^i}; \tag{12.50}$$

the derivative of the first factor is similar to the derivative of a scalar field, and hence we have

$$\frac{\partial \Phi_i(\xi, t)}{\partial t} = \left\{\frac{DF_r(x,t)}{Dt} + F_r(x,t)\frac{\partial v^s(x,t)}{\partial x^r}\right\}\frac{\partial x^r}{\partial \xi^i}. \tag{12.51}$$

But the factor $\partial x^r/\partial \xi^i$ on the right-hand side here is just that factor which occurs in the equation (such as (12.49)) defining the isomorphism at time t for covariant vector fields; we may therefore write (12.51) in the form

$$\frac{\partial \Phi_i(\xi, t)}{\partial t} \overset{t}{\rightarrow} \left(\delta^s_r\frac{D}{Dt} + \frac{\partial v^s(x,t)}{\partial x^r}\right)F_s(x,t). \tag{12.52}$$

For a contravariant body field $\Phi^i(\xi, t)$ and its associated space field $F^i(x, t)$, we have

$$F^i(x,t) \overset{t}{\rightleftharpoons} \Phi^i(\xi, t) = F^r(x,t)\frac{\partial \xi^i}{\partial x^r} \tag{12.53}$$

from an equation similar to (12.19). The time derivative of this equation will involve the quantity $\frac{\partial}{\partial t}\frac{\partial \xi^i}{\partial x^r}$; since $\frac{\partial}{\partial t}$ here is at constant ξ^i, the operations $\frac{\partial}{\partial t}$ and $\frac{\partial}{\partial x^r}$ do not commute, and to obtain a convenient expression (analogous to (12.50)) for this second derivative we differentiate the identity

$$\frac{\partial \xi^i}{\partial x^s}\frac{\partial x^s}{\partial \xi^j} = \delta^i_j$$

with respect to t at constant ξ^i. Thus we have

$$\begin{aligned}\left(\frac{\partial}{\partial t}\frac{\partial \xi^i}{\partial x^s}\right)\frac{\partial x^s}{\partial \xi^j} &= -\frac{\partial \xi^i}{\partial x^s}\left(\frac{\partial}{\partial t}\frac{\partial x^s}{\partial \xi^j}\right)\\ &= -\frac{\partial \xi^i}{\partial x^s}\left(\frac{\partial v^s}{\partial x^r}\frac{\partial x^r}{\partial \xi^j}\right) \qquad \text{by (12.50);}\end{aligned}$$

multiplying each side by $\partial\xi^j/\partial x^k$, summing over j, and applying the last identity (involving δ^i_j) to each side, we finally obtain the result

$$\frac{\partial}{\partial t}\frac{\partial \xi^i}{\partial x^k} = -\frac{\partial \xi^i}{\partial x^s}\frac{\partial v^s(x,t)}{\partial x^k}.$$

Differentiating (12.53) with respect to t at constant ξ^i, we have

$$\frac{\partial \Phi^i(\xi,t)}{\partial t} = \frac{DF^r(x,t)}{Dt}\frac{\partial \xi^i}{\partial x^r} + F^r(x,t)\left(\frac{\partial}{\partial t}\frac{\partial \xi^i}{\partial x^r}\right)$$

$$= \left\{\frac{DF^r(x,t)}{Dt}\delta^s_r - F^r(x,t)\frac{\partial v^s}{\partial x^r}\right\}\frac{\partial \xi^i}{\partial x^s};$$

the factor $\partial\xi^i/\partial x^s$ on the right-hand side is just that factor which occurs in the equation (e.g. in (12.53)) defining the isomorphism $\overset{t}{\to}$ for contravariant vector fields, and hence we have, finally, the result

$$\text{(12.54)} \qquad \frac{\partial \Phi^i(\xi,t)}{\partial t} \overset{t}{\to} \left(\delta^s_r \frac{D}{Dt} - \frac{\partial v^s(x,t)}{\partial x^r}\right) F^r(x,t).$$

This is similar in form to the corresponding result (12.52) for a covariant field, but the difference of sign should be noted.

The above results, (12.52) and (12.54), may be written in the following alternative form:

$$\text{(12.55)} \qquad \frac{\partial \Phi_i(\xi,t)}{\partial t} \overset{t}{\to} \frac{\partial F_i(x,t)}{\partial t} + v^k F_{i,k} + v^k{}_{,i} F_k,$$

$$\text{(12.56)} \qquad \frac{\partial \Phi^i(\xi,t)}{\partial t} \overset{t}{\to} \frac{\partial F^i(x,t)}{\partial t} + v^k F^i{}_{,k} - v^i{}_{,k} F^k,$$

where, following the usual notation, a comma followed by a letter suffix indicates covariant differentiation—in the present context (i.e. applied to space fields), with respect to the space metric tensor $g_{ij}(x)$. The proof of these results is straightforward: equations (12.52) and (12.54) have been proved for an arbitrary space coordinate system, and are therefore valid in a rectangular cartesian coordinate system, in particular; in such a system, however, covariant differentiation $(,k)$ reduces to partial differentiation (with respect to x^k) and the stated equations (12.55) and (12.56) therefore reduce to (12.52) and (12.54) and are hence valid when the space coordinate system is rectangular cartesian; but (12.55) and (12.56) are evidently tensor relations and are therefore valid whether the space coordinate system is rectangular cartesian or not. This completes the required proof. One can alternatively verify that the extra terms, implicit in (12.55) and (12.56) because of the covariant derivatives, cancel out, leaving the original equations (12.52) and (12.54).

The terms on the right-hand sides of (12.55) and (12.56) consist of (i) a partial time derivative, at constant place, which vanishes if the space field is constant; (ii) a term, involving the velocity and spatial derivatives of the space field, which is associated with the movement of the given particle through space; and (iii) a term involving the velocity gradient which (as we shall show below) can be expressed in terms of space fields describing rate of strain and vorticity, and therefore is associated with the changing shape and the rotation of the material element containing the given particle.

The above results for vector fields can be extended at once to deal with time derivatives of tensor fields of any rank, by inspecting the method of derivation given above and making the appropriate changes. The results for second rank tensor fields are as follows:

if

$$\Phi_{ij}(\xi, t) \stackrel{t}{\rightleftharpoons} F_{ij}(x, t),$$

then

$$\frac{\partial \Phi_{ij}(\xi, t)}{\partial t} \stackrel{t}{\rightarrow} \frac{\partial F_{ij}(x, t)}{\partial t} + v^k F_{ij,k} + v^k{}_{,i} F_{kj} + v^k{}_{,j} F_{ik}; \tag{12.57}$$

if

$$\Phi^{ij}(\xi, t) \stackrel{t}{\rightleftharpoons} F^{ij}(x, t),$$

then

$$\frac{\partial \Phi^{ij}(\xi, t)}{\partial t} \stackrel{t}{\rightarrow} \frac{\partial F^{ij}(x, t)}{\partial t} + v^k F^{ij}{}_{,k} - v^i{}_{,k} F^{kj} - v^j{}_{,k} F^{ik}. \tag{12.58}$$

Without giving a detailed proof of these statements, we may point out that for a second rank covariant field the equations corresponding to (12.49) (which formed the starting point for the previous derivations) will be similar in form but will have an extra factor of the form $\partial x^s/\partial \xi^j$ (cf. (12.21)); the time derivative of this equation will therefore have an additional term of the same form as the last term on the right-hand side of (12.55); the first two terms on the right-hand side of (12.55) came from the time derivative of the factor F_r in (12.49), and will therefore have a similar counterpart in the required equations (12.57). A similar argument accounts for the extra term in (12.58).

Let us now apply these results to obtain expressions for the space fields, $A^{(n)}_{ij}(x, t)$ say, which are isomorphic at time t to the nth rate-of-strain body fields $\partial^n \gamma_{ij}(\xi, t)/\partial t^n$; by definition, we thus have

$$A^{(n)}_{ij}(x, t) \stackrel{t}{\rightleftharpoons} \frac{\partial^n \gamma_{ij}(\xi, t)}{\partial t^n} \qquad (n = 1, 2, \ldots). \tag{12.59}$$

From the equation

$$(12.60)\qquad \frac{\partial^{n+1}\gamma_{ij}(\xi,t)}{\partial t^{n+1}} = \frac{\partial}{\partial t}\frac{\partial^n \gamma_{ij}(\xi,t)}{\partial t^n},$$

we immediately derive the recurrence relation

$$(12.61)\qquad A_{ij}^{(n+1)} = \frac{\partial A_{ij}^{(n)}(x,t)}{\partial t} + v^k A_{ij,k}^{(n)} + v^k{}_{,i} A_{kj}^{(n)} + v^k{}_{,j} A_{ik}^{(n)},$$

by using (12.57) with

$$\Phi_{ij} = \frac{\partial^n \gamma_{ij}}{\partial t^n} \quad\text{and}\quad F_{ij} = A_{ij}^{(n)}.$$

This relation in space fields is evidently much more complicated than its counterpart (12.60) in body fields.

From (12.61), we can obtain an expression for the rate-of-strain tensor $\frac{1}{2}A_{ij}^{(1)}$ in terms of velocity gradients. We may apply the above equations with $n=0$ if we take (12.59) as $\gamma_{ij} \overset{t}{\rightleftharpoons} A_{ij}^{(0)} = g_{ij}$ in this case. The first two terms on the right-hand side of (12.61) are then zero, because g_{ij} is independent of time and its covariant derivative is zero; the resulting equation may therefore be written in the form

$$(12.62)\qquad A_{ij}^{(1)} = v_{i,j} + v_{j,i}$$

where

$$(12.63)\qquad v_{i,j} = g_{ik} v^k{}_{,j}.$$

It is conventional to call $\frac{1}{2}A_{ij}^{(1)} \equiv \dot{e}_{ij}$ the *rate-of-strain tensor*, so that

$$(12.64)\qquad \dot{e}_{ij} = \tfrac{1}{2}(v_{i,j} + v_{j,i}),$$

and to write

$$(12.65)\qquad \omega_{ij} \equiv \tfrac{1}{2}(v_{i,j} - v_{j,i}),$$

where ω_{ij} is called the *vorticity tensor*. It follows that we may express the velocity gradient in the form

$$(12.66)\qquad v_{i,j} = \dot{e}_{ij} + \omega_{ij} = \dot{e}_{ji} - \omega_{ji},$$

since $\dot{e}_{ij}$ is symmetric and ω_{ij} is antisymmetric. This justifies the statement made above in the discussion of (iii) following equation (12.56).

The above discussion of time derivatives of arbitrary order of body fields and their space field counterparts is due to Oldroyd (1950a), apart from differences of terminology mentioned earlier. The space tensors $A_{ij}^{(n)}$ have been used by Rivlin and Ericksen (1955) in the case when the space coordinate system is rectangular cartesian and covariant derivatives are reduced to partial derivatives; this simplification can in fact be made whether the space coordinate system is rectangular cartesian or not, as one can readily see from the fact that (12.52) is an alternative form (of general validity) of (12.55).

The above ideas of one field being "dragged along" by a manifold moving through another manifold can be traced to Lie and to Schouten (1951); the associated time derivatives represented by the terms on the right-hand sides of (12.57) and (12.58) with omission of the partial time derivatives have been called *Lie derivatives* and have been treated in geometrical studies of one Riemannian manifold moving rigidly through another (Yano, 1957).

The Description of Stress

Space fields. A state of stress at time t can be described in terms of space fields by an absolute symmetric second rank contravariant tensor field of components $p^{ij}(x,t)$, say, referred to an arbitrary coordinate system x^i fixed in space. The traction, represented by a contravariant space vector of components F^i, across a surface $s(x,t) = \text{constant}$ is given by the equation

$$F^i = p^{ji} n_j, \tag{12.67}$$

where n_j, a covariant space vector field representing the unit normal to the surface, is given by

$$n_j(x,t) = \left(g^{\alpha\beta}\frac{\partial s}{\partial x^\alpha}\frac{\partial s}{\partial x^\beta}\right)^{-1/2}\frac{\partial s}{\partial x^j}. \tag{12.68}$$

The stress equations of motion may be written in the form

$$p^{\alpha i}{}_{,\alpha} = \rho(A^i - X^i) \tag{12.69}$$

where ρ is the density (defined as an absolute scalar), A^i is the acceleration, and X^i are the contravariant components of the external forces acting on unit mass of the material. The comma denotes covariant differentiation using the space metric tensor g_{ij}.

Body fields. Since all the above equations involve only one configuration (that at time t) of the material, they induce equations of the same form involving the corresponding body fields f^i, ν_i, and π^{ij}, where

$$F^i \xrightarrow{t} f^i, \quad n_i \xrightarrow{t} \nu_i, \quad p^{ij} \xrightarrow{t} \pi^{ij}. \tag{12.70}$$

We therefore have the equation

$$f^i = \pi^{ji}\nu_j \tag{12.71}$$

for the body traction vector f^i; the equation

$$\nu_j(\xi,t) = \left[\gamma^{\alpha\beta}(\xi,t)\frac{\partial\sigma}{\partial\xi^\alpha}\frac{\partial\sigma}{\partial\xi^\beta}\right]^{-1/2}\frac{\partial\sigma}{\partial\xi^j} \tag{12.72}$$

for the unit normal ν_j to the material surface $\sigma(\xi) = \text{constant}$; and we may write the stress equations of motion in the form

$$\pi^{\alpha i}{}_{,\alpha} = \rho(A^\alpha - X^\alpha)\frac{\partial\xi^i}{\partial x^\alpha}, \tag{12.73}$$

since the space vector $A^i - X^i$ induces the body vector $(A^\alpha - X^\alpha)\,\partial\xi^i/\partial x^\alpha$ in the body at time t, by (12.53).

Using known expressions (Madelung, 1943, p. 137) for the covariant derivative, which is here formed using the body metric tensor $\gamma_{ij}(\xi,t)$, the full expression for the left-hand side of (12.73), which represents the divergence of stress, may be written in the form

$$\pi^{\alpha i}{}_{,\alpha} = \gamma^{-1/2}\frac{\partial}{\partial\xi^\alpha}(\gamma^{1/2}\pi^{\alpha i}) + \Gamma^i{}_{\alpha\beta}\,\pi^{\alpha\beta}, \tag{12.74}$$

where $\gamma = \det\gamma_{ij}$ and

$$\Gamma^i{}_{\alpha\beta} \equiv \tfrac{1}{2}\gamma^{i\nu}\left(\frac{\partial\gamma_{\nu\alpha}}{\partial\xi^\beta} + \frac{\partial\gamma_{\nu\beta}}{\partial\xi^\alpha} - \frac{\partial\gamma_{\alpha\beta}}{\partial\xi^\nu}\right) \tag{12.75}$$

are the Christoffel symbols.

It will be seen that the stress equations of motion (12.73), when regarded as a system of differential equations to be solved simultaneously with the rheological equations of state, are more complicated than the corresponding equations (12.69) owing to the fact that the covariant derivative of the body stress tensor involves non-linear combinations of the unknown variables γ_{ij}, whereas the corresponding components g_{ij} in the space field equations are given functions of position. Thus the use of body fields, as an alternative to space fields, in general leads to simpler forms for rheological equations of state but to a more complicated form for the stress equations of motion. Nevertheless, certain problems have been solved using the body formalism throughout (Lodge, 1951) and a solution is in principle always obtainable. Stress equations of motion in terms of body fields have been given by Deuker (1941) and Green and Zerna (1950, 1954).

The reader may show without difficulty that

$$\pi^{ij}(\xi,t) \xrightarrow{t_0} \frac{\rho(\xi,t)}{\rho(\xi,t_0)}\bar{S}_{ij}(a,t,t_0)$$

where $\bar{S}_{ij}$ is Kirchhoff's stress tensor (Prager, 1961, Chapter IX, equation (4.6)), and $a^i = f^i(\xi,t_0)$ (from (12.12) above).

Time Derivatives of Stress

An important property of the body stress tensor π^{ij} is that it is unaffected by any rigid motion of the material: for, in a rigid motion, the body traction vector field f^i and the body field of normals ν_i to a material surface $\sigma(\xi) =$ constant are unaffected (cf. (12.72), which shows that ν_i changes only when γ_{ij}, and therefore the shape, changes). Since (12.71) is valid for all values of ν_i (subject to a single normalizing condition), it follows that π^{ij} are unaffected also. Since γ_{ij} are unaffected by any rigid motion, it follows that the covariant body stress tensor π_{ij}, defined by the equation

$$\text{(12.76)} \qquad \pi_{ij}(\xi, t) = \gamma_{ir}(\xi, t)\, \gamma_{js}(\xi, t)\, \pi^{rs}(\xi, t)$$

is also unaffected by any rigid motion.

It follows that quantities such as

$$\frac{\partial \pi^{ij}(\xi, t)}{\partial t} \quad \text{and} \quad \frac{\partial \pi_{ij}(\xi, t)}{\partial t}$$

depend only on changes in the state of stress and shape at a given particle, and can therefore occur in rheological equations of state without introducing any unwanted dependence on the absolute motion of the material relative to space.

Since, in a deforming material, no meaning can in general be assigned to the concept of a constant state of stress (Appendix 1), it is perhaps not surprising that there is no unique first-order time derivative of stress of rheological significance. In the present formalism, $\partial \pi^{ij}/\partial t$ and $\partial \pi_{ij}/\partial t$ appear to be on the same footing, and any invariant combination of them can also be used. In fact, as differentiation of (12.76) shows, these two derivatives differ by terms involving γ_{ij}, $\dfrac{\partial \gamma_{ij}}{\partial t}$, and π^{ij}, which could in any case occur in a rheological equation of state (Oldroyd, 1950a).

To obtain expressions for the space fields isomorphic to the time derivatives of body stress fields, we first note that from (12.76) and (12.23) it follows that

$$\text{(12.77)} \qquad \pi_{ij}(\xi, t) \overset{t}{\rightarrow} p_{ij}(x, t) = g_{ir}\, g_{js}\, p^{rs}(x, t).$$

Hence, using (12.57) with $\Phi_{ij} = \pi_{ij}$ and $F_{ij} = p_{ij}$, we have

$$\text{(12.78)} \qquad \frac{\partial \pi_{ij}(\xi, t)}{\partial t} \overset{t}{\rightarrow} \frac{\partial p_{ij}(x, t)}{\partial t} + v^k p_{ij,k} + v^k{}_{,i}\, p_{kj} + v^k{}_{,j}\, p_{ik}.$$

Similarly, using (12.58) with $\Phi^{ij} = \pi^{ij}$ and $F^{ij} = p^{ij}$, we have

$$(12.79) \qquad \frac{\partial \pi^{ij}(\xi,t)}{\partial t} \overset{t}{\to} \frac{\partial p^{ij}(x,t)}{\partial t} + v^k p^{ij}{}_{,k} - v^i{}_{,k} p^{kj} - v^j{}_{,k} p^{ik}.$$

By (12.66), the last two terms on the right-hand sides of these equations can be expressed in terms of the rate-of-strain tensor $\dot{e}_{ij}$ and the vorticity tensor ω_{ij}; the terms in ω_{ij} cannot be eliminated by any rheologically admissible combination of these two equations and owe their presence to the fact that $\partial p_{ij}/\partial t$ by itself has a dependence on the rotation of the material (relative to space) which must be eliminated for use in a rheological equation of state.

It is perhaps worth noting that the terms in $\dot{e}_{ij}$ can be eliminated by adding these two equations (after lowering the suffixes in the second equation); after some straightforward tensor manipulations, we obtain the result

$$(12.80) \qquad \frac{1}{2}\left(\frac{\partial \pi_{ij}}{\partial t} + \gamma_{ir}\gamma_{js}\frac{\partial \pi^{rs}}{\partial t}\right) \overset{t}{\to} \frac{\partial p_{ij}}{\partial t} + v^k p_{ij,k} - \omega_{ik} p^k_j - \omega_{jk} p^k{}_i.$$

The right-hand side represents a time derivative of stress due to Jaumann (cf. Prager, 1961, Chapter VIII, equation (1.7)).

Rheological Equations of State in Terms of Body Fields

The fundamental assumption underlying our treatment of rheological properties of continuous materials is that the stress at any given time t in an infinitesimally small material element containing a particle ξ^i is determined (possibly to within an arbitrary additive isotropic stress) by the shape of that element at time t and at all previous times and by the temperature T; there is no dependence on the absolute motion (relative to space) of the material element, nor on conditions in other material elements.

From the discussion given above, it is clear that this assumption is satisfied by any tensor functional relation between the body metric tensor at ξ^i and the body stress tensor at ξ^i:

$$(12.81) \qquad \pi^{ij}(\xi,t) = \mathscr{F}^{ij}_{t'=-\infty}^{\;t}\{\gamma_{rs}(\xi,t'),\, T(\xi,t')\}.$$

It may be convenient to replace the functional giving the stress explicitly in terms of shape history by a set of tensor equations, six of which will be independent, relating the quantities

$$(12.82) \qquad \pi^{ij}(\xi,t'), \quad \gamma_{ij}(\xi,t'), \quad T(\xi,t')\ (-\infty < t' \leqslant t).$$

In these equations, time derivatives and time integrals may occur; the equations should be expressible in a form which does not involve derivatives taken with respect to ξ^i, unless we have to alter the fundamental assumption to include the possibility that conditions in one material element may influence those in a neighbouring element.

In (12.81) or (12.82), there will also be quantities (not shown) representing material constants; if these can all be expressed as *scalar* body fields (together with the body metric field, if necessary), it is reasonable to call the material *isotropic*; if they cannot be so expressed but require tensor body fields which are not isotropic tensors, then it is reasonable to call the material *anisotropic* (Oldroyd, 1950a). If the material constants can be represented by body fields which are independent of time, then it is reasonable to say that the rheological properties of the material do not change with time. If the material constants can be described by body fields whose covariant derivative (formed with the use of the body metric tensor) is zero, then we may say that the material is *homogeneous*; since the body metric tensor is time-dependent, it follows that a material which is homogeneous at one instant will not in general be homogeneous at another. Exceptions occur (i) when the material is isotropic, for the material constants are then described by scalar fields, and the covariant derivative reduces to the partial derivative $\partial/\partial\xi^i$, and is not dependent on γ_{ij}; and (ii) when a homogeneous material is subjected to uniform strain, for the covariant derivative again reduces to the partial derivative $\partial/\partial\xi^i$, because a body coordinate system (with plane coordinate surfaces) can always be found such that γ_{ij} are independent of ξ^r and hence that the components of the affine connection (12.75) are zero. The notions of homogeneity and anisotropy in a deforming material are thus not elementary, presumably because, in an anisotropic material, homogeneity implies not only that the values of material "constants" should be the same at all particles of the body but also that the preferred directions in the material should be the same everywhere. Extensive treatments of anisotropic materials have been given by Rivlin and coworkers, e.g. Ericksen and Rivlin (1954) and Ericksen (1960b–e).

Uniform Stress and Strain

In any state t, one can always choose a cartesian body coordinate system in which all the coordinate surfaces are plane and the body metric tensor components $\gamma_{ij}(\xi,t)$ are independent of ξ^i. In a general deformation, such a coordinate system will not be cartesian in other states. In a uniform deformation, however, material planes remain planes (Chapter 2) and a cartesian body coordinate system therefore remains cartesian (oblique, not rectangular, for the mutual inclinations of coordinate planes belonging to different families will change). The body metric tensor components, referred to such a coordinate system, will therefore depend on the state t but not on the particle coordinates ξ^i.

Since the stress (or extra stress) depends on the history of γ_{ij}, it follows that the body stress (or extra stress) tensor components will also be independent of ξ^i. The covariant derivative of this tensor will therefore be zero, because it reduces to the partial derivative $\partial/\partial\xi^i$ when γ_{ij} are independent of ξ^i, and we may therefore say that the stress is uniform.

We now show that in these circumstances the body stress tensor components π^{ij} and the body metric tensor components γ_{ij} are equal to the stress components and shape components previously denoted by π^{ij} and γ_{ij} and defined in Chapters 2 and 3 above. More precisely, we show that, given any embedded basis $\mathbf{e}_i$, we can always choose a body coordinate system ξ^i such that this statement is true.

Let O, P_1, P_2, P_3 be four particles at the corners of the given basic parallelepiped, so that $\overrightarrow{OP}_r = \mathbf{e}_r$. Let us choose a cartesian body coordinate system ξ^i relative to which these particles have the following coordinates:

$$O = (0,0,0); \quad P_1 = (1,0,0); \quad P_2 = (0,1,0); \quad P_3 = (0,0,1).$$

Then the plane through OP_1P_2 is a coordinate surface $\xi^3 = 0$, etc.

In the present context, we may conveniently restrict our allowable body coordinate systems to be cartesian. It then follows that the coordinate differences for any two particles (whether neighbouring particles or not) are components of a contravariant vector; in particular, taking one particle at the origin O, it follows that the coordinates ξ^i of any other particle P are components of a contravariant vector which we may denote by $\mathbf{r} = \overrightarrow{OP}$. Hence the scalar product of two such vectors, $\overrightarrow{OP}_r$ and $\overrightarrow{OP}_s$, where $P_r = \xi^i_{(r)}$, $P_s = \xi^i_{(s)}$, is given by

$$\overrightarrow{OP}_r . \overrightarrow{OP}_s = \gamma_{ij}\,\xi^i_{(r)}\,\xi^j_{(s)}. \tag{12.83}$$

For the particles P_r at the corners of the given basic parallelepiped, we have $\xi^i_{(r)} = \delta^i_r$, and hence

$$\mathbf{e}_r . \mathbf{e}_s = \gamma_{ij}\,\delta^i_r\,\delta^j_s = \gamma_{rs}, \tag{12.84}$$

which proves the required result in respect of the metric tensor components. The contravariant components γ^{ij} must therefore agree in the two notations, because in each notation they are related to the covariant components by the same equation.

Further, if ξ^i are the coordinates of a particle P referred to the above body coordinate system, it is clear that $\overrightarrow{OP} = \xi^i \mathbf{e}_i$, which verifies that the symbols ξ^i so defined have the same significance as they had in earlier chapters. It follows that the equation of the plane, defined by the plane coordinates η_i or l_i, h as defined in Chapter 2, may be written in the form

$$(12.85) \qquad \xi^i \eta_i = 1 \quad \text{or} \quad \xi^i l_i = h.$$

In the notation of the present chapter (12.72), we may therefore write $\sigma(\xi) \equiv \xi^i \eta_i$, and hence the unit normal to the plane has the components

$$(12.86) \qquad \nu_i = l_i(\gamma^{rs} l_r l_s)^{-1/2} = l_i, \qquad \text{by (2.21).}$$

We may write equation (3.7), which expresses the traction vector **f** acting across this plane in terms of the base vectors $\mathbf{e}_i$, in the form $\mathbf{f} = f^i \mathbf{e}_i$ where

$$(12.87) \qquad f^i = \pi^{ji} l_j.$$

Then **f** may be regarded as a contravariant vector of components f^i, and therefore (12.71) and (12.87) must be identical,† showing that the quantities π^{ij}, as defined here and as defined in Chapter 3, are the same. This completes the required proof of the equivalence of the two formalisms.

It now follows at once that the rules stated in Chapter 8 for combining π^{ij} and γ_{ij} so as to give equations having a significance independent of the choice of base vectors are justified; for any such choice of base vectors, we can choose a corresponding body coordinate system, and therefore a change of basis is equivalent to a change from one allowable coordinate system to another. The rules stated in Chapter 8 are just the standard rules for forming tensors, and therefore lead to equations having a significance independent of the choice of coordinate system and hence also of the choice of basis.

It is also possible to give a relation between the two formalisms by confining one's attention to an infinitesimally small neighbourhood of any given particle in a material which undergoes any continuous motion, not necessarily involving only uniform strain; in such a neighbourhood, which may be regarded as a "tangent space" to the body manifold, the strain is uniform. The relations between the formalisms in this case are a little more involved than in the case of uniform strain throughout the manifold, but the main conclusion is the same, namely that the two formalisms are equivalent in the sense that properly invariant rheological equations of state take the same form in each formalism.

† With $l_i = \nu_i$.

Space Field Equations for Rubberlike Materials

As a further illustration of the process of transferring rheological equations of state from one manifold to another, using the isomorphism $\overset{t}{\rightarrow}$, we shall consider the equations given in earlier chapters for the rubberlike solid and for the rubberlike liquid. In view of the arguments just given concerning the equivalence of the uniform strain formalism and the general body field formalism, it follows that the equations previously derived for materials subjected to uniform strain can now be regarded as generally applicable whether the strain is uniform or not; the only change needed is to allow the variables π^{ij}, γ_{ij} and γ^{ij} to depend on ξ^i, the coordinates of a typical particle referred to an arbitrary body coordinate system, with the same value of ξ^i occurring throughout a given equation, and to interpret these variables as the components in this system of the body field of stress and the body metric tensors. Since body tensors at the same particle can be combined by the usual processes of addition, contraction, etc., it is seen that the equations so obtained are of tensor form and reduce to the original equations when the strain is uniform.

The equations for a rubberlike solid therefore take the form

$$(12.88)\qquad \begin{cases} \pi^{ij}(\xi,t)+p(\xi,t)\,\gamma^{ij}(\xi,t) = \mu_0\,\gamma^{ij}(\xi,t_0), \\ \det\gamma^{ij}(\xi,t) = \det\gamma^{ij}(\xi,t_0), \end{cases}$$

by generalizing (4.12) in this manner; μ_0, the modulus, is independent of ξ^i if the material is homogeneous.

Using (12.23), (12.40), and (12.70), it is evident that the isomorphism $\overset{t}{\rightarrow}$ gives rise to the following equations in space fields:

$$(12.89)\qquad \begin{cases} p^{ij}(x,t)+p(x,t)\,g^{ij}(x) = \mu_0\,B^{ij}(x,t), \\ \det g^{ij}(x) = \det B^{ij}(x,t). \end{cases}$$

To obtain a convenient expression for Finger's strain tensor B^{ij} which occurs in this equation, we note that, from (12.40), we have

$$(12.90)\qquad \gamma^{ij}(\xi,t_0) \overset{t}{\rightarrow} B^{ij}(x,t) = \left(\frac{\partial x^i}{\partial \xi^r}\frac{\partial x^j}{\partial \xi^s}\right)_t \gamma^{rs}(\xi,t_0), \qquad \text{from (12.20).}$$

The coordinate systems x^i, ξ^i are arbitrary (except that one is fixed in space and one in the body), and we may therefore choose them in any convenient way; for the particular application in this paragraph, let us choose any space system x^i and then choose a body system ξ^i which coincides with the space system *in the stress-free state* t_0. Using a^i and x^i to denote the space coordinates of the places occupied by a typical particle in states t_0 and t respectively, we then have

$$\xi^i = a^i, \quad \gamma^{rs}(\xi, t_0) = g^{rs}(a) \qquad \text{(by (12.17))},$$

and hence

$$B^{ij}(x,t) = \frac{\partial x^i}{\partial a^r}\frac{\partial x^j}{\partial a^s} g^{rs}(a). \tag{12.91}$$

The variables x^i and a^i here are related by equations of the form $x^i = f^i(a,t)$ and their inverse $a^i = \phi^i(x,t)$ which describe the deformation $t_0 \to t$ in terms of space coordinates and are obtained by putting $\xi^i = a^i$ in (12.12). When the space coordinate system is rectangular cartesian, we have $g^{rs}(a) = \delta^{rs}$ and hence

$$B^{ij}(x,t) = \sum_{r=1}^{3} \frac{\partial x^i}{\partial a^r}\frac{\partial x^j}{\partial a^r}. \tag{12.92}$$

The equations (6.9) for a rubberlike liquid, expressed in terms of the components of body fields referred to an arbitrary body coordinate system ξ^i, take the form

$$\pi^{ij}(\xi,t) + p(\xi,t)\,\gamma^{ij}(\xi,t) = \int_{-\infty}^{t} \mu(t-t')\,\gamma^{ij}(\xi,t')\,dt'. \tag{12.93}$$

From (12.19) with $t = t'$, $\Phi^{ij} = \gamma^{ij}$, and $F^{rs} = g^{rs}$, we see that

$$g^{ij}(x') \overset{t'}{\rightarrow} \gamma^{ij}(\xi,t') = \left(\frac{\partial \xi^i}{\partial x'^r}\frac{\partial \xi^j}{\partial x'^s}\right)_{t'} g^{rs}(x'), \tag{12.94}$$

where $x'^r = f^r(\xi,t')$ denote the coordinates, referred to an arbitrary space coordinate system, of the place occupied by a typical particle ξ^i at time t'.

We may now choose the body coordinate system so as to coincide with the space system *at the current time* t; then

$$\xi^i = x^i, \quad \pi^{ij}(\xi,t) = p^{ij}(x,t), \quad \gamma^{ij}(\xi,t) = g^{ij}(x),$$

where x^i are the space coordinates of the place occupied by the typical particle at time t, and hence, using (12.94), we obtain from (12.93) the required equation

$$p^{ij}(x,t) + p(x,t)\,g^{ij}(x) = \int_{-\infty}^{t} \mu(t-t')\frac{\partial x^i}{\partial x'^r}\frac{\partial x^j}{\partial x'^s} g^{rs}(x')\,dt' \tag{12.95}$$

in terms of components of space fields. Here, the variables x^i and x'^i are related by equations of the form $x^i = \phi^i(x',t')$ (obtained by putting $\xi^i = x^i$, $t = t'$ in (12.12)), which describe the motion.

If the space coordinate system is rectangular cartesian, then $g^{rs}(x') = \delta^{rs}$ and the equations take the form

$$(12.96) \qquad p^{ij}(x,t) + p(x,t)\,\delta^{ij} = \int_{-\infty}^{t} \mu(t-t') \sum_{r=1}^{3} \frac{\partial x^i}{\partial x'^r}\frac{\partial x^j}{\partial x'^r}\,dt'.$$

This is now in a form which can be recognized as being equivalent to that given by Lodge (1956, equation (2.4)), and can be shown to be equivalent to part of equation (B1), given by Green and Tobolsky (1946), when μ is an exponential function.

Space Field Equations in the Classical Theory of Elasticity

We proved in Chapter 8 that the stress–strain relations for an isotropic perfectly elastic solid reduce to the form (8.26) (in components of body fields) when the strain is small in the sense that the body strain components Δ^{ij}, defined by (8.22), are infinitesimally small. We now derive the corresponding equations in components of space fields, involving gradients of the displacement vector u^i, defined by the equation

$$(12.97) \qquad u^i = x^i - a^i,$$

where, as in the derivation of (12.92) above, a^i and x^i denote the components, relative to a rectangular cartesian coordinate system fixed in space, of the places occupied by a typical particle in the stress-free state t_0 and in an arbitrary state t.

The strain $t_0 \to t$ can be described either by the functions $x^i = f^i(a,t)$ or by the functions $u^i = u^i(x)$. Let us now assume that *the displacement gradients $\partial u^i/\partial x^j$ are so small that their products are negligible.* We then have the approximate equations

$$(12.98) \qquad \frac{\partial x^i}{\partial a^r} = \delta^i_r + \frac{\partial u^i}{\partial x^r},$$

which represent the solution, to first order, of the equations

$$\delta^i_k = \frac{\partial x^i}{\partial a^r}\frac{\partial a^r}{\partial x^k} = \frac{\partial x^i}{\partial a^r}\left(\delta^r_k - \frac{\partial u^r}{\partial x^k}\right),$$

which follow from (12.97). From (12.92) and (12.98), we obtain the following approximate expression for Finger's strain tensor

$$(12.99) \qquad B^{ij} - \delta^i_j \doteqdot 2\,e^{ij},$$

where

$$(12.100) \qquad e^{ij} \equiv \frac{1}{2}\left(\frac{\partial u^i}{\partial x^j} + \frac{\partial u^j}{\partial x^i}\right)$$

are the rectangular cartesian components of the infinitesimal strain tensor. In obtaining (12.99), products of displacement gradients have been omitted.

From (8.22), (12.40), and the fact that $\gamma^{ij} \xrightarrow{t} g^{ij} = \delta^i_j$, it follows that

$$\Delta^{ij} \xrightarrow{t} B^{ij} - \delta^i_j,$$

and hence, from (12.19) and (12.99), that

$$\Delta^{ij} \doteq 2\frac{\partial \xi^i}{\partial x^r}\frac{\partial \xi^j}{\partial x^s} e^{rs}. \tag{12.101}$$

Since the derivatives $\partial \xi^i/\partial x^r$ are bounded, it follows that *the body strain components Δ^{ij} are small when the displacement gradients $\partial u^i/\partial x^j$ are small.* (The converse is not true, as a consideration of the case $\partial u^i/\partial x^j = e^{ij} + \omega^{ij}$, where $e^{ij} = e^{ji}$ are small and $\omega^{ij} = -\omega^{ji}$ are finite, will show.)

The conditions under which (8.26) was derived from the general equations (8.1) for an isotropic perfectly elastic solid are thus satisfied when the displacement gradients are small. From (12.23), (12.40), and (12.70), it follows that in the state t the space equation isomorphic to the body equation (8.26) is

$$p^{ij} = \tfrac{1}{2}\lambda K_1 g^{ij} + \mu(B^{ij} - g^{ij}), \tag{12.102}$$

where

$$K_1 = g_{ij}(B^{ij} - g^{ij}), \qquad \text{from (8.23)}. \tag{12.103}$$

If we now use the fact that the space coordinate system is rectangular cartesian, so that $g^{ij} = \delta^i_j$, and the approximate equations (12.99), we obtain the equations

$$p^{ij} = \lambda(e^{11} + e^{22} + e^{33})\,\delta^i_j + 2\mu\, e^{ij} \tag{12.104}$$

in the form in which they are usually presented in the classical theory of elasticity. These equations have been derived in this way by Green and Zerna (1954, Chapter V).

Uni-directional Shear Flow

We can now generalize the description of shear flow given in Chapter 2 so as to allow the shearing surfaces and lines of shear to be curved. We first give a treatment for shearing surfaces of arbitrary shape, and show that, in so far as time derivatives and time integrals of strain are concerned, the behaviour of any given material element is determined by a single scalar function of time (the shear rate) and is the same whether the shear flow is curvilinear or rectilinear. This justifies the assumptions (9.4) and (9.5) made in connection with the determination of normal stress differences using various types of curvilinear shear flow. We then apply the general formalism to the various types of curvilinear shear flow of practical importance, and derive the appropriate expressions for the shear rate in each case, verifying the results obtained less rigorously in Chapter 9.

We use the definition (9.2) of uni-directional shear flow, and do not restrict the flow to be steady; since the shear flow is uni-directional, however, the lines of shear are constant in the material, and so, as we shall see, a non-steady flow can occur only if the shear rate varies with time.

For the present discussion, it is convenient to choose a particular body coordinate system ξ^i such that coordinate surfaces

$$(12.105)\quad \begin{cases} \xi^2 = \text{constant are shearing surfaces (9.2)(i);} \\ \xi^3 = \text{constant are orthogonal to the shearing surfaces (9.2)(iii).} \end{cases}$$

The choice of the third family of coordinate surfaces, $\xi^1 = $ constant, will for the present be left open.

The separation ds of two neighbouring particles, of relative coordinates $(d\xi^1, 0, d\xi^3)$, lying on the same shearing surface $\xi^2 = $ constant, is given by the equation

$$(ds)^2 = \gamma_{11}(d\xi^1)^2 + 2\gamma_{13}\, d\xi^1\, d\xi^3 + \gamma_{33}(d\xi^3)^2.$$

From the definition (9.2)(i) of a shearing surface, this ds must be independent of time for all values of $d\xi^1$ and $d\xi^2$; it follows (since $\gamma_{13} = \gamma_{31}$) that

$$(12.106)\qquad \frac{\partial \gamma_{11}}{\partial t} = \frac{\partial \gamma_{33}}{\partial t} = \frac{\partial \gamma_{13}}{\partial t} = \frac{\partial \gamma_{31}}{\partial t} = 0.$$

Since the volume is constant, we have

$$(12.107)\qquad \frac{\partial \gamma}{\partial t} = 0, \quad \gamma = \det \gamma_{ij}.$$

Since γ^{ij} are the elements of a matrix reciprocal to the matrix whose elements are γ_{ij}, we have

$$(12.108)\qquad \gamma^{22} = \gamma^{-1}(\gamma_{11}\gamma_{33} - \gamma_{13}\gamma_{31});$$

$$(12.109)\qquad \gamma_{11} = \gamma(\gamma^{22}\gamma^{33} - \gamma^{23}\gamma^{32}).$$

Here and elsewhere, the metric tensor components, γ_{ij} and γ^{ij}, and γ are evaluated throughout at the same value of ξ^i (and of t, where necessary).

It now follows, from (12.106), (12.107), and (12.108), that

$$\frac{\partial \gamma^{22}}{\partial t} = 0, \tag{12.110}$$

which, from (12.28), proves that the separation of neighbouring shearing surfaces is independent of time, as stated in (9.2)(iv).

It was also stated, in connection with (9.2), that (i) and (iv) imply (ii). The truth of this statement can now be readily seen: (9.4)(i) is equivalent to (12.106), which shows that γ_{11}, γ_{33}, γ_{13}, and γ_{31} are independent of time; (9.4)(iv) is, by (12.28), equivalent to (12.110), which implies that γ^{22} is independent of time; and hence (12.108), which is true generally, shows that γ must be independent of time, i.e. that the volume must be constant, which proves (9.4)(ii), as required.

The condition that the two families of coordinate surfaces (12.105) are orthogonal implies that

$$\gamma^{23} = \gamma^{32} = 0, \tag{12.111}$$

and hence, from (12.106), (12.107), (12.109), and (12.110), we see that

$$\frac{\partial \gamma^{33}}{\partial t} = 0, \tag{12.112}$$

showing that the separation of neighbouring surfaces of the family $\xi^3 =$ constant (orthogonal to the shearing surfaces) is also constant.

For later use, we note the following further results:

$$\frac{\partial \gamma^{13}}{\partial t} = \frac{\partial \gamma^{31}}{\partial t} = 0, \tag{12.113}$$

$$\frac{\partial \gamma^{11}}{\partial t} = 2\frac{\gamma^{12}}{\gamma^{22}}\frac{\partial \gamma^{12}}{\partial t}. \tag{12.114}$$

These may be obtained from (12.106), (12.107), (12.110), (12.111), and the equations

$$\gamma_{13} = \gamma(\gamma^{12}\gamma^{23} - \gamma^{13}\gamma^{22}), \quad \gamma_{33} = \gamma(\gamma^{11}\gamma^{22} - \gamma^{12}\gamma^{21}),$$

which follow from the fact that γ^{ij} and γ_{ij} are elements of reciprocal matrices; the results $\gamma_{ij} = \gamma_{ji}$ and $\gamma^{ij} = \gamma^{ji}$ are also needed.

To sum up these results, we see that

$$(12.115)\qquad \gamma^{ij} = \begin{pmatrix} \gamma^{11} & \gamma^{12} & \gamma^{13} \\ \gamma^{21} & \gamma^{22} & 0 \\ \gamma^{31} & 0 & \gamma^{33} \end{pmatrix}; \quad \frac{\partial \gamma^{ij}}{\partial t} = \frac{\partial \gamma^{12}}{\partial t} \begin{pmatrix} 2\dfrac{\gamma^{12}}{\gamma^{22}} & 1 & 0 \\ 1 & 0 & 0 \\ 0 & 0 & 0 \end{pmatrix}.$$

We may define the principal values of the rate-of-strain body tensor $\partial\gamma^{ij}/\partial t$ as the roots in ω of the equation

$$(12.116)\qquad \det\left[\frac{\partial \gamma^{ij}}{\partial t} - \omega\gamma^{ij}\right] = 0,$$

and the principal axis ν_i, corresponding to a principal value ω, as a solution of the equations

$$(12.117)\qquad \left(\frac{\partial \gamma^{ij}}{\partial t} - \omega\gamma^{ij}\right)\nu_j = 0 \qquad (i = 1, 2, 3).$$

Using the results (12.115), appropriate to shear flow with the particular coordinate system chosen, we readily find that one principal value is zero, that the corresponding principal direction is normal to the surface $\xi^3 = \text{constant}$, and that the other two principal values and their corresponding principal directions are given by the equations

$$(12.118)\qquad \begin{cases} \omega = \pm(\gamma\gamma^{33})^{1/2}\dfrac{\partial \gamma^{12}}{\partial t}, \\[2ex] \nu_i = \left(1, \quad \dfrac{\pm(\gamma\gamma^{33})^{-1/2} - \gamma^{12}}{\gamma^{22}}, \quad -\dfrac{\gamma^{12}}{\gamma^{33}}\right), \end{cases}$$

upper signs being taken together.

To relate these principal values to the shear rate G, as defined in Chapter 2 for the particular case of steady rectilinear shear flow, we note that, from (2.70) and (2.73), we have

$$\gamma = \gamma^{33} = 1 \quad \text{and} \quad \partial\gamma^{12}/\partial t = d\gamma^{12}/dt = -G,$$

and hence $G = \omega$ when the minus sign in (12.118) is taken. It will therefore be consistent with our previous definition if we extend the definition of shear rate G by means of the equation

$$(12.119)\qquad G = -(\gamma\gamma^{33})^{1/2}\frac{\partial \gamma^{12}}{\partial t},$$

which is valid for any uni-directional curvilinear shear flow and any body coordinate system chosen in accordance with (12.105).

In accordance with the sign convention for shear discussed in connection with Fig. 2.4 and equation (2.69), it can be seen that G, defined by (12.119), will be positive if the body coordinate system ξ^i is chosen so as to conform with the choice of base vectors $\mathbf{e}_i$ depicted in Fig. 2.4; according to the discussion of uniform strain given above in the present chapter, this means that the direction of ξ^i-increasing must coincide with the direction of $\mathbf{e}_i$ in Fig. 2.4, for $i = 1$, 2, and 3. With a different choice of directions, as in the case of the ξ^i-system chosen in the discussion of telescopic flow given below, G will be negative when defined by (12.119), and for consistency we should therefore replace the minus sign in (12.119) by a plus sign.

Using (12.119), we may write (12.115) in the form

$$\text{(12.120)} \qquad \frac{\partial \gamma^{ij}}{\partial t} = -\frac{G}{(\gamma\gamma^{33})^{1/2}}\begin{pmatrix} 2\gamma^{12}/\gamma^{22} & 1 & 0 \\ 1 & 0 & 0 \\ 0 & 0 & 0 \end{pmatrix}.$$

Remembering that γ, γ^{22} and γ^{33} are independent of time, by (12.107), (12.110), and (12.112), we may differentiate equation (12.120) n times, using Leibniz's method for the component in the position $i = j = 1$; we obtain the result

(12.121)

$$\frac{\partial^{n+1}\gamma^{ij}}{\partial t^{n+1}} = -\frac{\dfrac{\partial^n G}{\partial t^n}}{(\gamma\gamma^{33})^{1/2}}\begin{pmatrix} 2\gamma^{12}/\gamma^{22} & 1 & 0 \\ 1 & 0 & 0 \\ 0 & 0 & 0 \end{pmatrix} + \frac{2}{\gamma\gamma^{22}\gamma^{33}}\begin{pmatrix} Q_n & 0 & 0 \\ 0 & 0 & 0 \\ 0 & 0 & 0 \end{pmatrix},$$

where

$$\text{(12.122)} \qquad Q_n \equiv n\frac{\partial^{n-1}G}{\partial t^{n-1}}G + \frac{n(n-1)}{2!}\frac{\partial^{n-2}G}{\partial t^{n-2}}\frac{\partial G}{\partial t} + \ldots + G\frac{\partial^{n-1}G}{\partial t^{n-1}}.$$

In obtaining this result, we have used (12.107), (12.110), (12.112), and (12.119).

Again, on integrating (12.120) with respect to time from any instant t_1 up to the given instant t, remembering that γ, γ^{33}, and γ^{22} are independent of time, we see that the only non-zero elements in the resulting equation are

$$\text{(12.123)} \qquad \Delta^{12}(t, t_1) = \Delta^{21}(t, t_1) = -(\gamma\gamma^{33})^{-1/2}\int_{t_1}^{t} G(t')\,dt';$$

$$(12.124) \qquad \Delta^{11}(t,t_1) = -2(\gamma\gamma^{33})^{-1/2}(\gamma^{22})^{-1}\int_{t_1}^{t} G(t')\gamma^{12}(t')\,dt';$$

where $\Delta^{ij}(t,t_1) \equiv \gamma^{ij}(t) - \gamma^{ij}(t_1)$, in agreement with (12.31). To obtain an expression for $\gamma^{12}(t')$ in terms of G and constants, we use (12.123) with $t_1 = t'$; substituting this expression in the integrand of (12.124), we find that

$$(12.125) \qquad \Delta^{11}(t,t_1) = -2(\gamma\gamma^{22}\gamma^{33})^{-1}S_2(t,t_1) - 2(\gamma\gamma^{33})^{-1/2}(\gamma^{22})^{-1}\gamma^{12}(t)S_1(t,t_1),$$

where

$$(12.126) \qquad S_1(t,t_1) \equiv \int_{t_1}^{t} G(t')\,dt', \quad S_2(t,t_1) \equiv \int_{t_1}^{t} G(t')\,dt' \int_{t'}^{t} G(t'')\,dt''.$$

The foregoing results for the rate-of-strain tensors and the finite-strain tensor Δ^{ij} give values for their components whose physical significance is masked by their dependence on the arbitrary choice of the remaining coordinate surfaces $\xi^1 =$ constant. We therefore now calculate the *physical components* (McConnell, 1931) of these tensors relative to an orthogonal coordinate system obtained from the given system by making a special choice of the surfaces $\xi^1 =$ constant so that these surfaces are orthogonal to the other two families, $\xi^2 =$ constant and $\xi^3 =$ constant, *at the given instant t*. (They will not be orthogonal at any other instant, except in the degenerate case in which the motion is rigid or in a case such as oscillatory shear when the material might pass again through the same configuration.) The physical components $\widehat{\Phi^{ij}}$ of a given contravariant tensor Φ^{ij} are scalars which may be evaluated by means of the equations

$$(12.127) \qquad \widehat{\Phi^{ij}} = (\gamma^{ii}\gamma^{jj})^{-1/2}\Phi^{ij} \qquad (i,j \text{ not summed}),$$

where the metric tensor components γ^{ii}, γ^{jj} are evaluated at the instant t when the coordinate system is orthogonal, so that we also have

$$(12.128) \qquad \gamma^{ij}(t) = 0 \qquad (i \neq j).$$

Applying these equations to the tensors given by (12.120) and (12.121), we finally obtain the results

$$(12.129) \qquad \widehat{\frac{\partial\gamma^{ij}}{\partial t}} = \begin{pmatrix} 0 & -G & 0 \\ -G & 0 & 0 \\ 0 & 0 & 0 \end{pmatrix},$$

$$\widehat{\frac{\partial^{n+1}\gamma^{ij}}{\partial t^{n+1}}} = \begin{pmatrix} 2Q_n & -\dfrac{\partial^n G}{\partial t^n} & 0 \\ -\dfrac{\partial^n G}{\partial t^n} & 0 & 0 \\ 0 & 0 & 0 \end{pmatrix} \quad (n > 0), \tag{12.130}$$

for the physical components of the rate-of-strain tensors. In obtaining these equations, we have used the fact that

$$\gamma^{-1} = \gamma^{11}\gamma^{22}\gamma^{33} \quad \text{at time } t; \tag{12.131}$$

this follows from the equation $\gamma^{-1} = \det \gamma^{ij}$ when (12.128) is used.

Similarly, using (12.123), (12.125), (12.127), (12.128), and (12.131), the physical components (at time t) of the finite strain tensor

$$\Delta^{ij}(t, t_1) \equiv \gamma^{ij}(t) - \gamma^{ij}(t_1)$$

are found to be

$$\widehat{\Delta^{ij}} = \begin{pmatrix} -2S_2 & -S_1 & 0 \\ -S_1 & 0 & 0 \\ 0 & 0 & 0 \end{pmatrix}. \tag{12.132}$$

The integrals S_1 and S_2, defined by (12.126), depend only on the history of the shear rate G throughout the interval (t_1, t); in the particular case of steady shear flow, G is constant, and

$$S_1(t, t_1) = G(t - t_1), \quad S_2(t, t_1) = \tfrac{1}{2}G^2(t - t_1)^2. \tag{12.133}$$

Thus in this case the result (12.132) agrees with the values previously obtained for $\gamma^{ij}(t) - \gamma^{ij}(t_1)$ in steady rectilinear shear flow when the basis is orthonormal in state t ((2.70) with $t' = t_1$).

This is a particular illustration of a more general conclusion which we draw on the basis of the following two points: first, the physical components of a tensor at a point P are equal to the components referred to a local rectangular cartesian coordinate system whose coordinate planes are tangential at P to the coordinate surfaces of the orthogonal coordinate system used to evaluate the physical components; second, the above analysis applies to any type of uni-directional shear flow and the results (12.129), (12.130), and (12.132) show that *the physical components of the rate-of-strain tensors and the finite-strain tensor depend only on the shear rate history and not on the type of shear flow, whether curvilinear or rectilinear*.

It follows that, in so far as changes of shape at a given particle are concerned in a material undergoing uni-directional shear flow, the results for any curvilinear shear flow are the same as those for rectilinear shear flow derived in earlier chapters. (It can, however, be shown that the change from rectilinear to curvilinear shear flow does affect the value of quantities such as the covariant derivative of Δ^{ij}).

A similar conclusion can be drawn for rheological equations of state which (as we have assumed) contain no spatial (or covariant) derivatives of stress or strain; for any properly invariant relation between components of tensors yields a relation of the same form between their physical components, and therefore the physical components of stress or extra stress at time t at a given particle must be the same whether a uni-directional shear flow is rectilinear or curvilinear.

Differences between curvilinear and rectilinear shear flows are important (i) when, in the solution of the stress equations of motion in conjunction with the rheological equations of state, it is necessary to consider whether a given state of flow can be maintained by the application of surface tractions over the outer material surfaces alone; and (ii) in an incompressible material, where the value of an additive isotropic contribution to the stress at a given particle is governed by the curvature pattern of a curvilinear shear flow and the value of a component of traction normal to an outer material boundary.

The above calculations of uni-directional shear flow with a shear rate which varies with time in any manner are due to the author, and are here published for the first time. Similar calculations, using a space field formalism, have been made by Coleman and Noll for steady shear flow (1959a) and for oscillatory shear flow (1961).

We now consider some types of curvilinear shear flow of practical importance. We complete the discussion of Chapter 9 by calculating the shape variables and determining, in particular, the way in which shear rate depends on position.

Shear Flow between Concentric Cylinders in Relative Rotation

It is convenient to use a cylindrical polar space coordinate system such that

$$x^1 = \phi, \quad x^2 = r, \quad x^3 = z,$$

and the axis of coordinates ($r = 0$) coincides with the common cylinder axis (Fig. 9.2). In Couette flow, a given liquid cylinder $r =$ constant rotates rigidly with an angular velocity $\Omega(r,t)$. It follows that the surfaces $r =$ constant are the shearing surfaces, and the horizontal planes $z =$ constant are the material surfaces orthogonal to them throughout the motion.

We may therefore choose a body coordinate system ξ^i whose coordinate surfaces coincide with those of the space system at an arbitrary instant t_0, and such that

$$\xi^2 = r \quad \text{and} \quad \xi^3 = z \qquad \text{for all } t;$$

$$\xi^1 = \phi \qquad (\text{at } t_0).$$

This system is of the type (12.105) used in the above general treatment of shear flow. Further, we have

$$\frac{\partial \phi(\xi, t)}{\partial t} = \Omega(r, t) = \Omega(\xi^2, t),$$

and on integrating this with respect to time, using the above condition at $t = t_0$, we see that

$$\phi = \xi^1 + \int_{t_0}^{t} \Omega(\xi^2, t')\, dt'.$$

These equations together are the form which (12.12) take in the present case (the angle ϕ here should not be confused with the functions ϕ^i in (12.12)). The body coordinate surfaces $\xi^1 =$ constant are vertical planes (passing through the cylinder axis) at time t_0 and become at other times vertical surfaces whose cross-section by a horizontal plane is a family of spirals; it is not, however, necessary to picture these surfaces.

From the last equation, it follows that

$$\text{(12.134)} \qquad \frac{\partial \phi}{\partial \xi^1} = 1, \qquad \frac{\partial^2 \phi}{\partial \xi^2\, \partial t} = \frac{\partial \Omega}{\partial r}, \qquad \frac{\partial \phi}{\partial \xi^3} = 0.$$

The space metric tensor has the components

$$\text{(12.135)} \qquad g_{ij} = \begin{pmatrix} r^2 & 0 & 0 \\ 0 & 1 & 0 \\ 0 & 0 & 1 \end{pmatrix}$$

in this coordinate system, and hence, after some straightforward calculation using the above results in (12.16), we find that

$$\text{(12.136)} \qquad \gamma_{ij}(\xi, t) = \begin{pmatrix} r^2 & r^2 \dfrac{\partial \phi}{\partial \xi^2} & 0 \\ r^2 \dfrac{\partial \phi}{\partial \xi^2} & 1 + \left(r \dfrac{\partial \phi}{\partial \xi^2} \right)^2 & 0 \\ 0 & 0 & 1 \end{pmatrix}.$$

From this matrix, we find that $\gamma = r^2$ and hence that the reciprocal matrix is

$$\gamma^{ij}(\xi, t) = \begin{pmatrix} r^{-2} + \left(\frac{\partial \phi}{\partial \xi^2}\right)^2 & -\frac{\partial \phi}{\partial \xi^2} & 0 \\ -\frac{\partial \phi}{\partial \xi^2} & 1 & 0 \\ 0 & 0 & 1 \end{pmatrix}. \tag{12.137}$$

Differentiating this matrix with respect to time and using (12.134), we find that the expression (12.119) for the shear rate leads to the result

$$G = r\frac{\partial \Omega(r, t)}{\partial r}, \tag{12.138}$$

in agreement with (9.8).

Shear Flow between Parallel Plates in Relative Rotation

It is again convenient to use a cylindrical polar space coordinate system, but with x^2 and x^3 interchanged so that

$$x^1 = \phi, \quad x^2 = z, \quad x^3 = r.$$

The axis $r = 0$ coincides with the axis of rotation (Fig. 9.4). The shearing surfaces are now horizontal planes $z =$ constant, and the material surfaces orthogonal to them are vertical cylinders $r =$ constant; we may therefore choose a body coordinate system ξ^i whose surfaces coincide with those of the space coordinate system at an arbitrary instant t_0, and such that

$$\xi^2 = z \quad \text{and} \quad \xi^3 = r \qquad \text{for all } t,$$

$$\xi^1 = \phi \qquad \text{at } t_0.$$

For the angular velocity, we now have

$$\frac{\partial \phi(\xi, t)}{\partial t} = \Omega(z, t) = \Omega(\xi^2, t)$$

and therefore (12.134) are valid in the present case also, except that in place of the second of these equations we now have

$$\frac{\partial^2 \phi}{\partial \xi^2 \partial t} = \frac{\partial \Omega}{\partial z}.$$

The space metric tensor components are again given by (12.135), and a similar calculation shows that (12.136) and (12.137) are also valid in the present case; from these results, we find that

$$G = r\frac{\partial\Omega(z,t)}{\partial z}, \tag{12.139}$$

in agreement with (9.21).

Telescopic Flow through a Tube of Circular Cross-section

Let us take a cylindrical polar space coordinate system r, ϕ, z with axis $r = 0$ along the axis of the tube, and take

$$x^1 = z, \quad x^2 = r, \quad x^3 = \phi.$$

By *telescopic flow,* we mean a state of flow in which any given liquid cylinder $r =$ constant moves rigidly parallel to the tube axis, without rotation, with a speed $v(r,t)$. Such cylinders are therefore shearing surfaces, and the planes $\phi =$ constant (which pass through the tube axis) are evidently material planes orthogonal to the shearing surfaces (cf. Fig. 9.7).

We may therefore choose a body coordinate system ξ^i which coincides with the space system at an arbitrary instant t_0, and which is such that

$$\xi^2 = r \quad \text{and} \quad \xi^3 = \phi \qquad \text{for all } t;$$

$$\xi^1 = z \qquad \text{at } t_0.$$

For the motion of a given particle, we have

$$\frac{\partial z(\xi,t)}{\partial t} = v(r,t) = v(\xi^2,t),$$

which on integration leads to the result

$$z = \xi^1 + \int_{t_0}^{t} v(\xi^2,t')\,dt',$$

from which it follows that

$$\frac{\partial z}{\partial \xi^1} = 1, \quad \frac{\partial z}{\partial \xi^3} = 0, \quad \frac{\partial^2 z}{\partial \xi^2\,\partial t} = \frac{\partial v(r,t)}{\partial r}. \tag{12.140}$$

The space metric tensor has components

$$g_{ij} = \begin{pmatrix} 1 & 0 & 0 \\ 0 & 1 & 0 \\ 0 & 0 & r^2 \end{pmatrix}, \tag{12.141}$$

and hence, from (12.16) and (12.140), after some calculation we obtain the results

$$\gamma_{ij}(\xi, t) = \begin{pmatrix} 1 & z_2 & 0 \\ z_2 & 1+z_2{}^2 & 0 \\ 0 & 0 & r^2 \end{pmatrix}, \quad z_2 \equiv \frac{\partial z}{\partial \xi^2}, \tag{12.142}$$

from which we see that $\gamma = r^2$ and

$$\gamma^{ij}(\xi, t) = \begin{pmatrix} 1+z_2{}^2 & -z_2 & 0 \\ -z_2 & 1 & 0 \\ 0 & 0 & r^{-2} \end{pmatrix}. \tag{12.143}$$

From this equation, the expression (12.119) for the shear rate leads to the result

$$G = -\frac{\partial v(r,t)}{\partial r}, \tag{12.144}$$

when (12.140) is used, and the sign is changed because the directions ξ^1-, ξ^2-, and ξ^3-increasing coincide at a given particle O at time t_0 with the directions Oy_1, Oy_2, Oy_3 (Fig. 9.7), and these coincide with the directions $\mathbf{e}_1$, $-\mathbf{e}_2$, $\mathbf{e}_3$ of Fig. 2.4. [Cf. discussion following (12.119)].

Shear Flow between Cone and Plate in Relative Rotation

We now take a spherical polar space coordinate system r, θ, ϕ in which the axis $\theta = 0$ coincides with the cone axis, supposed vertical (Fig. 9.5), the origin $r = 0$ coincides with the cone apex (in contact with the plate), and we take

$$x^1 = \phi, \quad x^2 = \theta, \quad x^3 = r.$$

In the state of flow considered, each liquid cone $\theta =$ constant rotates rigidly about the cone axis with an angular velocity $\Omega(\theta, t)$. The surfaces $\theta =$ constant are therefore the shearing surfaces, and the spheres $r =$ constant are evidently material surfaces orthogonal to the shearing surfaces. We may therefore choose a body coordinate system ξ^i which coincides with the space system at an arbitrary instant t_0, and which is such that

$$\xi^2 = \theta \quad \text{and} \quad \xi^3 = r \qquad \text{for all } t;$$

$$\xi^1 = \phi \qquad \text{at } t_0.$$

For the motion of a given particle, we therefore have

$$\frac{\partial \phi(\xi, t)}{\partial t} = \Omega(\theta, t) = \Omega(\xi^2, t),$$

which gives, on integration,

$$\phi = \xi^1 + \int_{t_0}^{t} \Omega(\xi^2, t')\, dt'.$$

Hence

$$\frac{\partial \phi}{\partial \xi^1} = 1, \quad \frac{\partial \phi}{\partial \xi^3} = 0, \quad \frac{\partial^2 \phi}{\partial \xi^2\, \partial t} = \frac{\partial \Omega(\theta, t)}{\partial \theta}. \tag{12.145}$$

The space metric tensor is represented by the matrix

$$g_{ij} = \begin{pmatrix} r^2 \sin^2 \theta & 0 & 0 \\ 0 & r^2 & 0 \\ 0 & 0 & 1 \end{pmatrix} \tag{12.146}$$

in the present spherical polar coordinate system. Using this and the above results, we find that (12.16) now leads to the equation

$$\gamma_{ij}(\xi, t) = \begin{pmatrix} r^2 \sin^2 \theta & r^2 \phi_2 \sin^2 \theta & 0 \\ r^2 \phi_2 \sin^2 \theta & r^2(1 + \phi_2{}^2 \sin^2 \theta) & 0 \\ 0 & 0 & 1 \end{pmatrix}, \quad \phi_2 \equiv \frac{\partial \phi}{\partial \xi^2}. \tag{12.147}$$

Hence $\gamma = r^4 \sin^2 \theta$, and the reciprocal matrix is found to be

$$\gamma^{ij}(\xi, t) = \begin{pmatrix} r^{-2}(\phi_2{}^2 + \operatorname{cosec}^2 \theta) & -r^{-2} \phi_2 & 0 \\ -r^{-2} \phi_2 & r^{-2} & 0 \\ 0 & 0 & 1 \end{pmatrix}. \tag{12.148}$$

Using the time derivative of γ^{12} from this result together with (12.145), the expression (12.119) for the shear rate leads to the result

$$G = \sin \theta \frac{\partial \Omega(\theta, t)}{\partial \theta}, \tag{12.149}$$

in agreement with (9.35).

Curvilinear Shear Strain

We may define a curvilinear shear strain $t_1 \rightarrow t$ as a strain relating two states t_1, t in a curvilinear shear flow, defined by (9.2). We may describe such a strain by the values of $\gamma^{ij}(t) - \gamma^{ij}(t_1) = \Delta^{ij}$ relative to any body coordinate system of the type (12.105); for comparison with the values of $\gamma^{ij}(t)-\gamma^{ij}(t_1)$ defined for rectilinear shear in Chapter 2 and given by (2.66) (with $t_0 = t_1$) relative to a basis which is orthonormal in state t, it is convenient to evaluate the physical components of Δ^{ij} in relation to a (body) coordinate system which is instantaneously orthogonal in state t; the required values, $\widehat{\Delta^{ij}}$, are given by (12.132) above.

In fact, this equation can be further simplified (as a comparison with (2.66) suggests), for we have the result that, for any shear rate history $G = G(t')$,

$$2s_2(t, t_1) = [S_1(t, t_1)]^2. \tag{12.150}$$

This can be proved from the definitions (12.126) in a straightforward manner by considering the region of integration in the double integral for S_2.

It now follows, from a comparison of (12.132) and (2.66), that rectilinear shear, as defined in Chapter 2, is a particular case of the curvilinear shear defined above, and that $S_1(t, t_1) = s$, the magnitude of shear as defined in Chapter 2.

Appendices

Appendix 1

Constant Stress in a Deforming Material

The question of what is meant by a constant state of stress in a material whose shape is changing has arisen in the discussion of the requirement of using a description of stress which is not affected by any rigid-body motion (p. 59); in Chapter 12, in the discussion of time derivatives of stress, it was stated that in general no meaning can be assigned to the concept of a constant state of stress in a deforming material. In order to justify this statement, we first consider what is sometimes meant, and then what ought to be meant, by the phrase "constant stress" or "constant state of stress".

If a polymer solution is sheared at constant shear rate in a concentric cylinder viscometer, the pressure and torque exerted by the solution on the cylinder walls may at first vary with time and subsequently reach constant values; it is then often said that "the stress has reached a steady state" or that "the stress has become constant". Such statements are misleading, however, because the stress, or state of stress, in a material is determined by the tractions acting across three different surfaces (or three different families of surfaces, when the stress is non-uniform), whereas, in the experiment referred to, all we can say is that the traction across one surface (or one family of surfaces—the concentric liquid cylinders) has become constant. We have no grounds for asserting that the traction across any other material surface is constant; in fact, since other material surfaces are changing shape and orientation, it may not be clear what a constant traction across such a surface could mean.

It is clear, however, that any rheologically significant meaning must involve reference to lines embedded in the material rather than to axes fixed in space. It is sufficient to consider states of uniform stress and strain, in the first instance; the necessary generalization to non-uniform states can then be made as indicated in Chapter 12. A material plane then remains a material plane. It is also sufficient to consider *two* states, t_1 and t_2, related by any uniform strain, and to attempt to assign a meaning to the statement that the stress in state t_1 is equal to, or is the same as, the stress in state t_2; for we can then immediately extend the meaning to apply to any sequence of states.

The need to use reference lines embedded in the material may be clarified by the following example. Let us consider a sheet of perfectly elastic material in the stress-free state t_0; let Ox and Oy be two perpendicular axes embedded in the sheet. Then a state of stress t_1 which is a simple tension of magnitude T and direction Ox must be regarded as being different from a state of simple tension t_2 of magnitude T and direction Oy. If it is considered that the difference is unimportant, it should be realized that the two states of stress could lead to two strains, $t_0 \rightarrow t_1$ and $t_0 \rightarrow t_2$, which differed in magnitude as well as direction; this could happen, for example, if the perfectly elastic solid were anisotropic. It would not happen, however, if the material were isotropic (and perfectly elastic), for then the strains would be simple elongations, equal in magnitude, but having the directions Ox and Oy; again, if the material were a Newtonian liquid, the states of flow would differ only in regard to direction, not in magnitude of rate of elongation. If the material were viscoelastic, however, important differences in the states of flow in the two states of stress, t_1 and t_2, could occur, depending on the previous flow history.

The traction $\mathbf{f}$ acting across any given material plane, of unit normal $\mathbf{n}$ say, may be resolved into a part $\mathbf{f}_n$ acting normal to the plane and a part $\mathbf{f}_\tau$ acting parallel to the plane, so that we may write $\mathbf{f} = \mathbf{f}_n + \mathbf{f}_\tau$. We shall say that *a state of stress in a deforming material is constant* if, for every plane,

(i) the normal component of traction $\mathbf{f}_n$ is constant in magnitude and sign, and

(ii) the tangential component $\mathbf{f}_\tau$ is constant in magnitude, in sign, and in direction in the plane (i.e. $\mathbf{f}_\tau$ is always parallel to the same material line in the plane).

We shall now show that these conditions are so stringent that they can only be satisfied in the degenerate cases in which either the stress or the strain is isotropic; in all other cases, therefore, the stress cannot be constant in the material. This is the content of the following theorem, which is expressed in terms of stress and shape variables referred to an arbitrary set of embedded vectors.

Theorem. In order that the state of stress shall be constant in a uniform deformation $t_1 \rightarrow t_2$, it is necessary and sufficient that either

$$\text{(A 1)} \qquad \pi^{ij}(t_2) = \sigma\gamma^{ij}(t_2) \quad \text{and} \quad \pi^{ij}(t_1) = \sigma\gamma^{ij}(t_1)$$

(for some value of σ) or

$$\text{(A 2)} \qquad \gamma^{ij}(t_2) = \lambda^{-2}\gamma^{ij}(t_1) \quad \text{and} \quad \pi^{ij}(t_2) = \lambda^{-2}\pi^{ij}(t_1)$$

(for some value of λ).

The first of these possibilities evidently represents the case in which the stress is isotropic (and of magnitude σ) in both states. The second represents the case in which the deformation is isotropic, i.e. is a dilatation; the truth of this statement is evident from (2.45) and (2.56) when the basis is orthonormal in one of the two states considered, and hence also for any choice of basis, by the rules of Chapter 8. This case also includes the case of a rigid-body deformation when $\lambda = 1$. When $\lambda \neq 1$, we may note that the state of stress is constant although the components π^{ij} are not, according to (A 2).

The order of proof of the theorem will be as follows. We first prove that either (A 1) or (A 2) is sufficient to secure the constancy of normal components (condition (i)), and then that either (A 1) or (A 2) is necessary to satisfy this condition. Finally, we show that either (A 1) or (A 2) is sufficient to ensure the constancy of tangential components (condition (ii)).

Proof that (*A* 1) *or* (*A* 2) *is sufficient to satisfy* (*i*). The normal component of traction across a material plane is given, in magnitude and sign, by (3.17) in terms of the quantities l_i; these may be expressed in terms of a variable h and constants η_i by (2.24). Using (2.25), we then obtain the following expression for the difference of normal components on the same plane in the two states:

$$\text{(A 3)} \qquad \frac{(\mathbf{f}.\mathbf{n})_2 - (\mathbf{f}.\mathbf{n})_1}{(h_1 h_2)^2} = \sum_r \sum_s \sum_i \sum_j \{\pi^{ij}(t_2)\gamma^{rs}(t_1) - \pi^{ij}(t_1)\gamma^{rs}(t_2)\}\eta_r\eta_s\eta_i\eta_j.$$

The suffixes 1 and 2 here denote values appropriate to the states t_1 and t_2.

It can now be seen that the right-hand side of this equation is zero (for all values of η_i, and therefore for all planes) if either (A 1) or (A 2) is satisfied. The stated possibilities in the theorem are therefore *sufficient* to ensure that condition (i) is satisfied.

Proof that (*A* 1) *or* (*A* 2) *is necessary to satisfy* (*i*). We have to show that, if condition (i) is satisfied for all planes, then either (A 1) or (A 2) must hold. Assuming then that (i) is satisfied for all planes, it follows from (A 3) that

$$\text{(A 4)} \qquad \sum_r \sum_s \sum_i \sum_j \{\pi^{ij}(t_2)\gamma^{rs}(t_1) - \pi^{ij}(t_1)\gamma^{rs}(t_2)\}\eta_r\eta_s\eta_i\eta_j = 0$$

for all values of η_1, η_2, and η_3.

We now choose a basis which is orthonormal in state t_1 and has its base vectors parallel to the principal axes of stress in state t_1. We then have

$$\text{(A 5)} \qquad \gamma^{rs}(t_1) = \delta_{rs}, \quad \pi^{ij}(t_1) = \sigma_i \delta_{ij}, \qquad \text{by Examples 3, No. 7,}$$

where σ_1, σ_2, and σ_3 denote the principal values of stress in state t_1.

On substituting these expressions in (A 4) and simplifying the resulting equation, we obtain the result

$$\text{(A 6)} \qquad \sum_r \sum_s \left[\pi^{rs} - \gamma^{rs} \frac{\sigma_1 \eta_1^2 + \sigma_2 \eta_2^2 + \sigma_3 \eta_3^2}{\eta_1^2 + \eta_2^2 + \eta_3^2}\right] \eta_r \eta_s = 0,$$

where, for brevity, we have written $\pi^{rs}(t_2) \equiv \pi^{rs}$ and $\gamma^{rs}(t_2) \equiv \gamma^{rs}$. This equation is valid for all values of η_i. Taking $\eta_1 = 1$, $\eta_2 = \eta_3 = 0$, we see that $\pi^{11} = \sigma_1 \gamma^{11}$; with two similar results, we thus have

$$\text{(A 7)} \qquad \pi^{rr} = \sigma_r \gamma^{rr} \qquad (r = 1, 2, 3) \text{ (in state } t_2).$$

Let us now take $\eta_1 = 0$, $\eta_2 = x\eta_3$, where x is at our disposal. In this case, (A 6) reduces to a quadratic equation in x, after some reduction and the use of (A 7). Since this quadratic equation must be satisfied for all values of x, its coefficients must each be zero; this leads to the following equations:

$$\text{(A 8)} \qquad \begin{cases} \pi^{23} = \sigma_2 \gamma^{23} = \sigma_3 \gamma^{23}, \\ (\sigma_2 - \sigma_3)(\gamma^{22} - \gamma^{33}) = 0. \end{cases}$$

To satisfy these equations, we must have

either (i) $\sigma_2 = \sigma_3$ and $\pi^{23} = \sigma_3 \gamma^{23}$, *or* (iv) $\gamma^{22} = \gamma^{33}$ and $\pi^{23} = \gamma^{23} = 0$.

To satisfy equations obtained from (A 8) by cyclic interchange of suffixes (which must also be satisfied, as one can see by starting with the appropriate values for η_i), we therefore have, in conjunction with alternatives (i) and (iv), the following alternatives:

either (ii) $\sigma_3 = \sigma_1$ and $\pi^{31} = \sigma_1 \gamma^{31}$, *or* (v) $\gamma^{33} = \gamma^{11}$ and $\pi^{31} = \gamma^{31} = 0$;

either (iii) $\sigma_1 = \sigma_2$ and $\pi^{12} = \sigma_2 \gamma^{12}$, *or* (vi) $\gamma^{11} = \gamma^{22}$ and $\pi^{12} = \gamma^{12} = 0$.

Because of the symmetry of these equations with respect to cyclic interchange of the suffixes, the following selections of alternatives are all that need to be considered.

(i), (ii), and (iii). With these alternatives, it is seen that $\sigma_1 = \sigma_2 = \sigma_3$, so that the stress is isotropic in state t_1, and further, using (A 7), it is seen that $\pi^{rs} = \sigma_1 \gamma^{rs}$, so that the stress is isotropic in state t_2, and (A 1) is satisfied.

(iv), (v), and (vi). We now have $\gamma^{rs} = \gamma^{11} \delta_{rs}$, which means that the strain $t_1 \to t_2$ is a dilatation; also, from (A 5) and (A 7), we find that $\pi^{rs} = \gamma^{11} \pi^{rs}(t_1)$, so that (A 2) is satisfied.

(*i*), (*ii*), *and* (*vi*). Since $\pi^{12} = \gamma^{12} = 0$ (by (vi)), we can write $\pi^{12} = \sigma_2\gamma^{12}$, and hence the conditions of (iii) are valid (since (i) and (ii) imply that $\sigma_1 = \sigma_2$). We thus have case (A 1) again, as in the first set of alternatives considered above.

(*i*), (*v*), *and* (*vi*). On returning to the equation (A 6) and using the equations appropriate to (*i*), (*v*) and (*vi*), together with (A 7), we obtain, after some straightforward reduction, the following equation:

$$(\sigma_1 - \sigma_2)\,\gamma^{23}(\eta_1)^2\,\eta_2\,\eta_3 = 0.$$

Since this is to be satisfied for all values of η_1, η_2 and η_3, it follows that *either* $\sigma_1 = \sigma_2$ *or* $\gamma^{23} = 0$.

If $\sigma_1 = \sigma_2$, then (i), (v), (vi), and (A 7) lead to the results $\sigma_1 = \sigma_2 = \sigma_3$ and $\pi^{rs} = \sigma_1\gamma^{rs}$; with (A 5), it follows that (A 1) is satisfied.

If $\gamma^{23} = 0$, then (i), (v), and (vi) show that (iv) is also satisfied; this case has already been considered, and it has been shown that (A 2) is satisfied.

This completes the proof that either (A 1) or (A 2) is necessary if condition (i) of the definition is to be satisfied for all planes.

Proof that (*A* 1) *or* (*A* 2) *is sufficient to satisfy* (*ii*). If (A 1) is satisfied, the stress is isotropic in both states, and hence there is no tangential component of traction across any plane (Theorem (3.18), Corollary); condition (ii) of the definition is therefore satisfied.

It remains only to consider the case in which (A 2) is satisfied. It is for convenience in this stage of the argument that we have written the coefficient in (A 2) in the form λ^{-2}; this is legitimate, because $\gamma^{11}(t_2)$, $\gamma^{11}(t_1)$ and therefore also the coefficient must be positive.

It is convenient to represent the tangential traction $\mathbf{f}_\tau$ by a vector drawn from the particle O at the origin of any given set of embedded base vectors $\mathbf{e}_i$. We may express $\mathbf{f}_\tau$ in the form

$$\text{(A 9)} \qquad \mathbf{f}_\tau = \mu \sum_i \xi^i \mathbf{e}_i,$$

for suitable values of the quantities μ and ξ^i. Since the material line joining O to any given particle P is represented by a vector of the form $\sum_i \xi^i \mathbf{e}_i$, where ξ^i are constants, it follows that condition (ii) of the definition will be satisfied if we can choose μ and ξ^i in (A 9) so that ξ^i are constant and f_τ, the magnitude of $\mathbf{f}_\tau$, is constant; the sense of $\mathbf{f}_\tau$ will be constant in the material if we can choose values μ_1 and μ_2 for μ which have the same sign (positive, say) in the two states t_1 and t_2. Taking the scalar product of both sides of (A 9) with $\mathbf{e}^j$ and using (1.16), it follows that we have to show that, given (A 2), we can choose μ_2 and μ_1 so that

$$\text{(A 10)} \qquad \mu^{-1}\mathbf{f}_\tau . \mathbf{e}^j = \text{constant} \quad \text{and} \quad f_\tau = \text{constant}.$$

We have

$$\mathbf{f}_\tau = \mathbf{f} - f_n \mathbf{n}$$

$$= \sum_r l_r \left(\sum_s \pi^{rs} \mathbf{e}_s - f_n \mathbf{e}^r \right), \qquad \text{by (3.7) and (2.19).}$$

Hence

$$\mathbf{f}_\tau . \mathbf{e}^j = \sum_r l_r (\pi^{rj} - f_n \gamma^{rj}) \qquad \text{by (1.16) and (1.18).}$$

Using (A 2) and the fact that f_n, the magnitude of $\mathbf{f}_n$, is constant since we have shown that (A 2) is sufficient to ensure that condition (i) is satisfied, it follows that

$$(\mu^{-1}\mathbf{f}_\tau . \mathbf{e}^j)_2 - (\mu^{-1}\mathbf{f}_\tau . \mathbf{e}^j)_1 = \sum_r \left\{ \lambda^{-2} \left(\frac{l_r}{\mu} \right)_2 - \left(\frac{l_r}{\mu} \right)_1 \right\} \{\pi^{rj} - f_n \gamma^{rj}\}_1$$

where the suffixes 1 and 2 refer to values in states t_1 and t_2.

From (2.24), (2.25), (A 2), and the fact that η_i are constant, we find that

$$l_r(t_2)/l_r(t_1) = h_2/h_1 = \lambda.$$

Hence the right-hand side of the above equations is zero if we choose μ_1 and μ_2 so that

$$\mu_2/\mu_1 = \lambda^{-2} l_r(t_2)/l_r(t_1) = \lambda^{-1}.$$

Thus with this choice of the ratio μ_2/μ_1, it follows that the coefficients ξ^i in (A 9) are constant, as required, and hence from (A 2) and the fact that

$$(f_\tau)^2 = \mu^2 \sum_i \sum_j \xi^i \xi^j \gamma_{ij},$$

it also follows that f_τ is constant. This completes the proof of the theorem.

Appendix 2

The Limiting Value of a Certain Integral

We now prove that, as stated in (6.11), the integral

$$Y(t) \equiv \int_{-\infty}^{t_1} \mu(t-t')\gamma^{ij}(t')\,dt'$$

tends to zero as $t \to \infty$, if it is given that $\mu(\tau)$ is a positive decreasing function which tends to zero as $\tau \to \infty$ (cf. (6.2), (6.12)); that $Y(t_1)$ exists; and that (6.13) is true.

Since $Y(t_1)$ exists and μ is a decreasing function of its argument, it follows that $Y(t)$ exists for all $t \geqslant t_1$. This implies that, given any number $\epsilon > 0$, there exists a number t_0 such that $-\infty < t_0 \leqslant t_1$ and

$$\left| \int_{-\infty}^{t_0} \mu(t-t')\,\gamma^{ij}(t')\,dt' \right| < \epsilon \qquad \text{for all } t \geqslant t_1. \tag{A 11}$$

By (6.13), there exists a number $K(t_0)$ such that

$$\int_{t_0}^{t_1} |\gamma^{ij}(t')|\,dt' < K(t_0). \tag{A 12}$$

Since $\mu(\tau)$ is a decreasing positive function which tends to zero as $\tau \to \infty$, it follows that we can find a number τ_0 such that

$$\mu(t-t') \leqslant \mu(t-t_0) < \frac{\epsilon}{K(t_0)} \qquad \text{for all } t > \tau_0 \ (t_0 \leqslant t' \leqslant t_1).$$

We now have

$$\begin{aligned} |Y(t)| &\leqslant \left| \int_{-\infty}^{t_0} \mu(t-t')\,\gamma^{ij}(t')\,dt' \right| + \int_{t_0}^{t_1} \mu(t-t')\,|\gamma^{ij}(t')|\,dt' \\ &< \epsilon + \frac{\epsilon}{K(t_0)} \int_{t_0}^{t_1} |\gamma^{ij}(t')|\,dt' \qquad \text{when } t > \tau_0, \text{ by (A 11)}, \\ &< 2\epsilon \qquad \text{by (A 12)}. \end{aligned}$$

This proves the required result that $Y(t) \to 0$ as $t \to \infty$. I owe the above proof to Dr. R. K. Bullough.

Appendix 3

The Dirac Delta Function

Dirac (1947) has introduced a "function" $\delta(x)$ which satisfies the conditions

$$\begin{cases} \displaystyle\int_{-\infty}^{\infty} \delta(x)\,dx = 1, \\ \delta(x) = 0 \quad \text{for } x \neq 0. \end{cases} \tag{A 13}$$

In order to give a non-zero integral, it is clear that $\delta(x)$ must be indefinitely great at the origin, while being zero everywhere else. The question arises as to whether such a function is integrable, and whether in fact $\delta(x)$ can be regarded as a function at all since it has no definite value at the origin $x = 0$. Without attempting to answer these questions, we shall be content to state that the so-called "δ-function", $\delta(x)$, is a convenient notation for expressing certain physical ideas and that, provided its use is confined to certain simple contexts (namely, in the numerator in an integrand), a rigorous justification could be given by replacing the equations involving δ-functions by equations involving certain limiting processes.

For example, the δ-function itself may be regarded as the limit, as $\epsilon \to 0$, of a function which is equal to ϵ^{-1} inside an interval of width ϵ which includes the origin and is zero outside this interval.

The main use of the δ-function is illustrated by the equation

$$\text{(A 14)} \qquad \int_{-\infty}^{\infty} f(x)\,\delta(x)\,dx = f(0),$$

where $f(x)$ is any function of x which is continuous in an interval which includes the origin. The "validity" of this equation can be seen from the above limit for the δ-function: the integral in (A 14) can depend on the values of $f(x)$ only in the immediate neighbourhood of the origin, and hence, since $f(x)$ is continuous in such a neighbourhood, we can replace $f(x)$ in the integrand by $f(0)$ without sensible error; the stated result then follows from (A 13).

By changing the variable of integration from x to $x-a$, where a is any constant, it is seen that (A 13) leads to the equations

$$\text{(A 15)} \qquad \begin{cases} \displaystyle\int_{-\infty}^{\infty} \delta(x-a)\,dx = 1, & \\ \delta(x-a) = 0 & \text{for } x \neq a. \end{cases}$$

Hence, provided that $f(x)$ is continuous in an interval including the point $x = a$, we have the result

$$\text{(A 16)} \qquad \int_{-\infty}^{\infty} f(x)\,\delta(x-a)\,dx = f(a).$$

We may also note that the range of integration in the above equations may be reduced from $(-\infty, \infty)$ to any finite range provided that this range includes all points of singularity (e.g. the point $x = a$ for $\delta(x-a)$) of the δ-functions which are involved in the integrands. This follows because the value of the δ-function is zero except at the singularity.

It is perhaps instructive to note that the δ-function may be regarded as a generalization of the Kronecker delta, δ_{ij}. We may regard δ_{ij} as a function of a "variable" i (at fixed j) which can assume only the discrete values 1, 2, 3, ... Then the equations

$$\delta_{ij} = 0 \quad \text{for } i \neq j, \qquad \sum_i f_i \delta_{ij} = f_j$$

are evidently similar in form to the equations

$$\delta(x-a) = 0 \quad \text{for } x \neq a, \qquad \int_{-\infty}^{\infty} f(x)\,\delta(x-a)\,dx = f(a),$$

if we regard i, j, and $\sum_i$ as being on a similar footing to x, a, and $\int \ldots dx$, and recognize that the discrete range of values for the variable i corresponds to a continuous range of values for the variable x.

Bibliography

Adams, N. (1960). *Rheology Abstr.* **3**, No. 3, 28.

Adams, N. and Lodge, A. S. (1964). *Phil. Trans.* **A256**, 149.

Aeschlimann, W. (1952). "Untersuchungen über die Fadenzievermögen der viskose Flüssigkeiten." Dissertation, Bern.

Anthony, R. L., Caston, R. H. and Guth, E. (1942). *J. phys. Chem.* **46**, 826.

Barus, J. (1893). *Amer. J. Sci.* (3) **45**, 87.

Benbow, J. J., Brown, R. N. and Howells, E. R. (1961). *In* "Phénomènes de Relaxation et de Fluage en Rhéologie non-Linéaire", p. 65. Editions du C. N. R. S., Paris.

Benbow, J. J. and Howells, E. R. (1961). *Polymer* **2**, 429.

Berry, J. P., Scanlan, J. and Watson, W. F. (1956). *Trans. Faraday Soc.* **52**, 1137.

Bland, D. R. (1960). "The Theory of Linear Viscoelasticity." Pergamon Press, Oxford.

Boltzmann, L. (1874). *S.B. Akad. Wiss. Wien* **70**, 275.

Boltzmann, L. (1876). *Ann. Phys., Lpz.* **7**, 624.

Boyd, R. H. (1958). *J. appl. Phys.* **29**, 953.

Brillouin, L. (1925). *Ann. Phys., Paris* (10e Série) **3**, 251.

Brodnyan, J. G., Gaskins, F. H. and Philippoff, W. (1957). *Trans. Soc. Rheol.* **1**, 109.

Bueche, F. (1956). *J. chem. Phys.* **25**, 599.

Carslaw, H. S. and Jaeger, J. C. (1948). "Operational Methods in Applied Mathematics." Oxford University Press.

Carver, E. K. and van Wazer, J. R. (1947). *J. phys. Chem.* **51**, 751.

Ciferri, A. (1961). *Makromol. Chem.* **43**, 152.

Clegg, P. L. (1958). *In* "Rheology of Elastomers", ed. by P. Mason and N. Wookey, p. 174. Pergamon Press, London.

Coleman, B. D. and Noll, W. (1959a). *Arch. ration. Mech. Anal.* **3**, 289.

Coleman, B. D. and Noll, W. (1959b). *J. appl. Phys.* **30**, 1508.

Coleman, B. D. and Noll, W. (1961). *Ann. N.Y. Acad. Sci.* **89**, 672.

Cooper, W. (1955). *Chem. & Ind.* (*Rev.*) **74**, 1741.

Copson, E. T. (1935). "An Introduction to the Theory of Functions of a Complex Variable", p. 79. Clarendon Press, Oxford.

Crespi, G. and Flisi, U. (1963). *Makromol. Chem.* **60**, 191.

Deuker, E. A. (1941). *Dtsch. Math.* **5**, 546.

DeWitt, T. W. (1955). *J. appl. Phys.* **26**, 889.

DeWitt, T. W., Markovitz, H., Padden, F. J., Jr. and Zapas, L. J. (1955). *J. Colloid Sci.* **10**, 174.

Dirac, P. A. M. (1947). "The Principles of Quantum Mechanics", 3rd Ed., p. 58. Clarendon Press, Oxford.

Eliassaf, J., Silberberg, A. and Katchalsky, A. (1955). *Nature, Lond.* **176**, 1119.

Erbring, H. (1934). *Kolloidzschr.* **77**, 32.

Ericksen, J. L. (1960a). *In* "Viscoelasticity: Phenomenological Aspects", ed. by J. T. Bergen, p. 77. Academic Press, New York.

Ericksen, J. L. (1960b). *Arch. ration. Mech. Anal.* **4**, 231.

Ericksen, J. L. (1960c). *Kolloidzschr.* **172–3**, 117.

Ericksen, J. L. (1960d). *Trans. Soc. Rheol.* **4**, 29.

Ericksen, J. L. (1960e). *J. Polymer Sci.* **47**, 327.

Ericksen, J. L. and Rivlin, R. S. (1954). *J. ration. Mech. Anal.* **3**, 281.

Eringen, A. C. (1962). "Non-linear Theory of Continuous Media." McGraw-Hill, New York.

Ferry, J. D. (1942). *J. Amer. chem. Soc.* **64**, 1330.

Ferry, J. D. (1961). "Viscoelastic Properties of Polymers." Wiley, London.

Flory, P. J. (1953). "Principles of Polymer Chemistry." Cornell University Press, Ithaca, New York.

Flory, P. J. (1960). *Trans. Faraday Soc.* **56**, 722.

Fox, T. G., Gratch, S. and Loshaek, S. (1956). *In* "Rheology, Theory and Applications", ed. by F. Eirich, Vol. 1, p. 431. Academic Press, New York.

Fréchet, M. (1910). *Ann. Éc. Norm. Sup.* (3), **27**.

Frenkel, J. (1955). "Kinetic Theory of Liquids", pp. 199, 200. Dover, New York.

Fromm, H. (1948). *Z. angew. Math. Mech.* **28**, 43.

Garner, F. H. and Nissan, A. H. (1946). *Nature, Lond.* **158**, 634.

Garner, F. H., Nissan, A. H. and Wood, G. F. (1950). *Phil. Trans.* **A243, 37**.

Gaskins, F. H. and Philippoff, W. (1959). *Trans. Soc. Rheol.* **3**, 181.

Gee, G. (1946). *Trans. Faraday Soc.* **42**, 585.

Gill, S. J. and Gavis, J. (1956). *J. Polymer Sci.* **20**, 287.

Green, A. E. (1956). *J. ration. Mech. Anal.* **5**, 637.

Green, A. E. and Adkins, J. E. (1960). "Large Elastic Deformations and Nonlinear Continuum Mechanics." Clarendon Press, Oxford.

Green, A. E. and Rivlin, R. S. (1957). *Arch. ration. Mech. Anal.* **1**, 1.

Green, A. E. and Rivlin, R. S. (1960). *Arch. ration. Mech. Anal.* **4**, 387.

Green, A. E., Rivlin, R. S. and Spencer, J. M. (1959). *Arch. ration. Mech. Anal.* **3**, 82.

Green, A. E. and Zerna, W. (1950). *Phil. Mag.* **41**, 313.

Green, A. E. and Zerna, W. (1954). "Theoretical Elasticity." Clarendon Press, Oxford.

Green, M. S. and Tobolsky, A. V. (1946). *J. chem. Phys.* **14**, 80.

Greensmith, H. W. and Rivlin, R. S. (1953). *Phil. Trans.* **A245**, 399.

Grossman, P. U. A. (1961). *Kolloidzschr* **174**, 97.

Hencky, H. (1925). *Z. angew. Math. Mech.* **5**, 144.

Hencky, H. (1929). *Ann. Phys. Lpz.* (5), **2**, 617.

Hill, R. (1950). "The Mathematical Theory of Plasticity." Clarendon Press, Oxford.

Hull, H. H. (1961). *Trans. Soc. Rheol.* **5**, 115.

James, H. M. (1947). *J. chem. Phys.* **15**, 651.

James, H. M. and Guth, E. (1947). *J. Chem. Phys.* **15**, 669.

Jaumann, G. (1911). *S.B. Akad. Wiss. Wien* (IIa), **120**, 385.

Jensen, C. E. and Koefoed, J. (1954). *J. Colloid Sci.* **9**, 460.

Jha, S. D. (1955). *Kolloidzschr.* **143**, 174.

Jobling, A. and Roberts, J. E. (1958). *In* "Rheology, Theory and Applications", ed. by F. Eirich, Vol. II, p. 517, Academic Press, New York.

Jobling, A. and Roberts, J. E. (1959). *J. Polymer Sci.* **36**, 421, 433.

Jochims, J. (1932). *Kolloidzschr.* **61**, 250.

Kast, W. (1954). *ForschBer. Wirtsch. Verkehrsmin., Nordrhein-Westfalen,* No. 93.

Kaye, A. (1962). "Non-Newtonian Flow in Incompressible Fluids." College of Aeronautics Note No. 134, Cranfield, Bletchley, Bucks.

Kaye, A. (1963). *Nature, Lond.* **197**, 1001.

Képès, A. (1956). *J. Polymer Sci.* **22**, 409.

Khasanovitch, T. N. (1959). *J. appl. Phys.* **30**, 948.
Klare, H. and Gröbe, A. (1955). *Faserforsch. u. Textiltechnik* **6**, 97.
Kohlrausch, H. (1876). *Ann. Phys. Lpz.* **158**, 373.
Kotaka, T., Kurata, M. and Tamura, M. (1959). *J. appl. Phys.* **30**, 1705; *Bull. chem. Soc. Japan* **32**, 471.
Langlois, W. E. and Rivlin, R. S. (1959). "Steady Flow of Slightly Viscoelastic Fluids." Tech. Report No. 3, Division of Applied Mathematics, Brown University, Providence, R.I.
Leslie, F. M. and Tanner, R. I. (1961). *Quart. J. Mech. appl. Math.* **14**, 36.
Lodge, A. S. (1951). *Proc. Camb. phil. Soc.* **47**, 575.
Lodge, A. S. (1954). "Proc. 2nd Int. Cong. Rheol.", ed. by V. G. W. Harrison, p. 229. Butterworths, London.
Lodge, A. S. (1956). *Trans. Faraday Soc.* **52**, 120.
Lodge, A. S. (1958a). *In* "Rheology of Elastomers", ed. by P. Mason and N. Wookey, p. 70. Pergamon Press, London.
Lodge, A. S. (1958b). *Rheol. Acta* **1**, 158.
Lodge, A. S. (1960a). *Rheol. Abstr.* **3**, No. 3, 20.
Lodge, A. S. (1960b). *J. Sci. Instrum.* **37**, 401.
Lodge, A. S. (1960c). *Kolloidzschr.* **171**, 46.
Lodge, A. S. (1961a). *Rheol. Abstr.* **4**, No. 3, 29.
Lodge, A. S. (1961b). *In* "Phénomènes de Relaxation et de Fluage en Rhéologie Non-linéaire", p. 51. Editions du C.N.R.S., Paris.
Lodge, A. S. (1961c). *Chem. & Ind. (Rev.)* **80**, 1261.
Lodge, A. S. (1964). *La Scuola in Azione.* In press.
Lodge, A. S., Evans, D. J. and Scully, D. B. (1964). In press.
Lodge, A. S. and Weissenberg, K. (1950). *In* "Some Recent Developments in Rheology", ed. by V. G. W. Harrison, p. 129. United Trade Press, London.
Love, A. E. H. (1944). "The Mathematical Theory of Elasticity", 4th Ed. Dover, New York.
McConnell, A. J. (1931). "Applications of the Absolute Differential Calculus." Blackie, Glasgow. Dover reprint: "Applications of Tensor Analysis."
McKennell, R. (1954). "Proc. 2nd Int. Cong. Rheol.", ed. by V. G. W. Harrison, p. 350. Butterworths, London.
Madelung, E. (1943). "Mathematische Hilfsmittel des Physikers." Dover, New York.
Markovitz, H. (1957). *Trans. Soc. Rheol.* **1**, 37.
Markovitz, H. (1962). "Int. Symp. on 2nd Order Effects in Elasticity, Plasticity, and Fluid Dynamics, Haifa." In press.
Markovitz, H., Elyash, L. J., Padden, F. J., Jr. and DeWitt, T. W. (1955). *J. Colloid Sci.* **10**, 165.
Markovitz, H. and Williamson, R. B. (1957). *Trans. Soc. Rheol.* **1**, 25.
Maxwell, J. C. (1868). *Phil. Mag.* (4), **35**, 129, 185.
Mell, C. C. (1956). *J. Oil Col. Chem. Ass.* (Nov. 1956) 832.
Merrington, A. C. (1943). *Nature, Lond.* **152**, 663.
Milne, E. A. (1948). "Vectorial Mechanics", p. 36. Methuen, London.
Mooney, M. (1940). *J. appl. Phys.* **11**, 582.
Mooney, M. (1951). *J. Colloid Sci.* **6**, 96.
Mooney, M. and Ewart, R. H. (1934). *Physics* **5**, 350.
Nason, H. K. (1945). *J. appl. Phys.* **16**, 338.
Neubert, D. and Saunders, D. W. (1958). *Rheol. Acta* **1**, 151.
Nitschmann, H. and Schrade, J. (1948). *Helv. chim. Acta* **31**, 297.

Noll, W. (1955). *J. ration. Mech. Anal.* **4,** 3.
Noll, W. (1958). *Arch. ration Mech. Anal.* **2,** 197.
Oldroyd, J. G. (1950a). *Proc. roy. Soc.* **A200,** 523.
Oldroyd, J. G. (1950b). *Proc. roy. Soc.* **A202,** 345.
Oldroyd, J. G. (1958). *Proc. roy. Soc.* **A245,** 278.
Padden, F. J. and DeWitt, T. W. (1954). *J. appl. Phys.* **25,** 1086.
Peterlin, A. (1956). *In* "Rheology: Theory and Applications", ed. by F. R. Eirich, Vol. 1, p. 615. Academic Press, New York.
Philippoff, W. (1956). *J. appl. Phys.* **27,** 984.
Philippoff, W. (1960). *Trans. Soc. Rheol.* **4,** 169.
Philippoff, W., Gaskins, F. H. and Brodnyan, J. G. (1957). *J. appl. Phys.* **28,** 1118.
Pilpel, N. (1954). *Trans. Faraday Soc.* **50,** 1369.
Pipkin, A. C. and Rivlin, R. S. (1960). *Arch. ration. Mech. Anal.* **4,** 129.
Pipkin, A. C. and Rivlin, R. S. (1961). *Arch. ration. Mech. Anal.* **8,** 297.
Pollett, W. F. O. (1954). "Proc. 2nd Int. Cong. Rheol.", ed. by V. G. W. Harrison, p. 85. Butterworths, London.
Pollett, W. F. O. (1955). *Brit. J. appl. Phys.* **6,** 199.
Pollett, W. F. O. (1958). *Rheol. Acta* **1,** 257.
Poynting, J. H. (1909). *Proc. roy. Soc.* **A82,** 546.
Poynting, J. H. (1912). *Proc. roy. Soc.* **A86,** 534.
Poynting, J. H. (1913). *India Rubber J.* (October 4th), p. 6.
Prager, W. (1945). *J. appl. Phys.* **16,** 837.
Prager, W. (1961). "Introduction to the Mechanics of Continua." Ginn, Boston.
Rabinowitsch, B. (1929). *Z. phys. Chem.* **A145,** 1.
Reiner, M. (1945). *Amer. J. Maths.* **67,** 350.
Reiner, M. (1948). *Amer. J. Maths.* **70,** 433.
Reiner, M. (1960). *Phys. Fluids* **3,** 427.
Rigbi, Z. (1953). *S.P.E.J.* **9,** 22.
Rivlin, R. S. (1947). *J. appl. Phys.* **18,** 444.
Rivlin, R. S. (1948). *Proc. roy. Soc.* **A193,** 260.
Rivlin, R. S. (1955). *J. ration. Mech. Anal.* **4,** 681.
Rivlin, R. S. (1956a). *Quart. appl. Math.* **14,** 83.
Rivlin, R. S. (1956b). *J. ration. Mech. Anal.* **5,** 179.
Rivlin, R. S. (1960). *Arch. ration. Mech. Anal.* **4,** 262.
Rivlin, R. S. and Ericksen, J. L. (1955). *J. ration. Mech. Anal.* **4,** 323.
Rivlin, R. S. and Saunders, D. W. (1951). *Phil. Trans.* **A243,** 251.
Roberts, J. E. (1952). "The pressure distribution in laminar shearing motion and comparison with predictions from various theories." U.K. Ministry of Supply Report A.D.E. 13/52.
Roberts, J. E. (1954). "Proc. 2nd Int. Cong. Rheol.", ed. by V. G. W. Harrison, p. 91. Butterworths, London.
Roberts, J. E. (1957). *Nature, Lond.* **179,** 487.
Rouse, P. E. Jr. (1953). *J. chem. Phys.* **21,** 1272.
Russell, R. J. (1946). "The determination of the basic rheological constants governing the flow of pseudoplastic substances", Ph.D. Thesis, University of London.
Sakiadis, B. C. (1962). *Amer. Inst. Chem. Engng. J.* **8,** 317.
Scanlan, J. and Watson, W. F. (1958). *Trans. Faraday Soc.* **54,** 740.
Schouten, J. A. (1951). "Tensor Analysis for Physicists." Oxford University Press.
Schwedoff, T. (1889). *Journal de Physique* (2), **8,** 341.
Scott-Blair, G. W. and Burnett, J. (1957). *Lab. Practice* **6,** 570.
Spencer, R. S. and Dillon, R. E. (1948). *J. Colloid Sci.* **3,** 163.

Spencer, R. S. and Dillon, R. E. (1949). *J. Colloid Sci.* **4**, 241.

Tobolsky, A. V. (1958). *In* "Rheology: Theory and Applications", ed. by F. R. Eirich, Vol. 2, p. 63. Academic Press, New York.

Tobolsky, A. V., Andrews, R. D. and Hanson, E. E. (1946). *J. appl. Phys.* **17**, 352.

Toms, B. A. and Strawbridge, D. J. (1953). *Trans. Faraday Soc.* **49**, 1225.

Toms, B. A. and Strawbridge, D. J. (1954). "Proc. 2nd Int. Cong. Rheol.", ed. by V. G. W. Harrison, p. 99. Butterworths, London.

Tordella, J. P. (1956). *J. appl. Phys.* **27**, 454.

Trapeznikov, A. A. and Assonova, T. V. (1958). *Colloid J.* **20**, No. 3, 376.

Trapeznikov, A. A., Morozov, A. S. and Petrzhik, G. G. (1960). *Dokl. Akad. Nauk SSSR* **133**, 637 (cf. *Chem. Abstr.* **55**, 11030d).

Trapeznikov, A. A. and Shalopalkina, T. G. (1956). *Dokl. Akad. Nauk SSSR* **111**, 380 (cf. *Chem. Abstr.* **51**, 14378c).

Treloar, L. R. G. (1958). "The Physics of Rubber Elasticity", 2nd Ed. Clarendon Press, Oxford.

Trouton, F. T. (1906). *Proc. roy. Soc.* **A77**, 426.

Truesdell, C. (1951). *J. Math. pures appl.* **30**, 111.

Truesdell, C. (1952). *J. ration. Mech. Anal.* **1**, 125.

Truesdell, C. (1955). *J. ration. Mech. Anal.* **4**, 83, 1019.

Truesdell, C. (1956). *J. appl. Phys.* **26**, 441.

Truesdell, C. and Toupin, R. A. (1960). The Classical Field Theories. *In* "Handbuch der Physik", Vol. III, p. 1. Springer, Berlin.

Voigt, W. (1889). *Abh. Ges. Wiss. Göttingen* **36**, No. 1.

Voigt, W. (1892). *Ann. Phys., Lpz.* (2) **46**, 671.

Volterra, V. and Pérès, J. (1936). "Théorie Générale des Fonctionelles", Vol. I, p. 61. Gauthier-Villars, Paris.

Wall, F. T. (1942). *J. chem. Phys.* **10**, 485.

Ward, A. F. H. and Jenkins, G. M. (1958). *Rheol. Acta* **1**, 110.

Ward, A. F. H. and Lord, P. (1957). *J. sci. Instrum.* **34**, 363.

Watkins, J. M. (1956). *J. appl. Phys.* **27**, 419.

Weatherburn, C. E. (1942). "Elementary Vector Analysis", Chapters I–IV. Bell, London.

Weber, N. and Bauer, W. H. (1956). *J. phys. Chem.* **60**, 270.

Weissenberg, K. (1931). *Abh. preuss. Akad. Wiss.* No. 2.

Weissenberg, K. (1935). *Arch. Sci. phys. nat.* (5), **17**, 1.

Weissenberg, K. (1946). "Rep. Gen. Conf. Brit. Rheol. Club", p. 36. Nelson, Edinburgh.

Weissenberg, K. (1947). *Nature, Lond.* **159**, 310.

Weissenberg, K. (1949). "Proc. 1st Int. Cong. Rheol", p. I–29. North-Holland, Amsterdam.

Weissenberg, K. and Freeman, S. M. (1948). *Nature, Lond.* **161**, 324.

Whitehead, A. N. and Russell, B. (1927). "Principia Mathematica", 2nd Ed., *100. Cambridge University Press, London.

Yamamoto, M. (1956). *J. phys. Soc. Japan* **11**, 413.

Yamamoto, M. (1957). *J. phys. Soc. Japan* **12**, 1148.

Yamamoto, M. (1958). *J. phys. Soc. Japan* **13**, 1200.

Yamamoto, M. and Inagaki, H. (1952). *Busseiron Kenkyu* No. 55, 26.

Yano, K. (1957). "The Theory of Lie Derivatives and its Applications." North-Holland, Amsterdam.

Zaremba, S. (1903). *Bull. Int. Acad. Sci. Cracovie*, 594.

Zaremba, S. (1937). *Mém. Sci. Math.*, No. 82.

List of Symbols

This list includes symbols that occur frequently in the text, together with the number of the page containing the definition or first occurrence.

Page	Symbol	Definition
2	$\mathbf{e}_1 . \mathbf{e}_2$	scalar product of vectors $\mathbf{e}_1$ and $\mathbf{e}_2$
2	$\mathbf{e}_1 \wedge \mathbf{e}_2$	vector product of vectors $\mathbf{e}_1$ and $\mathbf{e}_2$
1	e	magnitude of the vector $\mathbf{e}$
5	O, P_1, P_2, P_3	four non-coplanar particles
6, 8	i, j, k, l, m, n	suffixes and superfixes assuming values 1, 2 and 3
6	$\mathbf{e}_i$	$\overrightarrow{\mathrm{OP}}_i$ (embedded base vectors)
5	v	$\mathbf{e}_1 \wedge \mathbf{e}_2 . \mathbf{e}_3$ (volume of basic parallelepiped)
7, 309	δ_{ij}, δ_i	1 if $i = j$; 0 if $i \neq j$ (Kronecker delta)
8	$\mathbf{e}^i$	$\mathbf{e}^1 = v^{-1} \mathbf{e}_2 \wedge \mathbf{e}_3$ etc. (reciprocal base vectors)
9	ξ^i	$\overrightarrow{\mathrm{OP}}.\mathbf{e}^i$ (convected coordinates of a particle P)
9	γ_{ij}	$\mathbf{e}_i . \mathbf{e}_j$ (shape variables)
9	γ^{ij}	$\mathbf{e}^i . \mathbf{e}^j$ (reciprocal shape variables)
10	γ, γ_0	$\det \gamma_{ij}(t)$, $\det \gamma_{ij}(t_0)$
10	Γ^{ij}, Γ_{ij}	cofactor of γ_{ji} in $\det \gamma_{ij}$, of γ^{ji} in $\det \gamma^{ij}$
19	t_0, t, t'	labels for states; instants of time
19	x_i	rectangular cartesian coordinates of a place referred to axes fixed in space
27	$\mathbf{n}$	unit vector normal to a (material) plane
27	h, h_0, h'	distance between a plane and particle O in states t, t_0, t'
27	l_i	$\mathbf{n}.\mathbf{e}_i$ (direction cosines of $\mathbf{n}$ when basis is orthonormal)
28	η_i	convected coordinates of a plane
32	λ_a, λ_b, λ_c	principal elongation ratios for a strain $t_0 \to t$
47, 48	J_1, J_2, J_3	strain invariants $\sum_{a,b,c} \lambda_a^2$, $\sum_{a,b,c} \lambda_a^4$, $\lambda_a^2 \lambda_b^2 \lambda_c^2$

Page	Symbol	Definition
161	K_1, K_2, K_3	strain invariants $\sum_{a,b,c} (\lambda_a^2-1)$, $\sum_{a,b,c} (\lambda_a^2-1)^2$, $(\lambda_a^2-1)(\lambda_b^2-1)(\lambda_c^2-1)$
36	$\bar{G}$	$e_1^{-1}de_1/dt$ (elongation rate)
39	ϵ	angle of shear
38, 40	s	$\tan\epsilon$ (magnitude of shear)
41	χ	angle between a principal axis of shear strain and a line of shear
42	$G, \dot{s}$	shear rate
45	α, ω	amplitude and angular frequency of oscillatory shear
49, 165	$\omega_n, \bar{\omega}$	principal values of $d^n\gamma_{ij}/dt^n$, $d\gamma^{ij}/dt$
51	$\mathbf{f}$	traction across plane of normal $\mathbf{n}$
55	$\mathbf{f}^i$	traction across plane of normal $\mathbf{e}^i$
55	p_{ij}	cartesian stress components ($\mathbf{f}^i.\mathbf{e}^j$ in an orthonormal basis)
57	π^{ij}	$\mathbf{e}^i\mathbf{f}^i.\mathbf{e}^j$ (stress components in a general embedded basis)
68	$\bar{\pi}_{ij}$	stress components reciprocal to π^{ij}
100	π_{ij}	$\sum_l \sum_m \gamma_{il}\gamma_{jm}\pi^{lm}$
56	p, p_0	magnitude of hydrostatic pressure
62	Π^{ij}	$\pi^{ij}+p\gamma^{ij}$ ("extra" stress)
67	$\sigma_a, \sigma_b, \sigma_c$	principal values of stress
58	α, α^i	areas of faces of a tetrahedron
66	χ'	angle between a principal axis of stress and a line of shear
56, 66, 77	σ	magnitude of a shear stress; principal value of stress; Poisson's ratio
72, 77	μ_0, E	shear modulus, Young's modulus
66	ρ	density
84	k, T	Boltzmann's constant, absolute temperature
84	N_0, cN_0	concentrations of network junctions and network chains ($c \sim 2$)
85	S, F	entropy, Helmholtz free energy — per unit volume (p. 84)
85	W, U	work done by tractions, internal energy — per unit mass (p. 155)

Page	Symbol	Definition
93, 96	η	viscosity (p_{21}/G)
98	$\bar{\eta}$	elongational viscosity
99	$\dot{\gamma}^{ij}$	$d\gamma^{ij}/dt$ (rate-of-strain variables)
121, 163	L_i	rate-of-strain invariants
102	$\mu(t-t')$	memory function
102	μ_r	$\int_0^\infty \mu(\tau)\,\tau^r d\tau$ (r = 0, 1, 2)
103	a_s, τ_s	constants in an exponential form for $\mu(t-t')$
110	β	$\mu_2 G/\mu_1$
110	$I_r(t)$	$\int_t^\infty \mu(\tau)\,(\tau-t)^r d\tau$ (r = 0, 1, 2)
112	A, B, C, D	integrals of $\mu(t-t')$ arising in oscillatory shear flow
118	$N(t-t')$	network junction age distribution function
125	μ_0^*	modulus of a rubberlike liquid
125	$\gamma^{ij}(t_1^*)$	instantaneously recoverable state at time t_1
132	h_2^*, h_2	instantaneous and delayed separation ratios for shearing planes in free recovery after steady shear flow
132	ϵ^*	instantaneous shear recovery angle
132	λ	$\{1+(\mu_0\mu_2-\mu_1^2)\,G^2\mu_0^{-2}\}^{1/6}$
140, 148	s_0, s_∞	magnitudes of instantaneous and ultimate constrained shear recovery
144	$\bar{x}(p)$	Laplace transform of $x(t)$
154	A, B, C	coefficients in a stress–strain relation
161	Δ^{ij}	$\gamma^{ij}(t_0)-\gamma^{ij}(t)$ (strain components)
162	a, b, c	coefficients in a relation between stress and rate-of-strain variables
174	$\mathscr{F}$, $\mathscr{F}^{ij}$	functionals
186	$Oy_1\,y_2\,y_3$	local rectangular axes in curvilinear shear flow (Oy_1 in direction of shear; Oy_2 normal to shearing surface)
183	p_{11}, p_{22}, p_{33}	normal stress components in shear flow referred to $Oy_1\,y_2\,y_3$
188	Ω, Ω_0	angular velocity
188	r, z, ϕ	cylindrical polar coordinates

Page	Symbol	Definition
199	r, θ, ϕ	spherical polar coordinates
192, 202	M	total torque on the wall of a rotational viscometer
193	ν	$2d\log G/d\log p_{21}$
196	$\widehat{rr}, \widehat{r\phi}, \widehat{rz}$, etc.	local cartesian stress components relative to an orthogonal coordinate system r, z, ϕ
196	F_r, F_ϕ, F_z	components of body force per unit mass
196	g	acceleration due to gravity
199, 202	$\Delta\theta, R$	gap angle and plate radius in cone-and-plate apparatus
205	p_a	atmospheric pressure
206	ψ	angle between normal to free liquid boundary and radius vector
210	F	total thrust on plate due to normal stress effect
217	τ, τ_R	$p_{21}(r)$, $p_{21}(R)$ (values of shear stress in telescopic flow)
217	Q	volume flowing through tube in unit time
218	T	total traction normal to cross-section at tube exit
226	M_n, M_w	number- and weight-average molecular weights
224	A, B, C	polymeric liquids of specified compositions
310	x^i	coordinates of a place referred to a general space coordinate system
310	ξ^i	coordinates of a particle referred to a general body coordinate system
312	$v^i(x, t)$	velocity (a contravariant space vector field)
312	$g_{ij}(x)$	space metric tensor ($x \equiv x^1, x^2, x^3$)
313	$\gamma_{ij}(\xi, t)$	body metric tensor ($\xi \equiv \xi^1, \xi^2, \xi^3$)
314	$\overset{t}{\rightarrow}$	isomorphism between space fields and body fields generated by a state t
319	$C_{ij}, \overline{C}_{ij}$	Cauchy's strain tensors
319	$B^{ij}, \overline{B}^{ij}$	Finger's strain tensors
320	$U_{ij}, \overline{U}_{ij}$	Almansi's and Green's strain tensors
322	D/Dt	hydrodynamic operator

Page	Symbol	Definition
326	$v_{i,j}$	covariant derivative of v_i formed with g_{ij} ($v_i = g_{ik}v^k$)
326	$\dot{e}_i$	$\frac{1}{2}(v_{i,j}+v_{j,i})$ (rate-of-strain space tensor)
326	ω_{ij}	$\frac{1}{2}(v_{i,j}-v_{j,i})$ (vorticity space tensor)
327	$p^{ij}(x, t)$	contravariant space stress tensor field
327	$\pi^{ij}(\xi, t)$	contravariant body stress tensor field
328	$\Gamma^i_{\alpha\beta}$	Christoffel symbols formed from γ_{ij}
336	u^i	rectangular cartesian components of displacement vector
336	e^{ij}	infinitesimal strain components
341	Q_n	a function of shear rate and its time derivatives
342	$\widehat{\Phi^{ij}}$	physical components of a tensor Φ^{ij} relative to a specified orthogonal coordinate system
352	$\mathbf{f}_n$, $\mathbf{f}_\tau$	normal and tangential resolutes of traction across a plane of normal **n**
357	$\delta(x)$	Dirac's delta function

Author Index

Numbers in italics indicate the page on which the reference is listed

Subject Index

D

S